oroonoko

& OTHER PROSE NARRATIVES

WITHDRAWN

oroonoko

& OTHER PROSE NARRATIVES

by

APHRA BEHN

Edited by Montague Summers

Benjamin Blom
New York

PR
3317
.O7
1967

First published 1916
as volume five of
THE WORKS OF APHRA BEHN
Reissued 1967 by
Benjamin Blom, Inc. New York 10452
under the title
OROONOKO & Other Prose Narratives
Library of Congress Catalog Card No. 67-25151

PRINTED IN THE U.S.A.

12667

CONTENTS.

CONTENTS

THE ADVENTURE
OF THE BLACK LADY.

THE ADVENTURE
OF THE *BLACK LADY*.

ABOUT the Beginning of last *June* (as near as I can
remember) *Bellamora* came to Town from *Hampshire*, and
was obliged to lodge the first Night at the same Inn where
the Stage-Coach set up. The next Day she took Coach
for *Covent-Garden*, where she thought to find Madam
Brightly, a Relation of hers, with whom she design'd to
continue for about half a Year undiscover'd, if possible, by
her Friends in the Country : and order'd therefore her
Trunk, with her Clothes, and most of her Money and
Jewels, to be brought after her to Madame *Brightly's* by
a strange Porter, whom she spoke to in the Street as she
was taking Coach ; being utterly unacquainted with the
neat Practices of this fine City. When she came to
Bridges-Street, where indeed her Cousin had lodged near
three or four Years since, she was strangely surprized that
she could not learn anything of her ; no, nor so much as
meet with anyone that had ever heard of her Cousin's Name :
Till, at last, describing Madam *Brightly* to one of the
House-keepers in that Place, he told her, that there was
such a kind of Lady, whom he had sometimes seen there
about a Year and a half ago ; but that he believed she was
married and remov'd towards *Soho*. In this Perplexity she
quite forgot her Trunk and Money, *&c*, and wander'd in
her Hackney-Coach all over St. *Anne's* Parish ; inquiring
for Madam *Brightly*, still describing her Person, but in
vain ; for no Soul could give her any Tale or Tidings of
such a Lady. After she had thus fruitlessly rambled, till
she, the Coachman, and the very Horses were even tired,

by good Fortune for her, she happen'd on a private House, where lived a good, discreet, ancient Gentlewoman, who was fallen to Decay, and forc'd to let Lodgings for the best Part of her Livelihood : From whom she understood, that there was such a kind of Lady, who had lain there somewhat more than a Twelvemonth, being near three Months after she was married ; but that she was now gone abroad with the Gentleman her Husband, either to the Play, or to take the fresh Air ; and she believ'd would not return till Night. This Discourse of the Good Gentlewoman's so elevated *Bellamora's* drooping Spirits, that after she had beg'd the liberty of staying there till they came home, she discharg'd the Coachman in all haste, still forgetting her Trunk, and the more valuable Furniture of it.

When they were alone, *Bellamora* desired she might be permitted the Freedom to send for a Pint of Sack ; which, with some little Difficulty, was at last allow'd her. They began then to chat for a matter of half an Hour of things indifferent : and at length the ancient Gentlewoman ask'd the fair Innocent (I must not say foolish) one, of what Country, and what her Name was : to both which she answer'd directly and truly, tho' it might have prov'd not discreetly. She then enquir'd of *Bellamora* if her Parents were living, and the Occasion of her coming to Town. The fair unthinking Creature reply'd, that her Father and Mother were both dead ; and that she had escap'd from her Uncle, under the pretence of making a Visit to a young Lady, her Cousin, who was lately married, and liv'd above twenty Miles from her Uncle's, in the Road to *London*, and that the Cause of her quitting the Country, was to avoid the hated Importunities of a Gentleman, whose pretended Love to her she fear'd had been her eternal Ruin. At which she wept and sigh'd most extravagantly. The discreet Gentlewoman endeavour'd to comfort her by all the softest and most powerful Arguments in her Capacity; promising her all the friendly Assistance that she could

expect from her, during *Bellamora's* stay in Town : which
she did with so much Earnestness, and visible Integrity,
that the pretty innocent Creature was going to make her
a full and real Discovery of her imaginary insupportable
Misfortunes; and (doubtless) had done it, had she not been
prevented by the Return of the Lady, whom she hop'd to
have found her Cousin *Brightly*. The Gentleman, her
Husband just saw her within Doors, and orderd the Coach
to drive to some of his Bottle-Companions; which gave
the Women the better Opportunity of entertaining one
another, which happen'd to be with some Surprize on all
Sides. As the Lady was going up into her Apartment,
the Gentlewoman of the House told her there was a young
Lady in the Parlour, who came out of the Country that
very Day on purpose to visit her : The Lady stept immediately to see who it was, and *Bellamora* approaching to
receive her hop'd-for Cousin, stop'd on the sudden just as
she came to her; and sigh'd out aloud, Ah, Madam! I
am lost—It is not your Ladyship I seek. No, Madam
(return'd the other) I am apt to think you did not intend
me this Honour. But you are as welcome to me, as you
could be to the dearest of your Acquaintance : Have you
forgot me, Madame *Bellamora*? (continued she.) That
Name startled the other : However, it was with a kind
of Joy. Alas! Madam, (replied the young one) I now
remember that I have been so happy to have seen you;
but where and when, my Memory can't tell me. 'Tis
indeed some Years since, (return'd the Lady) But of that
another time.—Mean while, if you are unprovided of a
Lodging, I dare undertake, you shall be welcome to this
Gentlewoman. The Unfortunate returned her Thanks;
and whilst a Chamber was preparing for her, the Lady entertain'd her in her own. About Ten o'Clock they parted,
Bellamora being conducted to her Lodging by the Mistress
of the House, who then left her to take what Rest she
could amidst her so many Misfortunes; returning to the

other Lady, who desir'd her to search into the Cause of *Bellamora's* Retreat to Town.

The next Morning the good Gentlewoman of the House coming up to her, found *Bellamora* almost drown'd in Tears, which by many kind and sweet Words she at last stopp'd; and asking whence so great Signs of Sorrow should proceed, vow'd a most profound Secrecy if she would discover to her their Occasion; which, after some little Reluctancy, she did, in this manner.

I was courted (said she) above three Years ago, when my Mother was yet living, by one Mr. *Fondlove*, a Gentleman of good Estate, and true Worth; and one who, I dare believe, did then really love me : He continu'd his Passion for me, with all the earnest and honest Sollicitations imaginable, till some Months before my Mother's Death; who, at that time, was most desirous to see me disposed of in Marriage to another Gentleman, of much better Estate than Mr. *Fondlove*; but one whose Person and Humour did by no means hit with my Inclinations : And this gave *Fondlove* the unhappy Advantage over me. For, finding me one Day all alone in my Chamber, and lying on my Bed, in as mournful and wretched a Condition to my then foolish Apprehension, as now I am, he urged his Passion with such Violence, and accursed Success for me, with reiterated Promises of Marriage, whensoever I pleas'd to challenge 'em, which he bound with the most sacred Oaths, and most dreadful Execrations : that partly with my Aversion to the other, and partly with my Inclinations to pity him, I ruin'd my self.—Here she relaps'd into a greater Extravagance of Grief than before; which was so extreme that it did not continue long. When therefore she was pretty well come to herself, the antient Gentlewoman ask'd her, why she imagin'd herself ruin'd : To which she answer'd, I am great with Child by him, Madam, and wonder you did not perceive it last Night. Alas ! I have not a Month to go : I am asham'd, ruin'd, and damn'd, I fear, for ever lost. Oh ! fie, Madam, think not so, (said the other) for the Gentleman may yet prove true, and marry you. Ay, Madam (replied *Bellamora*) I doubt not that he would marry me ; for soon after my Mother's Death, when I came to be at my own Disposal, which happen'd about two Months after, he offer'd, nay most earnestly sollicited me to it, which still he perseveres to do. This is strange ! (return'd the other) and it appears to me to be your own Fault, that you are yet miserable. Why did you not, or why will you not consent to your own Happiness ? Alas ! (cry'd *Bellamora*) 'tis the only Thing I dread in this World : For, I am certain, he can never love me after. Besides, ever since I have abhorr'd the Sight of him : and this is the only Cause that obliges me to forsake my Uncle, and all my Friends and Relations in the Country, hoping in this populous and publick Place to be most private, especially, Madam, in your House, and in your Fidelity and Discretion. Of the last you may assure yourself, Madam, (said the other :) but what Provision have you made for the Reception of the young Stranger that you carry about you ? Ah, Madam ! (cryd *Bellamora*) you have brought to my Mind another Misfortune : Then she acquainted her with the suppos'd loss of her Money and Jewels, telling her withall, that she had but three Guineas and some Silver left, and the Rings she wore, in her present possession. The good Gentlewoman of the House told her, she would send to enquire at the Inn where she lay the first Night she came to Town ; for, haply, they might give some Account of the Porter to whom she had entrusted her Trunk ; and withal repeated her Promise of all the Help in her Power, and for that time left her much more composed than she found her. The good Gentlewoman went directly to the other Lady, her Lodger, to whom she recounted *Bellamora's* mournful Confession ; at which the Lady appear'd mightily concern'd : and at last she told her Landlady, that she would take Care that *Bellamora* should lie in according to her Quality : For, added she, the Child, it seems, is my own Brother's.

As soon as she had din'd, she went to the *Exchange*, and bought Child-bed Linen ; but desired that *Bellamora* might not have the least Notice of it : And at her return dispatch'd a Letter to her Brother *Fondlove* in *Hampshire*, with an Account of every Particular ; which soon brought him up to Town, without satisfying any of his or her Friends with the Reason of his sudden Departure.   Mean while, the good Gentlewoman of the House had sent to the *Star Inn* on *Fish-street-Hill*, to demand the Trunk, which she rightly suppos'd to have been carried back thither : For by good Luck, it was a Fellow that ply'd thereabouts, who brought it to *Bellamora's* Lodgings that very Night, but unknown to her.   *Fondlove* no sooner got to *London*, but he posts to his Sister's Lodgings, where he was advis'd not to be seen of *Bellamora* till they had work'd farther upon her, which the Landlady began in this manner ; she told her that her Things were mis-carried, and she fear'd, lost ; that she had but a little Money her self, and if the Overseers of the Poor (justly so call'd from their over-looking 'em) should have the least Suspicion of a strange and unmarried Person, who was entertain'd in her House big with Child, and so near her Time as *Bellamora* was, she should be troubled, if they could not give Security to the Parish of twenty or thirty Pounds, that they should not suffer by her, which she could not ; or otherwise she must be sent to the House of Correction, and her Child to a Parish-Nurse. This Discourse, one may imagine, was very dreadful to a Person of her Youth, Beauty, Education, Family and Estate : However, she resolutely protested, that she had rather undergo all this, than be expos'd to the Scorn of her Friends and Relations in the Country.   The other

told her then, that she must write down to her Uncle a
Farewell-Letter, as if she were just going aboard the
Pacquet-Boat for *Holland*, that he might not send to
enquire for her in Town, when he should understand
she was not at her new-married Cousin's in the Country;
which accordingly she did, keeping her self close Prisoner
to her Chamber; where she was daily visited by *Fondlove's*
Sister and the Landlady, but by no Soul else, the first
dissembling the Knowledge she had of her Misfortunes.
Thus she continued for above three Weeks, not a Servant
being suffer'd to enter her Chamber, so much as to make
her Bed, lest they should take Notice of her great Belly :
but for all this Caution, the Secret had taken Wind, by
the means of an Attendant of the other Lady below, who
had over-heard her speaking of it to her Husband. This
soon got out of Doors, and spread abroad, till it reach'd
the long Ears of the Wolves of the Parish, who next Day
design'd to pay her a Visit : But *Fondlove*, by good Providence, prevented it; who, the Night before, was usher'd
into *Bellamora's* Chamber by his Sister, his Brother-in-Law,
and the Landlady. At the Sight of him she had like
to have swoon'd away : but he taking her in his Arms,
began again, as he was wont to do, with Tears in his
Eyes, to beg that she would marry him ere she was
deliver'd; if not for his, nor her own, yet for the Child's
Sake, which she hourly expected; that it might not be
born out of Wedlock, and so be made uncapable of
inheriting either of their Estates; with a great many
more pressing Arguments on all Sides : To which at last
she consented; and an honest officious Gentleman, whom
they had before provided, was call'd up, who made an
End of the Dispute : So to Bed they went together that
Night; next Day to the *Exchange*, for several pretty
Businesses that Ladies in her Condition want. Whilst
they were abroad, came the Vermin of the Parish, (I
mean, the Overseers of the Poor, who eat the Bread from

'em) to search for a young Blackhair'd Lady (for so was
Bellamora) who was either brought to Bed, or just ready
to lie down.   The Landlady shew'd 'em all the Rooms
in her House, but no such Lady could be found.   At last
she bethought her self, and led 'em into her Parlour,
where she open'd a little Closet-door, and shew'd 'em
a black Cat that had just kitten'd: assuring 'em, that she
should never trouble the Parish as long as she had Rats
or Mice in the House; and so dismiss'd 'em like Logger-
heads as they came.

THE COURT OF
THE KING OF BANTAM.

THE COURT OF
THE KING OF *BANTAM*.

THIS Money certainly is a most devilish Thing! I'm sure the Want of it had like to have ruin'd my dear *Philibella*, in her Love to *Valentine Goodland*; who was really a pretty deserving Gentleman, Heir to about fifteen hundred Pounds a Year; which, however, did not so much recommend him, as the Sweetness of his Temper, the Comeliness of his Person, and the Excellency of his Parts: In all which Circumstances my obliging Acquaintance equal'd him, unless in the Advantage of their Fortune. Old Sir *George Goodland* knew of his Son's Passion for *Philibella*; and tho' he was generous, and of a Humour sufficiently complying, yet he could by no means think it convenient, that his only Son should marry with a young Lady of so slender a Fortune as my Friend, who had not above five hundred Pound, and that the Gift of her Uncle Sir *Philip Friendly*: tho' her Virtue and Beauty might have deserv'd, and have adorn'd the Throne of an *Alexander* or a *Cæsar*.

Sir *Philip* himself, indeed, was but a younger Brother, tho' of a good Family, and of a generous Education; which, with his Person, Bravery, and Wit, recommended him to his Lady *Philadelphia*, Widow of Sir *Bartholomew Banquier*, who left her possess'd of two thousand Pounds *per Annum*, besides twenty thousand Pounds in Money and Jewels; which oblig'd him to get himself dubb'd, that she might not descend to an inferior Quality. When he was in Town, he liv'd—let me see! in the *Strand*; or, as near as I can remember, somewhere about *Charing-Cross*; where first of all Mr. *Would-be King*, a Gentleman of a large

Estate in Houses, Land and Money, of a haughty, extravagant and profuse Humour, very fond of every new Face, had the Misfortune to fall passionately in love with *Philibella*, who then liv'd with her Uncle.

This Mr. *Would-be* it seems had often been told, when he was yet a Stripling, either by one of his Nurses, or his own Grandmother, or by some other Gypsy, that he should infallibly be what his Sirname imply'd, a King, by Providence or Chance, ere he dy'd, or never. This glorious Prophecy had so great an Influence on all his Thoughts and Actions, that he distributed and dispers'd his Wealth sometimes so largely, that one would have thought he had undoubtedly been King of some Part of the *Indies*; to see a Present made to-day of a Diamond Ring, worth two or three hundred Pounds, to Madam *Flippant*; to-morrow, a large Chest of the finest *China* to my Lady *Fleecewell*; and next Day, perhaps, a rich Necklace of large Oriental Pearl, with a Locket to it of Saphires, Emeralds, Rubies, &c., to pretty Miss *Ogle-me*, for an amorous Glance, for a Smile, and (it may be, tho' but rarely) for the mighty Blessing of one single Kiss. But such were his Largesses, not to reckon his Treats, his Balls, and Serenades besides, tho' at the same time he had marry'd a virtuous Lady, and of good Quality: But her Relation to him (it may be fear'd) made her very disagreeable: For a Man of his Humour and Estate can no more be satisfy'd with one Woman, than with one Dish of Meat; and to say Truth, 'tis something unmodish. However, he might have dy'd a pure Celibate, and altogether unexpert of Women, had his good or bad Hopes only terminated in Sir *Philip's* Niece. But the brave and haughty Mr. *Would-be* was not to be baulk'd by Appearances of Virtue, which he thought all Womankind only did affect; besides, he promis'd himself the Victory over any Lady whom he attempted, by the Force of his damn'd Money, tho' her Virtue were ever so real and strict.

With *Philibella* he found another pretty young Creature, very like her, who had been a *quondam* Mistress to Sir *Philip*: He, with young *Goodland*, was then diverting his Mistress and Niece at a Game at Cards, when *Would-be* came to visit him; he found 'em very merry, with a Flask or two of Claret before 'em, and Oranges roasting by a large Fire, for it was *Christmas-time*. The Lady *Friendly* understanding that this extraordinary Man was with Sir *Philip* in the Parlour, came in to 'em, to make the number of both Sexes equal, as well as in Hopes to make up a Purse of Guineas toward the Purchase of some new fine Business that she had in her Head, from his accustom'd Design of losing at Play to her. Indeed, she had Part of her Wish, for she got twenty Guineas of him; *Philibella* ten; and *Lucy*, Sir *Philip's* quondam, five: Not but that *Would-be* intended better Fortune to the young ones, than he did to Sir *Philip's* Lady; but her Ladyship was utterly unwilling to give him over to their Management, tho' at the last, when they were all tir'd with the Cards, after *Would-be* had said as many obliging things as his present Genius would give him leave, to *Philibella* and *Lucy*, especially to the first, not forgetting his Baisemains to the Lady *Friendly*, he bid the Knight and *Goodland* adieu; but with a Promise of repeating his Visit at six a-clock in the Evening on *Twelfth-Day*, to renew the famous and antient Solemnity of chusing King and Queen; to which Sir *Philip* before invited him, with a Design yet unknown to you, I hope.

As soon as he was gone, every one made their Remarks on him, but with very little or no Difference in all their Figures of him. In short, all Mankind, had they ever known him, would have universally agreed in this his Character, That he was an Original; since nothing in Humanity was ever so vain, so haughty, so profuse, so fond, and so ridiculously ambitious, as Mr. *Would-be King*. They laugh'd and talk'd about an Hour longer, and then young *Goodland* was oblig'd to see *Lucy* home in his Coach; tho' he had rather have sat up all Night in the same House with *Philibella*, I fancy, of whom he took but an unwilling Leave; which was visible enough to every one there, since they were all acquainted with his Passion for my fair Friend.

About twelve a-clock on the Day prefix'd, young *Goodland* came to dine with Sir *Philip*, whom he found just return'd from Court, in a very good Humour. On the Sight of *Valentine*, the Knight ran to him, and embracing him, told him, That he had prevented his Wishes, in coming thither before he sent for him, as he had just then design'd. The other return'd, that he therefore hoped he might be of some Service to him, by so happy a Prevention of his intended Kindness. No doubt (reply'd Sir *Philip*) the Kindness, I hope, will be to us both; I am assur'd it will, if you will act according to my Measures. I desire no better Prescriptions for my Happiness (return'd *Valentine*) than what you shall please to set down to me: But is it necessary or convenient that I should know 'em first? It is, (answer'd Sir *Philip*) let us sit, and you shall understand 'em.—I am very sensible (continu'd he) of your sincere and honourable Affection and Pretension to my Niece, who, perhaps, is as dear to me as my own Child could be, had I one; nor am I ignorant how averse Sir *George* your Father is to your Marriage with her, insomuch that I am confident he would disinherit you immediately upon it, merely for want of a Fortune somewhat proportionable to your Estate: but I have now contrived the Means to add two or three thousand Pounds to the five hundred I have design'd to give with her; I mean, if you marry her, *Val*, not otherwise; for I will not labour so for any other Man. What inviolable Obligations you put upon me! (cry'd *Goodland*.) No Return, by way of Compliments, good *Val*, (said the Knight:) Had I not engag'd to my Wife, before Marriage, that I would not dispose of any part of what she brought me, without her Consent, I would certainly make *Philibella's* Fortune answerable to your Estate : And besides, my Wife is not yet full eight and twenty, and we may therefore expect Children of our own, which hinders me from proposing any thing more for the Advantage of my Niece.—But now to my Instructions ;—*King* will be here this Evening without fail, and, at some Time or other to-night, will shew the Haughtiness of his Temper to you, I doubt not, since you are in a manner a Stranger to him : Be sure therefore you seem to quarrel with him before you part, but suffer as much as you can first from his Tongue ; for I know he will give you Occasions enough to exercise your passive Valour. I must appear his Friend, and you must retire Home, if you please, for this Night, but let me see you as early as your Convenience will permit to-morrow : my late Friend *Lucy* must be my Niece too. Observe this, and leave the rest to me. I shall most punctually, and will in all things be directed by you, (said *Valentine*.) I had forgot to tell you (said *Friendly*) that I have so order'd matters, that he must be King to-night, and *Lucy* Queen, by the Lots in the Cake. By all means (return'd *Goodland ;*) it must be Majesty.

Exactly at six a'clock came *Wou'd-be* in his Coach and six, and found Sir *Philip*, and his Lady, *Goodland*, *Philibella*, and *Lucy* ready to receive him ; *Lucy* as fine as a Dutchess, and almost as beautiful as she was before her Fall. All things were in ample Order for his Entertainment. They play'd till Supper was serv'd in, which was between eight and nine. The Treat was very seasonable and splendid. Just as the second Course was set on the Table, they were all on a sudden surpriz'd, except *Would-be*, with a Flourish of Violins, and other Instruments, which proceeded to entertain 'em with the best and newest Airs in the last new Plays, being then in the Year 1683. The Ladies were curious to know to whom they ow'd the chearful

part of their Entertainment: On which he call'd out,
Hey! *Tom Farmer! Aleworth! Eccles! Hall!* and the
rest of you! Here's a Health to these Ladies, and all
this honourable Company. They bow'd; he drank, and
commanded another Glass to be fill'd, into which he put
something yet better than the Wine, I mean, ten Guineas:
Here, *Farmer*, (said he then) this for you and your Friends.
We humbly thank the honourable Mr. *Would-be King*.
They all return'd, and struck up with more Spriteliness
than before. For Gold and Wine, doubtless, are the best
Rosin for Musicians.

After Supper they took a hearty Glass or two to the
King, Queen, Duke, *&c.* And then the mighty Cake,
teeming with the Fate of this extraordinary Personage,
was brought in, the Musicians playing an Overture at the
Entrance of the *Alimental Oracle;* which was then cut
and consulted, and the royal Bean and Pea fell to those
to whom Sir *Philip* had design'd 'em. 'Twas then the
Knight began a merry Bumper, with three Huzza's, and,
Long live King Would-be! to *Goodland*, who echo'd and
pledg'd him, putting the Glass about to the harmonious
Attendants; while the Ladies drank their own Quantities
among themselves, *To his aforesaid Majesty.* Then of
course you may believe Queen *Lucy's* Health went merrily
round, with the same Ceremony: After which he saluted
his Royal Consort, and condescended to do the same
Honour to the two other Ladies.

Then they fell a dancing, like Lightning; I mean,
they mov'd as swift, and made almost as little Noise; But
his Majesty was soon weary of that; for he long'd to be
making love both to *Philibella* and *Lucy*, who (believe me)
that Night might well enough have passed for a Queen.

They fell then to Questions and Commands; to cross
Purposes: *I think a Thought, what is it like?* &c. In all
which, his *Would-be* Majesty took the Opportunity of
shewing the Excellency of his Parts, as, How fit he was

to govern ! How dextrous at mining and countermining ! and, How he could reconcile the most contrary and distant Thoughts ! The Musick, at last, good as it was, grew troublesome and too loud ; which made him dismiss them : And then he began to this effect, addressing himself to *Philibella :* Madam, had Fortune been just, and were it possible that the World should be govern'd and influenc'd by two Suns, undoubtedly we had all been Subjects to you, from this Night's Chance, as well as to that Lady, who indeed alone can equal you in the Empire of Beauty, which yet you share with her Majesty here present, who only could dispute it with you, and is only superior to you in Title. My Wife is infinitely oblig'd to your Majesty, (interrupted Sir *Philip*) who in my Opinion, has greater Charms, and more than both of them together. You ought to think so, Sir *Philip* (returned the new dubb'd King) however you should not liberally have express'd your self, in Opposition and Derogation to Majesty :— Let me tell you 'tis a saucy Boldness that thus has loos'd your Tongue !—What think you, young Kinsman and Counsellor ? (said he to *Goodland*.) With all Respect due to your sacred Title, (return'd *Valentene*, rising and bowing) Sir *Philip* spoke as became a truly affectionate Husband ; and it had been Presumption in him, unpardonable, to have seem'd to prefer her Majesty, or that other sweet Lady, in his Thoughts, since your Majesty has been pleas'd to say so much and so particularly of their Merits : 'Twould appear as if he durst lift up his Eyes, with Thoughts too near the Heaven you only would enjoy. And only can deserve, you should have added, (said *King*, no longer *Would-be*.) How ! may it please your Majesty (cry'd *Friendly*) both my Nieces ! tho' you deserve ten thousand more, and better, would your Majesty enjoy them both ? Are they then both your Nieces ? (asked Chance's King). Yes, both, Sir (return'd the Knight,) her Majesty's the eldest, and in that Fortune has shewn some Justice. So she has (reply'd the titular Monarch : My Lot is fair (pursu'd he) tho' I can be bless'd but with one.

> *Let Majesty with Majesty be join'd,*
> *To get and leave a Race of Kings behind.*

Come, Madam (continued he, kissing *Lucy*, this, as an Earnest of our future Endeavours. I fear (return'd the pretty Queen) your Majesty will forget the unhappy *Statira*, when you return to the Embraces of your dear and beautiful *Roxana*. There is none beautiful but you (reply'd the titular King) unless this Lady, to whom I yet could pay my Vows most zealously, were't not that Fortune has thus pre-engaged me. But, Madam (continued he) to shew that still you hold our Royal Favour, and that, next to our Royal Consort, we esteem you, we greet you thus (kissing *Philibella ;*) and as a Signal of our continued Love, wear this rich Diamond : (here he put a Diamond Ring on her Finger, worth three hundred Pounds.) Your Majesty (pursu'd he to *Lucy*) may please to wear this Necklace, with this Locket of Emeralds. Your Majesty is bounteous as a God ! (said *Valentine*.) Art thou in Want, young Spark ? (ask'd the King of *Bantam*) I'll give thee an Estate shall make thee merit the Mistress of thy Vows, be she who she will. That is my other Niece, Sir, (cry'd *Friendly*.) How ! how ! presumptious Youth ! How are thy Eyes and Thoughts exalted ? ha ! To Bliss your Majesty must never hope for, (reply'd *Goodland*.) How now ! thou Creature of the basest Mold ! Not hope for what thou dost aspire to ! *Mock-King;* thou canst not, dar'st not, shalt not hope it : (return'd *Valentine* in a heat.) Hold, *Val*, (cry'd Sir *Philip*) you grow warm, forget your Duty to their Majesties, and abuse your Friends, by making us suspected. Good-night, dear *Philibella*, and my Queen ! Madam, I am your Ladyship's Servant (said *Goodland :*) Farewel, Sir *Philip* : Adieu, thou Pageant ! thou Property-King ! I shall see thy Brother on the Stage ere long ; but first I'll visit thee : and in the meantime, by way of Return to thy proffer'd Estate, I shall add a real Territory to the rest of thy empty Titles; for from thy Education, barbarous manner of Conversation, and Complexion, I think I may justly proclaim thee, *King of* Bantam—So, *Hail, King that Would-be! Hail thou King of* Christmas ! *All-hail, Wou'd-be King of* Bantam—and so he left 'em.—They all seem'd amazed, and gaz'd on one another, without speaking a Syllable ; 'till Sir *Philip* broke the Charm, and sigh'd out, Oh, the monstrous Effects of Passion ! Say rather, Oh, the foolish Effects of a mean Education ! (interrupted his Majesty of *Bantam*.) For Passions were given us for Use, Reason to govern and direct us in the Use, and Education to cultivate and refine that Reason. But (pursu'd he) for all his Impudence to me, which I shall take a time to correct, I am oblig'd to him, that at last he has found me out a Kingdom to my Title ; and if I were Monarch of that Place (believe me, Ladies) I would make you all Princesses and Duchesses ; and thou, my old Companion, *Friendly*, should rule the Roast with me. But these Ladies should be with us there, where we could erect Temples and Altars to 'em ; build Golden Palaces of Love, and Castles—in the Air (interrupted her Majesty, *Lucy* I. smiling.) 'Gad take me (cry'd King *Wou'd-be*) thou dear Partner of my Greatness, and shalt be, of all my Pleasures ! thy pretty satirical Observation has oblig'd me beyond Imitation. I think your Majesty is got into a Vein of Rhiming to-night, (said *Philadelphia*.) Ay ! Pox of that young insipid Fop, we could else have been as great as an Emperor of *China*, and as witty as *Horace* in his Wine ; but let him go, like a pragmatical, captious, giddy Fool as he is ! I shall take a Time to see him. Nay, Sir, (said *Philibella*) he has promis'd your Majesty a Visit in our Hearing. Come, Sir, I beg your Majesty to pledge me this Glass to your long and happy Reign ; laying aside all Thoughts of ungovern'd Youth :

Besides, this Discourse must needs be ungrateful to her Majesty, to whom, I fear, he will be marry'd within this Month ! How ! (cry'd *King and no King*) married to my Queen ! I must not, cannot suffer it ! Pray restrain your self a little, Sir (said Sir *Philip*) and when once these Ladies have left us, I will discourse your Majesty further about this Business. Well, pray, Sir *Philip*, (said his Lady) let not your Worship be pleas'd to sit up too long for his Majesty : About five o'Clock I shall expect you ; 'tis your old Hour. And yours, Madam, to wake to receive me coming to Bed—Your Ladyship understands me, (return'd *Friendly*.) You're merry, my Love, you're merry, (cry'd *Philadelphia :*) Come, Niece, to Bed ! to Bed ! Ay, (said the Knight) Go, both of you and sleep together, if you can, without the Thoughts of a Lover, or a Husband. His Majesty was pleas'd to wish them a good Repose ; and so, with a Kiss, they parted for that time.

Now we're alone (said Sir *Philip*) let me assure you, Sir, I resent this Affront done to you by Mr. *Goodland*, almost as highly as you can : and tho' I can't wish that you should take such Satisfaction, as perhaps some other hotter Sparks would ; yet let me say, his Miscarriage ought not to go unpunish'd in him. Fear not (reply'd t'other) I shall give him a sharp Lesson. No, Sir (return'd *Friendly*) I would not have you think of a bloody Revenge ; for 'tis that which possibly he designs on you : I know him brave as any Man. However, were it convenient that the Sword should determine betwixt you, you should not want mine: The Affront is partly to me, since done in my House ; but I've already laid down safer Measures for us, tho' of more fatal Consequence to him : that is, I've form'd them in my Thoughts. Dismiss your Coach and Equipage, all but one Servant, and I will discourse it to you at large. 'Tis now past Twelve ; and if you please, I would invite you to take up as easy a Lodging here, as my House will afford. (Accordingly they were dismiss'd, and he proceeded :)—As I hinted to you before, he is in love with my youngest Niece, *Philibella*; but her Fortune not exceeding five hundred Pound, his Father will assuredly disinherit him, if he marries her : tho' he has given his Consent that he should marry her eldest Sister, whose Father dying ere he knew his Wife was with child of the youngest, left *Lucy* three thousand Pounds, being as much as he thought convenient to match her handsomly ; and accordingly the Nuptials of young *Goodland* and *Lucy* are to be celebrated next *Easter*. They shall not, if I can hinder them (interrupted his offended Majesty.) Never endeavour the Obstruction (said the Knight) for I'll shew you the Way to a dearer Vengeance : Women are Women, your Majesty knows ; she may be won to your Embraces before that time, and then you antedate him your Creature. A Cuckold, you mean (cry'd King in Fancy :) O exquisite Revenge ! but can you consent that I should attempt it ? What is't to me ? We live not in *Spain*, where all the Relations of the Family are oblig'd to vindicate a Whore : No, I would wound him in his most tender Part. But how shall we compass it ? (ask'd t'other.) Why thus, throw away three thousand Pounds on the youngest Sister, as a Portion, to make her as happy as she can be in her new Lover, Sir *Frederick Flygold*, an extravagant young Fop, and wholly given over to Gaming ; so, ten to one, but you may retrieve your Money of him, and have the two Sisters at your Devotion. Oh, thou my better Genius than that which was given to me by Heaven at my Birth ! What Thanks, what Praises shall I return and sing to thee for this ! (cry'd King *Conundrum*.) No Thanks, no Praises, I beseech your Majesty, since in this I gratify my self—You think I am your Friend ? and, you will agree to this ? (said *Friendly*, by way of Question.) Most readily, (returned the Fop King :) Would it were broad Day, that I might send for the Money to my Banker's ; for in all my Life, in all my Frolicks, Encounters and Extravagances, I never had one so grateful, and so pleasant as this will be, if you are in earnest, to gratify both my Love and Revenge! That I am in earnest, you will not doubt, when you see with what Application I shall pursue my Design : In the mean Time, *My Duty to your Majesty; To our good Success in this Affair.* While he drank, t'other return'd, *With all my Heart;* and pledg'd him. Then *Friendly* began afresh: Leave the whole Management of this to me; only one thing more I think necessary, that you make a Present of five hundred Guineas to her Majesty, the Bride that must be. By all means (return'd the wealthy King of *Bantam;*) I had so design'd before. Well, Sir (said Sir *Philip*) what think you of a set Party or two at *Piquet,* to pass away a few Hours, till we can sleep? A seasonable and welcome Proposition (returned the King;) but I won't play above twenty Guineas the Game, and forty the Lurch. Agreed (said *Friendly;*) first call in your Servant; mine is here already. The Slave came in, and they began, with unequal Fortune at first; for the Knight had lost a hundred Guineas to Majesty, which he paid in Specie; and then propos'd fifty Guineas the Game, and a hundred the Lurch. To which t'other consented; and without winning more than three Games, and those not together, made shift to get three thousand two hundred Guineas in debt to Sir *Philip;* for which Majesty was pleas'd to give him Bond, whether *Friendly* would or no,

Seal'd and deliver'd in the Presence of,

The Mark of *(W.) Will. Watchful.*
And, *(S) Sim. Slyboots.*

A couple of delicate Beagles, their mighty Attendants.

It was then about the Hour that Sir *Philip's* (and, it may be, other Ladies) began to yawn and stretch; when the Spirits refresh'd, troul'd about, and tickled the Blood with Desires of Action; which made Majesty and Worship think of a Retreat to Bed : where in less than half an Hour,

or before ever he cou'd say his Prayers, I'm sure the first
fell fast asleep; but the last, perhaps, paid his accustom'd
Devotion, ere he begun his Progress to the Shadow of
Death. However, he waked earlier than his Cully Majesty,
and got up to receive young *Goodland*, who came according
to his Word, with the first Opportunity. Sir *Philip* receiv'd
him with more than usual Joy, tho' not with greater
Kindness, and let him know every Syllable and Accident
that had pass'd between them till they went to Bed: which
you may believe was not a little pleasantly surprizing to
Valentine, who began then to have some Assurance of his
Happiness with *Philibella*. His Friend told him, that he
must now be reconcil'd to his *Mock-Majesty*, tho' with
some Difficulty; and so taking one hearty Glass a-piece,
he left *Valentine* in the Parlour to carry the ungrateful
News of his Visit to him that Morning. King—was in
an odd sort of taking, when he heard that *Valentine* was
below; and had been, as Sir *Philip* inform'd *Majesty*, at
Majesty's Palace, to enquire for him there: But when he
told him, that he had already school'd him on his own
Behalf, for the Affront done in his House, and that he
believ'd he could bring his Majesty off without any loss
of present Honour, his Countenance visibly discover'd
his past Fear, and present Satisfaction; which was much
encreas'd too, when *Friendly* shewing him his Bond for
the Money he won of him at play, let him know, that if
he paid three thousand Guineas to *Philibella*, he would
immediately deliver him up his Bond, and not expect the
two hundred Guineas overplus. His Majesty of *Bantam*
was then in so good a Humour, that he could have made
Love to Sir *Philip;* nay, I believe he could have kiss'd
Valentine, instead of seeming angry. Down they came,
and saluted like Gentlemen: But after the Greeting was
over, *Goodland* began to talk something of Affront, Satisfaction, Honour, *&c.* when immediately *Friendly* interpos'd,
and after a little seeming Uneasiness and Reluctancy,

reconcil'd the hot and cholerick Youth to the cold phleg-matick King.

Peace was no sooner proclaim'd, than the King of *Bantam* took his Rival and late Antagonist with him in his own Coach, not excluding Sir *Philip* by any means, to *Locket's*, where they din'd : Thence he would have 'em to Court with him, where he met the Lady *Flippant*, the Lady *Harpy*, the Lady *Crocodile*, Madam *Tattlemore*, Miss *Medler*, Mrs. *Gingerly*, a rich Grocer's Wife, and some others, besides Knights and Gentlemen of as good Humours as the Ladies; all whom he invited to a Ball at his own House, the Night following; his own Lady being then in the Country. Madam *Tattlemore*, I think was the first he spoke to in Court, and whom first he surpriz'd with the happy News of his Advancement to the Title of King of *Bantam*. How wondrous hasty was she to be gone, as soon as she heard it ! 'Twas not in her Power, because not in her Nature, to stay long enough to take a civil Leave of the Company ; but away she flew, big with the empty Title of a fantastick King, proclaiming it to every one of her Acquaintance, as she passed through every Room, till she came to the *Presence-Chamber*, where she only whisper'd it ; but her Whispers made above half the honourable Company quit the Presence of the King of *Great-Britain*, to go make their Court to his Majesty of *Bantam* : some cry'd, *God bless your Majesty!* Some *Long live the King of* Bantam ! Others, *All Hail to your Sacred Majesty;* In short, he was congratulated on all Sides. Indeed I don't hear that his Majesty King *Charles* II. ever sent an Ambassador to compliment him ; tho' possibly, he saluted him by his Title the first time he saw him afterwards : For, you know, he is a wonderful good-natur'd and well-bred Gentleman.

After he thought the Court of *England* was universally acquainted with his mighty Honour, he was pleas'd to think fit to retire to his own more private Palace, with Sir *Philip* and

Goodland, whom he entertain'd that Night very handsomly, till about seven o'Clock; when they went together to the Play, which was that Night, *A King and no King*. His Attendant-Friends could not forbear smiling, to think how aptly the Title of the Play suited his Circumstances. Nor could he choose but take Notice of it behind the Scenes, between Jest and Earnest; telling the Players how kind Fortune had been the Night past, in disposing the Bean to him; and justifying what one of her Prophetesses had foretold some Years since. I shall now no more regard (said he) that old doating Fellow *Pythagoras's* Saying *Abstineto a Fabis*, That is, (added he, by way of Construction) *Abstain from Beans*: for I find the Excellency of 'em in Cakes and Dishes; from the first, they inspire the Soul with mighty Thoughts; and from the last our Bodies receive a strong and wholesom Nourishment. That is, (said a Wag among those sharp Youths, I think 'twas my Friend the Count) these puff you up in Mind, Sir, those in Body. They had some further Discourse among the Nymphs of the Stage, ere they went into the Pit; where Sir *Philip* spread the News of his Friend's Accession to the Title, tho' not yet to the Throne of *Bantam*; upon which he was there again complimented on that Occasion. Several of the Ladies and Gentlemen who saluted him, he invited to the next Night's Ball at his Palace.

The Play done, they took each of them a Bottle at the *Rose*, and parted till Seven the Night following; which came not sooner than desired : for he had taken such Care, that all things were in readiness before Eight, only he was not to expect the Musick till the End of the Play. About Nine, Sir *Philip*, his Lady, *Goodland*, *Philibella*, and *Lucy* came. Sir *Philip* return'd him *Rabelais*, which he had borrow'd of him, wherein the Knight had written, in an old odd sort of a Character, this Prophecy of his own making ; with which he surpriz'd the Majesty of *Bantam*, who vow'd he had never taken Notice of it before ; but

he said, he perceiv'd it had been long written by the
Character ; and here it follows, as near as I can remember:

> *When* M. D. C. *come* L. *before*,
> *Three* XXX's, *two* II's *and one* I. *more* ;
> *Then* KIN G, *tho' now but Name to thee*,
> *Shall both thy Name and Title be.*

They had hardly made an End of reading it, ere the whole
Company, and more than he had invited, came in, and
were receiv'd with a great deal of Formality and Magnificence.   *Lucy* was there attended as his Queen ; and
Philibella, as the Princess her Sister.   They danc'd then
till they were weary ; and afterwards retired to another
large Room, where they found the Tables spread and
furnished with all the most seasonable cold Meat; which
was succeeded by the choicest Fruits, and the richest
Desert of Sweetmeats that Luxury could think on, or at
least that this Town could afford.   The Wines were all
most excellent in their Kind ; and their Spirits flew about
thro' every Corner of the House : There was scarce a
Spark sober in the whole Company, with drinking repeated
Glasses to the Health of the King of *Bantam*, and his
Royal Consort, with the Princess *Philibella's* who sat
together under a Royal Canopy of State, his Majesty
between the two beautiful Sisters : only *Friendly* and
Goodland wisely manag'd that part of the Engagement
where they were concern'd, and preserv'd themselves
from the Heat of the Debauch.

Between Three and Four most of them began to draw
off, laden with Fruit and Sweetmeats, and rich Favours
compos'd of Yellow, Green, Red and White, the Colours
of his new Majesty of *Bantam*.   Before Five they were
left to themselves ; when the Lady *Friendly* was discompos'd, for want of Sleep, and her usual Cordial, which
obliged Sir *Philip* to wait on her Home, with his two
Nieces : But his Majesty would by no means part with

Goodland; whom, before Nine that Morning, he made
as drunk as a Lord, and by Consequence, one of his Peers;
for Majesty was then, indeed, as great as an Emperor:
He fancy'd himself *Alexander*, and young *Valentine* his
Hephestion; and did so be-buss him, that the young
Gentleman fear'd he was fallen into the Hands of an
Italian. However, by the kind Persuasions of his con-
descending and dissembling Majesty, he ventur'd to go
into Bed with him; where King *Would-be* fell asleep,
hand-over-head: and not long after, *Goodland*, his new-
made Peer, follow'd him to the cool Retreats of *Morpheus*.

About Three the next Afternoon they both wak'd, as
by consent, and called to dress. And after that Business
was over, I think they swallow'd each of 'em a Pint of
Old-Hock, with a little Sugar, by the way of healing.
Their Coaches were got ready in the mean time; but the
Peer was forced to accept of the Honour of being carried
in his Majesty's to Sir *Philip's*, whom they found just
risen from Dinner, with *Philadelphia* and his two Nieces.
They sat down, and ask'd for something to relish a Glass
of Wine, and Sir *Philip* order'd a cold Chine to be set
before 'em, of which they eat about an Ounce a-piece;
but they drank more by half, I dare say.

After their little Repast, *Friendly* call'd the *Would-be-
Monarch* aside, and told him, that he would have him go
to the Play that Night, which was *The London-Cuckolds*;
promising to meet him there in less than half an Hour
after his Departure: telling him withal, that he would
surprize him with a much better Entertainment than
the Stage afforded. *Majesty* took the Hint, imagining,
and that rightly, that the Knight had some Intrigue in
his Head, for the Promotion of the Commonwealth of
Cuckoldom: In order therefore to his Advice, he took
his leave about a quarter of an Hour after.

When he was gone, Sir *Philip* thus bespoke his pretended Niece: Madam, I hope your Majesty will not

refuse me the Honour of waiting on you to a Place where you will meet with better Entertainment than your Majesty can expect from the best Comedy in Christendom. *Val,* (continued he) you must go with us, to secure me against the Jealousy of my Wife. That, indeed (return'd his Lady) is very material ; and you are mightily concern'd not to give me Occasion, I must own. You see I am now, (replied he:) But—come ! on with Hoods and Scarf ! (pursued he, to *Lucy*.) Then addressing himself again to his Lady ; Madam, (said he) we'll wait on you. In less Time than I could have drank a Bottle to my Share, the Coach was got ready, and on they drove to the Play-House. By the way, said *Friendly* to *Val.*—Your Honour, noble Peer, must be set down at *Long's* ; for only *Lucy* and I must be seen to his Majesty of *Bantam :* And now, I doubt not, you understand what you must trust to.—To be robb'd of her Majesty's Company, I warrant (return'd the other) for these long three Hours. Why (cry'd *Lucy*) you don't mean, I hope, to leave me with his Majesty of *Bantam ?* 'Tis for thy Good, Child ! 'Tis for thy Good (return'd *Friendly*.) To the *Rose* they got then ; where *Goodland* alighted, and expected Sir *Philip ;* who led *Lucy* into the King's Box, to his new Majesty ; where, after the first Scene, he left them together. The over-joy'd fantastick Monarch would fain have said some fine obliging Things to the Knight, as he was going out; but *Friendly's* Haste prevented 'em, who went directly to *Valentine,* took one Glass, call'd a Reckoning, mounted his Chariot, and away Home they came : where I believe he was welcome to his Lady ; for I never heard any thing to the contrary.

In the mean Time, his Majesty had not the Patience to stay out half the Play, at which he was saluted by above twenty Gentlemen and Ladies by his new and mighty Title : but out he led Miss Majesty ere the third Act was half done ; pretending, that it was so damn'd a bawdy Play, that he knew her Modesty had been already but

too much offended at it; so into his Coach he got her.
When they were seated, she told him she would go to no
Place with him, but to the Lodgings her Mother had taken
for her, when she first came to Town, and which still
she kept. Your Mother, Madam, (cry'd he) why, is Sir
Philip's Sister living then? His Brother's Widow is, Sir,
(she reply'd.) Is she there? (he ask'd.) No, Sir, (she
return'd;) she is in the Country. Oh, then we will
go thither to chuse. The Coach-man was then order'd
to drive to *Jermain-Street*; where, when he came in to the
Lodgings, he found 'em very rich and modishly furnish'd.
He presently call'd one of his Slaves, and whisper'd him
to get three or four pretty Dishes for Supper; and then
getting a Pen, Ink and Paper, writ a Note to *C—d* the
Goldsmith with *Temple-Bar*, for five hundred guineas;
which *Watchful* brought him, in less than an Hour's
time, when they were just in the Height of Supper;
Lucy having invited her Landlady, for the better Colour
of the Matter. His *Bantamite* Majesty took the Gold
from his Slave, and threw it by him in the Window, that
Lucy might take Notice of it; (which you may assure
yourself she did, and after Supper wink'd on the goodly
Matron of the House to retire, which she immediately
obey'd.) Then his Majesty began his Court very earnestly
and hotly, throwing the naked Guineas into her Lap:
which she seemed to refuse with much Disdain; but
upon his repeated Promises, confirm'd by unheard of
Oaths and Imprecations, that he would give her Sister
three thousand Guineas to her Portion, she began by
Degrees to mollify, and let the Gold lie quietly in her
Lap: And the next Night, after he had drawn Notes
on two or three of his Bankers, for the Payment of
three thousand Guineas to Sir *Philip*, or Order, and
received his own Bond, made for what he had lost at
Play, from *Friendly*, she made no great Difficulty to admit
his Majesty to her Bed. Where I think fit to leave 'em

for the present; for (perhaps) they had some private Business.

The next Morning before the Titular King was (I won't say up, or stirring, but) out of Bed, young *Goodland* and *Philibella* were privately marry'd; the Bills being all accepted and paid in two Days Time. As soon as ever the fantastick Monarch could find in his Heart to divorce himself from the dear and charming Embraces of his beautiful Bedfellow, he came flying to Sir *Philip*, with all the Haste that Imagination big with Pleasure could inspire him with, to discharge it self to a suppos'd Friend. The Knight told him, that he was really much troubled to find that his Niece had yielded so soon and easily to him; however, he wish'd him Joy: To which the other return'd, that he could never want it, whilst he had the Command of so much Beauty, and that without the ungrateful Obligations of Matrimony, which certainly are the most nauseous, hateful, pernicious and destructive of Love imaginable. Think you so, Sir? (ask'd the Knight;) we shall hear what a Friend of mine will say on such an Occasion, to-morrow about this Time: but I beseech your Majesty to conceal your Sentiments of it to him, lest you make him as uneasy as you seem to be in that Circumstance. Be assur'd I will, (return'd the other:) But when shall I see the sweet, the dear, the blooming, the charming *Philibella?* She will be with us at Dinner. Where's her Majesty? (ask'd Sir *Philip*) Had you enquir'd before, she had been here; for, look, she comes! *Friendly* seems to regard her with a Kind of Displeasure, and whisper'd Majesty, that he should express no particular Symptoms of Familiarity with *Lucy* in his House, at any Time, especially when *Goodland* was there, as then he was above with his Lady and *Philibella*, who came down presently after to Dinner.

About Four o'Clock, as his Majesty had intrigu'd with her, *Lucy* took a Hackney-Coach, and went to her

Lodgings; whither about an Hour after, he follow'd her, Next Morning, at nine, he came to *Friendly's*, who carry'd him up to see his new-married Friends—But (O Damnation to Thoughts!) what Torments did he feel, when he saw young *Goodland* and *Philibella* in bed together; the last of which return'd him humble and hearty Thanks for her Portion and Husband, as the first did for his Wife. He shook his Head at Sir *Philip*, and without speaking one Word, left 'em, and hurry'd to *Lucy*, to lament the ill Treatment he had met with from *Friendly*. They coo'd and bill'd as long as he was able; she (sweet Hypocrite) seeming to bemoan his Misfortunes; which he took so kindly, that when he left her, which was about three in the Afternoon, he caus'd a Scrivener to draw up an Instrument, wherein he settled a hundred Pounds a Year on *Lucy* for her Life, and gave her a hundred Guineas more against her Lying-in: (For she told him, and indeed 'twas true, that she was with child, and knew her self to be so from a very good Reason—) And indeed she was so —by the *Friendly* Knight. When he return'd to her, he threw the obliging Instrument into her Lap; (it seems he had a particular Kindness for that Place—) then call'd for Wine, and something to eat; for he had not drank a Pint to his Share all the Day, (tho' he had ply'd it at the Chocolate-House.—) The Landlady, who was invited to sup with 'em, bid 'em good-night, about eleven; when they went to bed, and partly slept till about six; when they were entertain'd by some Gentleman of their Acquaintance, who play'd and sung very finely, by way of *Epithalamium*, these Words and more:

> *Joy to great* Bantam!
> *Live long, love and wanton!*
> *And thy Royal Consort!*
> *For both are of one Sort*, &c.

The rest I have forgot. He took some Offence at the

Words; but more at the Visit that Sir *Philip*, and *Goodland*, made him, about an Hour after, who found him in Bed with his Royal Consort; and after having wish'd 'em Joy, and thrown their Majesties own Shoes and Stockings at their Head, retir'd. This gave Monarch in Fancy so great a Caution that he took his Royal Consort into the Country, (but above forty Miles off the Place where his own Lady was) where, in less than eight Months, she was deliver'd of a Princely Babe, who was Christen'd by the Heathenish Name of *Hayoumorecake Bantam*, while her Majesty lay in like a pretty Queen.

THE
UNFORTUNATE HAPPY LADY:
A TRUE HISTORY.

THE
UNFORTUNATE HAPPY LADY:
A True History.

I cannot omit giving the World an account, of the uncommon Villany of a Gentleman of a good Family in
England practis'd upon his Sister, which was attested to
me by one who liv'd in the Family, and from whom I had
the whole Truth of the Story. I shall conceal the unhappy
Gentleman's own, under the borrow'd Names of Sir
William Wilding, who succeeded his Father Sir *Edward*,
in an Estate of near 4000*l.* a Year, inheriting all that
belong'd to him, except his Virtues. 'Tis true, he was
oblig'd to pay his only Sister a Portion of 6000*l.* which
he might very easily have done out of his Patrimony in a
little Time, the Estate being not in the least incumbred.
But the Death of his good Father gave a loose to the
Extravagancy of his Inclinations, which till then was
hardly observable. The first Discovery he made of his
Humour, was in the extraordinary rich Equipage he
prepar'd for his Journey to *London*, which was much
greater than his fair and plentiful Fortune cou'd maintain,
nor were his Expences any way inferior to the Figure he
made here in Town ; insomuch, that in less than a Twelve-
Month, he was forc'd to return to his Seat in the Country,
to Mortgage a part of his Estate of a Thousand Pounds a
Year, to satisfy the Debts he had already contracted in his
profuse Treats, Gaming and Women, which in a few
Weeks he effected, to the great Affliction of his Sister
Philadelphia, a young Lady of excellent Beauty, Education,
and Virtue ; who, fore-seeing the utter Ruin of the Estate,

if not timely prevented, daily begg'd of him, with Prayers and Tears, that might have mov'd a *Scythian* or wild *Arab*, or indeed any thing but him, to pay her her Portion. To which, however, he seemingly consented, and promis'd to take her to Town with him, and there give her all the Satisfaction she cou'd expect : And having dipp'd some paltry Acres of Land, deeper than ever Heaven dipp'd 'em in Rain, he was as good as his Word, and brought her to Town with him, where he told her he would place her with an ancient Lady, with whom he had contracted a Friendship at his first coming to *London ;* adding, that she was a Lady of incomparable Morals, and of a matchless Life and Conversation. *Philadelphia* took him in the best Sense, and was very desirous to be planted in the same House with her, hoping she might grow to as great a Perfection in such excellent Qualifications, as she imagined 'em. About four Days therefore after they had been in Town, she sollicits her Brother to wait on that Lady with her : He reply'd, that it is absolutely Necessary and Convenient that I should first acquaint her with my Design, and beg that she will be pleas'd to take you into her Care, and this shall be my chief Business to Day : Accordingly, that very Hour he went to the Lady *Beldams,* his reverend and honourable Acquaintance, whom he prepar'd for the Reception of his Sister, who he told her was a Cast-Mistress of his, and desir'd her Assistance to prevent the Trouble and Charge, which she knew such Cattle would bring upon young Gentlemen of plentiful Estates. To morrow Morning about Eleven, I'll leave her with your Ladyship, who, I doubt not, will give her a wholesome Lesson or two before Night, and your Reward is certain. My Son, (return'd she) I know the Greatness of your Spirit, the Heat of your Temper has both warm'd and inflam'd me ! I joy to see you in Town again—Ah ! That I could but recal one twenty Years for your Sake !—Well—no matter. —I won't forget your Instructions, nor my Duty to

Morrow : In the mean time, I'll drink your Health in a Bottle of *Sherry* or two. O ! Cry your Mercy, good my Lady *Beldam*, (said the young Debauchee) I had like to have forfeited my Title to your Care, in not remembring to leave you an Obligation. There are three Guinea's, which, I hope, will plead for me till to Morrow.—So— Your Ladyship's Servant humbly kisses your Hand. Your Honours most Obedient Servant, most gratefully Acknowledges your Favours.—Your humble Servant, Good Sir *William*, added she, seeing him leave her in haste.

Never were three Persons better pleas'd for a Time than this unnatural Man, his sweet innocent Sister, and the Lady *Beldam ;* upon his return to *Philadelphia,* who could not rest that Night, for thinking on the Happiness she was going to enjoy in the Conversation of so virtuous a Lady as her Brother's Acquaintance, to whom she was in Hopes that she might discover her dearest Thoughts, and complain of Sir *William's* Extravagance and Unkindness, without running the Hazzard of being betray'd ; and at the same Time, reasonably expect from so pious a Lady all the Assistance within her Capacity. On the other side, her Brother hugg'd himself in the Prospect he had of getting rid of his own Sister, and the Payment of 6000*l.* for the Sum of forty or fifty Guineas, by the Help and Discretion of this sage Matron ; who, for her part, by this Time, had reckon'd up, and promis'd to herself an Advantage of at least three hundred Pounds, one way or other by this bargain.

About Ten the next Morning, Sir *William* took Coach with his Sister, for the old Lady's Enchanted Castle, taking only one Trunk of hers with them for the present, promising her to send her other Things to her the next Day. The young Lady was very joyfully and respectfully received by her Brother's venerable Acquaintance, who was mightily charm'd with her Youth and Beauty. A Bottle of the Best was then strait brought in, and not long after a very splendid Entertainment for Breakfast: The Furniture was all very modish and rich, and the Attendance was suitable. Nor was the Lady *Beldam's* Conversation less obliging and modest, than Sir *William's* Discourse had given *Philadelphia* occasion to expect. After they had eaten and drank what they thought Convenient, the reverend old Lady led 'em out of the Parlour to shew 'em the House, every Room of which they found answerably furnish'd to that whence they came. At last she led 'em into a very pleasant Chamber, richly hung, and curiously adorn'd with the Pictures of several beautiful young Ladies, wherein there was a Bed which might have been worthy the Reception of a Dutchess: This, Madam, (said she) is your Apartment, with the Anti-chamber, and little Withdrawing-Room. Alas, Madam! (returned the dear innocent unthinking Lady) you set too great a Value on your Servant; but I rather think your Ladyship designs me this Honour for the sake of Sir *William*, who has had the Happiness of your Acquaintance for some Months: Something for Sir *William*, (returned the venerable Lady *Beldam*) but much more for your Ladyship's own, as you will have Occasion to find hereafter. I shall Study to deserve your Favours and Friendship, Madam, reply'd *Philadelphia*: I hope you will, Madam, said the barbarous Man. But my Business now calls me hence; to Morrow at Dinner I will return to you, and Order the rest of your Things to be brought with me. In the mean while (pursu'd the Traytor, kissing his Sister, as he thought and hop'd the last time) be as chearful as you can, my Dear! and expect all you can wish from me. A thousand Thanks, my dearest Brother, return'd she, with Tears in her Eyes: And Madam, (said he to his old mischievous Confederate, giving her a very rich Purse which held 50 Guineas) be pleas'd to accept this Trifle, as an humble Acknowledgment of the great Favour you do this Lady, and the Care of her, which you promise; and I'm sure she cannot want.

—So, once more, (added he) my Dear! and, Madam! I
am your humble Servant *Jusqu' a Revoir*, and went out
bowing. Heavens bless my dear Brother! (cry'd *Philadelphia*) your Honour's most Faithful and obedient Servant,
said the venerable *Beldam*.

No sooner was the treacherous Brother gone, than the
old Lady taking *Philadelphia* by the Hand, led her into
the Parlour; where she began to her to this Effect: *If I
mistake not, Madam, you were pleas'd to call Sir* William
*Brother once or twice of late in Conversation: Pray be pleas'd
to satisfy my Curiosity so far as to inform me in the Truth
of this Matter? Is it really so or not?* *Philadelphia* reply'd,
blushing, your Ladyship strangely surprizes me with this
Question: For, I thought it had been past your Doubt
that it is so. Did not he let you know so much himself?
I humbly beg your Pardon, Madam, (returned the true
Offspring of old Mother *Eve*) that I have so visibly disturb'd
you by my Curiosity: But, indeed, Madam, Sir *William*
did not say your Ladyship was his Sister, when he gave
me the Charge of you, as of the nearest and dearest Friend
he had in the World. Now our Father and Mother are
dead, (said the sweet Innocent) who never had more
Children than us two, who can be a nearer or dearer
Friend unto me, than my Brother Sir *William*, or than I
his Sister to him? None? Certainly, you'll excuse me,
Madam, (answer'd t'other) a Wife or Mistress may. A
Wife indeed, (return'd the beautiful Innocent) has the
Pre-eminence, and perhaps, a Mistress too, if honourably
lov'd and sought for in Marriage: But, (she continu'd)
I can assure your Ladyship that he has not a Wife, nor
did I ever hear he had a Mistress yet. Love in Youth (said
old Venerable) is very fearful of Discovery. I have known,
Madam, a great many fine young Gentlemen and Ladies,
who have conceal'd their violent Passions and greater
Affection, under the Notion and Appellation of Brother
and Sister. And your Ladyship imagines, Sir *William*

and I do so? reply'd *Philadelphia*, by way of Question.
'Twere no imprudence, if you did, Madam, return'd old
Lady *Beldam*, with all the Subtlety she had learn'd from
the Serpent. Alas! Madam, (reply'd she) there is nothing
like Secrecy in Love: 'Tis the very Life and Soul of it! I
have been young myself, and have known it by Experience.
But, all this, Madam, (interrupted *Philadelphia*, something
nettl'd at her Discourse) all this can't convince me, that
I am not the true and only Sister both by Father and
Mother of Sir *William Wilding*; however, he wou'd
impose upon your Ladyship, for what Ends, indeed, I
know not, unless (unhappily, which Heaven forbid!) he
designs to gain your Ladship's Assistance in defeating me
of the Portion left me by my Father: But, (she continued
with Tears) I have too great an Assurance of your Virtue,
to Fear that you will consent to so wicked a Practise.
You may be confident, Madam, (said t'other) I never
will. And, supposing that he were capable of perpetrating
so base an Act of himself, yet if your Ladyship will be
guided and directed by me, I will shew you the Means
of living Happy and Great, without your Portion, or your
Brother's Help; so much I am charm'd with your Beauty
and Innocence.

But, pray, Madam, (pursu'd she) what is your Portion?
And what makes you doubt your Brother's Kindness?
Philadelphia then told her, how much her Brother was to
pay her, and gave her an Account of his Extravagancies,
as far as she knew 'em; to which t'other was no Stranger;
and (doubtless) cou'd have put a Period to her Sorrows
with her Life, had she given her as perfect a Relation of
his riotous and vicious Practices, as she was capable of:
But she had farther Business with her Life, and, in short,
bid her be of good Comfort, and lay all her Care on her,
and then she cou'd not miss of continual Happiness. The
sweet Lady took all her Promises for sterling, and kissing
her Impious Hand, humbly return'd her Thanks. Not

long after they went to Dinner; and in the Afternoon, three or four young Ladies came to visit the Right Reverend the Lady *Beldam* ; who told her new Guest, that these were all her Relations, and no less than her own Sister's Children. The Discourse among 'em was general and very modest, which lasted for some Hours : For, our Sex seldom wants matter of Tattle. But, whether their Tongues were then miraculously wearied, or that they were tir'd with one continued Scene of Place, I won't pretend to determine : But they left the Parlour for the Garden, where after about half an Hour's Walk, there was a very fine Desert of Sweetmeats and Fruits brought into one of the Arbours. *Cherbetts*, *Ros Solis*, rich and small Wines, with Tea, Chocolate, &c. compleated the old Lady's Treat ; the Pleasure of which was much heighten'd by the Voices of two of her Ladyship's Sham-Nieces, who sung very charmingly. The Dear, sweet Creature, thought she had happily got into the Company of Angels : But (alas!) they were Angels that had fallen more than once. She heard talk of Nunneries, and having never been out of her own Country till within four or five Days, she had certainly concluded she had been in one of those Religious-Houses now, had she but heard a Bell ring, and seen 'em kneel to Prayers, and make use of their Beads, as she had been told those happy people do. However it was, she was extremely pleas'd with the Place and Company. So nearly do's Hell counterfeit Heaven sometimes. At last, said one of the white Devils, wou'd my dear *Tommy* were here ! O Sister ! (cry'd another) you won't be long without your wish : For my Husband and he went out together, and both promis'd to be here after the Play. Is my Brother Sir *Francis* with him there ? (ask'd the first) yes, (answer'd the third) Sir *Thomas* and Sir *Francis* took Coach from St. *James's*, about two Hours since : We shall be excellent Company when they come, (said a fourth) ; I hope they'll bring the Fiddlers with 'em, added the first : Don't you love

Musick, Madam? (ask'd the old Lady *Beldam*) Sometimes, Madam, (reply'd *Philadelphia*) but now I am out o'tune myself.   A little harmless Mirth will chear your drooping Spirits, my dear, (return'd t'other, taking her by the Hand) come! These are all my Relations, as I told you, Madam; and so consequently are their Husbands. Are these Ladies all marry'd, Madam? *Philadelphia* ask'd. All, all, my dear Soul! (reply'd the insinuating Mother of Iniquity;) and thou shalt have a Husband too, e're long. Alas, Madam! (return'd the fair Innocent) I have no Merit, nor Money : Besides, I never yet could Love so well as to make Choice of one Man before another.

How long have you liv'd then, Madam? (ask'd the Lady *Beldam*) too long by almost sixteen Years, (reply'd *Philadelphia*) had Heaven seen good.   This Conversation lasted till Word was brought that Sir *Francis* and Sir *Thomas*, with Two other Gentlemen were just lighted at the Gate : Which so discompos'd the fair Innocent, that trembling, she begg'd leave to retire to her Chamber.   To which, after some Perswasion to the contrary, the venerable *Beldam* waited on her.   For, these were none of the Sparks to whom *Philadelphia* was design'd to be Sacrific'd. In her Retirement, the Beautiful dear Creature had the Satisfaction of venting her Grief in Tears, and addressing herself to Heaven, on which only she trusted, notwithstanding all the fair Promises of her reverend Hostess; she had not been retir'd above an Hour, e're a She-attendant waited on her, to know if she wanted any thing, and what she wou'd please to have for her Supper; if she wou'd not give her Lady the Honour of her Company below? To which she return'd, that she wou'd not Sup, and that she wanted nothing but Rest, which she wou'd presently seek in Bed.   This Answer brought up the Officious old Lady herself; who, by all Means wou'd needs see her undress'd, for other Reasons more than a bare Compliment; which she perform'd with a great deal of Ceremony, and a

Diligence that seem'd more than double. For she had then the Opportunity of observing the Delicacy of her Skin, the fine turn of her Limbs, and the richness of her Night-dress, part of the Furniture of her Trunk. As soon as she had cover'd herself, she kiss'd and wish'd her a good Repose. The dear Soul, as Innocent and White as her Linen, return'd her Thanks, and address'd herself to Sleep; out of which she was waken'd by a loud Consort of Musick, in less than two Hours time, which continu'd till long after Midnight. This occasion'd strange and doubtful Thoughts in her, tho' she was altogether so unskill'd in these Mysteries, that she cou'd not guess the right Meaning. She apprehended, that (possibly) her Brother had a Mistress, from the Lady *Beldam's* Discourse, and that this was their Place of Assignation: Suspecting too, that either Sir *Francis*, or Sir *Thomas*, of whom she had heard not long before, was Sir *William*, her Brother. The Musick and all the Noise in the House ceas'd about four a Clock in the Morning; when she again fell into a Sleep, that took away the Sense of her Sorrows, and Doubts 'till Nine; when she was again visited from her Lady, by the same She-attendant, to know how she had rested, and if she wou'd Please to Command her any Service. *Philadelphia* reply'd, That she had rested very well most Part of the Morning, and that she wanted nothing, but to know how her Lady had Slept, and whether she were in Health, unless it were the Sight of her Brother. The Servant return'd with this Answer to her Lady, while *Philadelphia* made shift to rise, and begin to Dress without an Assistant; but she had hardly put on anything more than her Night-gown, e're the Lady *Beldam* herself came in her *Dishabille*, to assure her of her Brother's Company with 'em at Dinner, exactly at One a Clock; and finding *Philadelphia* doing the Office of a Waiting-woman to herself, call'd up the same Servant, and in a great Heat (in which however she took Care to make Use of none of her familiar develish Dialect) ask'd the Reason

that she durst leave the Lady when she was Rising. The
Wench trembling, reply'd, That indeed the Lady did not
let her know that she had any Thoughts of Rising. Well
then (said her seeming offended Lady) stir not from her
now, I charge you, 'till she shall think fit to dismiss you,
and Command your Absence. Dear Madam, Good
Morrow to you, (said she to *Philadelphia*) I'll make haste
and Dress too. Good Morrow to your Ladyship (return'd
the design'd Victim) when she was *Habille*, she desir'd
the Servant to withdraw ; after which she betook herself
to her Devotion ; at the end of which the Lady *Beldam*
return'd, attended by a Servant, who brought some Bread
and Wine for her Breakfast ; which might then be seasonable enough to *Philadelphia ;* who cou'd not forbear discovering the Apprehensions she had of her Brother's
Unkindness, still entertaining her *Reverence*, with the Fear
she had of his Disappointment that Day at Dinner ; which
t'other oppos'd with all the seeming Reasons her Art cou'd
suggest, 'till the Clock had struck Twelve ; when a Servant
came to tell the Lady *Beldam*, that one Sir *William Wilding*
wou'd certainly wait on her precisely at One, and desir'd
that he might Dine in the young Lady's Apartment, to
avoid being seen by any Visitants that might come ; and
besides, that he had invited a Gentleman, his particular
Friend, to Dinner with him there. This Message being
deliver'd aloud by the Servant, was no little Satisfaction
to the poor desponding young Lady, who discours'd very
chearfully of indifferent Matters, 'till the Clock gave 'em
Notice that the Hour was come ; within three Minutes
after which, Word was brought to the Lady *Beldam*, that
a Gentleman below enquir'd for Sir *William Wilding*,
whom she immediately went down to receive, and led up
to *Philadelphia*. Madam, (cry'd the great Mistress of her
Art) this is the Gentleman whom Sir *William* has invited
to Dinner with us ; and I am very Happy to see him, for
he is my worthy Friend, and of a long Acquaintance.

Trust me, Madam, he is a Man of Honour, and has a very large Estate: I doubt not (added she) that you will find his Merits in his Conversation. Here *Gracelove*, for that was the Gentleman's Name, saluted *Philadelphia*, and acquitted himself like a Person of good Sense and Education, in his first Address to her; which she return'd with all the Modesty and ingenuous Simplicity that was still proper to her. At last she ask'd him how long he thought it wou'd be e're Sir *William* came? To which he reply'd, that Sir *William* told him, unless he were there exactly at half an Hour after One, they shou'd not stay Dinner for him; that he had not parted with him much above a Quarter of an Hour, when he left him engag'd with particular Company, about some weighty Business: But however, that, if he shou'd be so unhappy as to lose their Conversation at Dinner, he wou'd not fail to wait on 'em by Four at farthest. The young Lady seem'd a little uneasie at this; but the Gentleman appearing so very Modest, and speaking it with such an assur'd Gravity, took away all Thoughts of Suspicion. To say Truth, *Gracelove* was a very honest, modest, worthy and handsome Person; and had the Command, at present, of a many Thousand Pounds, he was by Profession a *Turkey* Merchant: He had Travell'd much, for his Age, not having then reach'd Thirty, and had seen most of the Courts in *Christendom*: He was a Man of a sweet Temper, of just Principles, and of inviolable Friendship, where he promis'd; which was no where, but where 'twas merited. The Minute came then at length, but without any Sir *William*; so Dinner was serv'd up in the Room next to *Philadelphia's* Bed-chamber. What they had was Nice and Seasonable; and they were all Three as Pleasant as cou'd be expected, without Sir *William*; to whose Health the Glass went round once or twice. Dinner over, and the Table clear'd, the old Lady *Beldam* entreated Mr. *Gracelove* to entertain the young Lady with a Discourse of his Travels, and of the most remarkable Passages and Encounters of 'em, which he perform'd with a Modesty and Gravity peculiar to himself ; and in some part of his Discourse mov'd the innocent Passions of the beauteous and compassionate *Philadelphia ;* who was as attentive as she us'd to be in Church at Divine Service. When the old Lady perceiv'd that he had made an end, or at least, that he desir'd to proceed no farther, she took Occasion to leave 'em together, in haste ; pretending, that she had forgotten to give Orders to one of her Servants, about a Business of Moment, and that she wou'd return to 'em in a very little Time. The Gentleman, you may believe, was very well pleas'd with her Retreat, since he had a Discourse to make to *Philadelphia* of a quite contrary Nature to the Preceding, which requir'd Privacy : But how grateful her Absence was to *Philadelphia*, we may judge by the Sequel. Madam, (said *Gracelove*) how do you like the Town ? Have you yet seen any Man here whom you cou'd Love ? Alas, Sir ! (she reply'd) I have not seen the Town, only in a Coach, as I pass'd along, nor ever was in any House, except this and another, where my Brother lodg'd : And to your other Question I must Answer, that I Love all Men. That's generous, indeed, Madam ! (cry'd he) there is then some hope that I am one of the Number. No doubt, Sir, (she return'd) that I Love you as well as any, except Sir *William*. Is he the happy Man then, Madam ? (said *Gracelove*.) If to be loved best by me, may make any Man happy, doubtless it must be he, for he is my own Brother. I fancy, Madam, (return'd he) that you may make me as dear a Relation to you, as Sir *William*. How is that possible, Sir ? she ask'd. Thus, Madam, (replied he, drawing closer to her) by our nearer Approaches to one another. O, Heaven defend me ! (cried she aloud) what do you mean ? Take away your Hand ; you uncivil Man ! Help ! Madam ! my Lady ! O, (said *Gracelove*) she's gone purposely out of hearing. Am I betray'd then ? She cried. Betray'd ! as if your pretty innocent Ladyship did not know where you were lodged. Ah, Lady, (said he) this Faint will never do. Come, Child, (pursued he) here are an hundred Guineas for you; and I promise you Yearly as much, and Two Hundred with every Child that I shall get on thy sweet Body: Faith I love thee, thou pretty Creature. Come! let's be better acquainted! you know my Meaning. Hell does, no doubt of (she return'd!) O Monster a Man! I hate the Sight of you. With that she flung from him, and ran into the Bed-chamber, where she thought to have locked herself in; but the Key was conveyed into his Pocket. Thither, therefore, he pursued her, crying, Ah, Madam, this is the proper Field for our Dispute. Perceiving her Error, and animated by Despair, she rushed between him and the Door, into the outward Room again, he still following, and dodging her from Chair to Chair, she still Shrieking. At last (cried he) a Parley, Madam, with you. Let me ask you one Question, and will you Answer me directly and truly to it? Indeed, I will, (said she) if it be Civil. Don't you know then, that you are in a naughty House, and that old *Beldam* is a rank Procuress, to whom I am to give Two hundred Guineas for your Maidenhead? O Heaven (cried she, kneeling with Tears gushing out from her dear Eyes) thou Asserter and Guardian of Innocence! protect me from the impious Practices intended against me! Then looking steadfastly on him, Sir, (pursued she) I can but Difficultly guess what you mean: But I find, that unless you prove what at first you seemed to me, I would say, an honest worthy Gentleman, I shall be in danger of eternal Ruin. You, Sir, are the only Person that may yet Preserve me. Therefore I beseech you, Sir, hear my Story, with the Injuries and Afflictions that so dreadfully torment me; of which, I am sure, none of those *Barbarians*, of which you had Occasion to speak but now, would have been guilty! O hear, and help me! for Heaven's Sake, hear and help me! I will,

poor Creature, (return'd he) methinks I now begin to see
my Crime and thy Innocence in thy Words and Looks.
Here she recounted to him all the Accidents of her Life,
since her Father's Decease, to that very Day, e're *Gracelove*
came to Dinner.   And now (cry'd she, sobbing and weeping) how dare I trust this naughty Brother again? Can I
be safe with him, think you, Sir? O! no; thou dear sweet
Creature! by no Means. O infernal Monsters! Brother
and Bawd! If you distrust that I am yet his Sister, here,
Sir, take this Key, (said she) and open that Trunk within,
where you will find Letters from him to me in his own
Hand; and from my own dear dead Father too, Sir *Edward*,
that gracious, that good Man! He shew'd us both the
Paths of Virtue: which I have not yet forsaken.   Pray
satisfy me, Sir, and see the Truth! For your Satisfaction
I will, Madam, (said he) but I am now fully convinc'd
that you have greater Beauties within, than those I admire
without.   Saying this, he open'd the Trunk, where he
read a Line or two from her Father, and as many from
her Brother, which having again laid down, return'd to
her, with this Advice: I see, Madam, (said he) that you
have Money there, and several Things of Value, which I
desire you to secure about you this Moment; for I mean
to deliver you out of this cursed Place, if you dare put any
Confidence in a Stranger, after your own Brother has
acted the Part of so great a Villain; if you dare trust a
Stranger too, Madam, who had himself a Design upon
you; Heaven forgive me for it! but by all Things sacred,
I find my Error: I pity you, and I fear I shall love you.
Do you fear that, Sir? (said she) Why I love you dearly
now, because I see you are going to be good again; that is,
you are going to be your self again. I hope, nay, I resolve
I will, tho' it cost me my Life (said he.) Can you submit,
Madam, to attend on a young Lady of my Acquaintance
here in Town, 'till I can provide better for you? O I can
be any Thing; a Chamber-Maid, a Cook-Maid, a Scullion,

what you shall think fit, tho' never so mean, that is not naughty. Well, Madam, (said he) compose your self then, and seem a little pleasant when I bring up that old Factoress of Hell. I will endeavour it, Sir, she return'd ; and he went down to the Devil's chief Agent, to whom he said, that the poor Thing was at first very uneasy, but that now she had consented to go along with him for an Hour or two to some other Place, doubting your Secrecy ; for she would not have her Brother know it, as she calls him, for a thousand Worlds, and more Money. Well, my Son, (reply'd old *Beldam*) you may take her with you : But you remember your Bargain. O fie, Mother ! (cry'd he) did you ever know me false to you? No, no, you smock'd-fac'd Wag, (said she) but be sure you bring her again to Night, for fear Sir *William* should come. Never doubt it ! Come up with me, (cry'd he) you'll see a strange Alteration, I believe. To *Philadelphia* they came then, whom they found walking about the Room, and looking something more pleasantly than she had ever done since she came thither. After she had taken her Money, and other Things of Value, so, Madam, (said *Beldam*) how does your Ladiship now ? I find, the Sight of a young handsome Gentleman has work'd Wonders with you in a little Time : I understand you are going to take a Walk with my worthy Friend here, and 'tis well done : I dare trust you with him, but with no other Man living, except Sir *William*. Madam, (return'd the fair afflicted Lady) I am strangely oblig'd to you for your Care of me, and am sure I shall never be able to return your Obligations as I ought, and as I could wish. You won't stay late, Mr. *Gracelove?* (said the Mother of Mischief.) No, no, (reply'd he) I will only shew the Lady a Play, and return to Supper. What is play'd to Night ? (ask'd the old One) *The Cheats*, Mother, *the Cheats*. (answer'd *Gracelove*.) Ha, (said *Beldam*, laughing) a very pretty Comedy, indeed ! Ay, if well play'd, return'd he. At these Words, they went down, where a Coach was

call'd ; which carry'd 'em to Counsellor *Fairlaw's* House,
in *Great Lincolns-Inn-Fields*, whom they found accidentally
at Home ; but his Lady and Daughter were just gone to
Chapel, being then turn'd of Five. *Gracelove* began his
Apology to the good old Counsellor, who was his Relation,
for bringing a strange Lady thither, with a Design to
place her in his Family : But Sir, continu'd he, if you
knew her sorrowful Story, you would be as ambitious of
entertaining her, as I am earnest to entreat it of you. A
very beautiful Lady 'tis, (return'd the Counsellor) and very
modest, I believe. That I can witness (reply'd t'other.)
Alas, Sir ! (said the fair Unfortunate) I have nothing but
my Modesty and honest Education to recommend me to
your Regard. I am wrong'd and forsaken by my nearest
Relation ; then she wept extravagantly : That Gentleman
can give you an Account of my Misfortunes, if he pleases,
with greater Ease and less Trouble than my self. Not
with less Trouble, believe me, Madam; (return'd *Gracelove*)
and then began to inform *Fairlaw* in every Point of her
unhappy Circumstances. The good old Gentleman heard
'em with Amazement and Horror ; but told her, however,
that she need not despond, for he would take Care to right
her against her Brother ; and, that in the mean Time she
should be as welcome to him as any of his nearest Kindred,
except his Wife and Daughter. *Philadelphia* would have
knelt to thank him ; but he told her, that humble Posture
was due to none but Heaven, and the King sometimes.
In a little While after, the Lady *Fairlaw* and her Daughter
came Home, who were surpriz'd at the Sight of a Stranger,
but more at her Beauty, and most of all at her Story,
which the good old Gentleman himself could not forbear
relating to 'em : Which ended, the Mother and Daughter
both kindly and tenderly embrac'd her, promising her all
the Assistance within their Power, and bid her a thousand
Welcomes. *Gracelove* stay'd there 'till after Supper, and
left her extremely satisfy'd with her new Station. 'Twas

here she fix'd then; and her Deportment was so obliging, that they would not part with her for any Consideration. About three Days after her coming from that lewd Woman's House, *Gracelove* took a Constable and some other Assistants, and went to *Beldam's* to demand the Trunk, and what was in it, which at first her Reverence deny'd to return, 'till Mr. Constable produc'd the Emblem of his Authority, upon which it was deliver'd, without so much as re-minding *Gracelove* of his Bargain; who then pretended he would search the House for Sir *William Wilding*; but her graceless Reverence swore most devoutly that he had never been there, and that she had neither seen nor heard from him since the Day he left *Philadelphia* with her. With these Things, and this Account he return'd to Counsellor *Fairlaw's*, who desir'd *Gracelove*, if possible, to find out Sir *William*, and employ'd several others on the same Account. In less than a Month's Time *Gracelove* had the good Fortune to find him at his Lodgings in *Soho-Square*, where he discours'd him about his Sister's Portion, and desir'd Sir *William* to take some speedy Care for the Payment of it; otherwise she had Friends that would oblige him to it, tho' never so contrary to his Intentions. *Wilding* ask'd where she was? t'other enquir'd where he left her? Sir *William* reply'd, that he had plac'd her with an old grave Gentlewoman of his Acquaintance, and that he thought she was there still. No, Sir, (return'd *Gracelove*) I have deliver'd her out of the Jaws of Perdition and Hell. Come, Sir *William*, (answer'd he) 'twas impiously done, to leave your beautiful, young, and virtuous Sister, to the Management of that pernicious Woman. I found her at old *Beldam's*, who would have prostituted her to me for two hundred Guineas; but her heavenly Virtues might have secur'd and guarded her from more violent Attempts than mine. Blush, if you can, Sir! and repent of this! It will become you. If not, Sir, you will hear farther from your Servant, added he, and left him staring

after him. This Discourse was a great Mortification to
the Knight, whose Conscience, harden'd as it was, felt
yet some Pain by it. He found he was not like to continue
safe or at Ease there, where he immediately retreated into
a Place of Sanctuary, call'd the *Savoy*, whither his whole
Equipage was remov'd as soon as possible, he having left
Order with his Servants, to report that he went out of
Town that very Afternoon for his own Country. *Gracelove*
in the mean Time return'd to the Counsellor's, with a
great deal of Joy, for having discover'd Sir *William* at his
Lodgings, which was likewise no little Satisfaction to
Fairlaw, his Lady and Daughter; *Philadelphia* only was
disturb'd when she heard the good old Gentleman threaten
to lay her Brother fast enough: But, alas! he was too
cunning for 'em; for in a whole Twelvemonth after, all
which Time they made Enquiry, and narrowly search'd
for him, they could not see him, nor any one that could
give an Account of him, for he had chang'd his true Name
and Title, for that of 'Squire *Sportman*. The farther Pursuit
of him then seem'd fruitless to 'em, and they were forc'd
to be contented with their Wishes to find him.

Gracelove by this Time had entertain'd the sincerest
Affections and noblest Passion that Man can be capable
of, for *Philadelphia*; of which he had made her sensible,
who had at that Time comply'd with his honourable
Demands, had she not entreated him to expect a kind Turn
of Providence, which might, (happily) e're long, put her
in Possession of her Right; without which, she told him,
she could not consent to marry him, who had so plentiful
a Fortune, and she nothing but her Person and Innocence.
How, Madam! (cry'd he) have you no Love in Store for
me! Yes, Sir, (return'd she) as much as you can wish I
have in Store for you, and so I beg it may be kept 'till a
better Opportunity. Well, Madam, (said he) I must leave
you for some Months, perhaps for a whole Year; I have
receiv'd Letters of Advice that urge the Necessity of my

going to *Turkey*; I have not a Week's Time to endeavour so dreaded a Separation as I must suffer; therefore, thou beautiful, thou dear, thou virtuous Creature, let me begin now! Here, thou tenderest Part of my Soul! (continu'd he, giving her a rich Diamond Ring) wear this 'till my Return! I hope the Sight of it may sometimes re-call the dying Memory of *Gracelove* to your better-busy'd Thoughts. Ah, *Gracelove!* (said she) nothing can so well, nothing I am sure can better employ my Thoughts, than thy dear self : Heaven only excepted. They enlarg'd a great deal more on this Subject at that Time; but the Night before his Departure was entirely spent in Sighs, Vows, and Tears, on both Sides. In the Morning, after he had again entreated his Cousin's, and the Lady's, and her Daughter's Care and Kindness to *Philadelphia*, the remaining and best Part of his Soul, with one hearty Kiss, accompany'd with Tears, he took a long Farewel of his dear Mistress, who pursu'd him with her Eyes, 'till they could give her no farther Intelligence of him; and they help'd her Kindness to him, and eas'd her Grief for his Absence in weeping for above a Week together, when in private. He never omitted writing to her and his Cousin by every Opportunity, for near nine Months, as he touch'd at any Port; but afterwards they could not hear from him for above half a Year; when, by Accident, the Counsellor met a Gentleman of *Gracelove's* Acquaintance at a Coffee-House, who gave him an Account, that the Ship and he were both cast away, near five Months since; that most if not all of the Ship's Company perish'd; of which, 'twas fear'd, *Gracelove* was one, having never since been heard of. That his Loss in that Ship amounted to above twelve thousand Pounds: With this dreadful and amazing News the good old Gentlemen returns Home, afflicts his poor sorrowful Lady and Daughter, and almost kills unhappy *Philadelphia*; who the next Day, by mere Chance, and from a Stranger, who came on Business to the Counsellor, heard, that one Sir *William Wilding*, an

extravagant, mad, young Spark of such a County, who lately
went by the borrow'd Name and Title of 'Squire *Sportman*,
had mortgag'd all his Estate, which was near four thousand
a Year, and carry'd the Money over with him into *France*
on Saturday last. This, added to the former News, put
so great a Check on her Spirits, that she immediately
dropp'd down in a Swoon; whence she only recover'd, to
fall into what was of a much more dangerous Consequence,
a violent Feaver, which held her for near six Weeks, e're
she could get Strength enough to go down Stairs: In all
which Time, Madam *Fairlaw* and *Eugenia*, her Daughter,
attended her as carefully and constantly, as if they had
been her own Mother and Sister: The good old Counsellor
still commending and encouraging their Care. The Roses
and Lillies at last took their Places again; but the Clouds
of her Sorrow were still but too visible. Two Years more
past, without one Word of Advice from *Gracelove*, or any
Account of him from any one else; insomuch, that they
all concluded he was certainly dead: And, 'twas true,
indeed, that his Ship and he were cast away, much about
that Time that the Gentleman gave *Fairlaw* a Relation:
That 'twas certain he had lost above 12000 *l.* and had like
to have lost his Life; but being very expert in Swimming,
he got to Shoar upon the Coast of *Barbary*, the Wreck
happening not to be above three Leagues thence; he was
in almost as bad a Condition as if he had been drown'd,
for here he was made a Prisoner to one of the Natives;
in which miserable Circumstance he lanquish'd for above
six Years, for Want of a Ransom; which he had often
endeavour'd to raise by Letters, that he sent hither to his
Friends (in *England*;) amongst which Counsellor *Fairlaw*
was one of his most particular and assur'd. But however
Providence or Accident, if you please, order'd it, not a
Line came to the Hands of any of his Friends; so that had
not Heaven had yet a future Blessing in Store for him, he
had certainly have better perish'd in the Sea, than to have

fall'n into the Power of a People less merciful than Seas, Winds, or hungry wild Beasts in Pursuit of their Prey. But this could not be learn'd (it seems) from any Man but himself, upon his Return, after his Redemption.

Two Years more pass'd on; towards the latter of which the old Lady *Fairlaw* took her Bed, desperately sick, insomuch that she was given over by all her Physicians; she continu'd in great Misery for near two Months; in all which Time *Philadelphia* was constantly with her all the Day, or all the Night; much about that Time she dy'd; and, dying, told her Husband, that she had observ'd he had a particular Esteem or Kindness for *Philadelphia*; which was now a great Satisfaction to her; since she was asssur'd, that if he marry'd her, she would prove an excellent Nurse to him, and prolong his Life by some Years. As for *Eugenia*, (added she) you need not be concern'd; I'm sure she will consent to any Thing that you shall propose, having already so plentifully provided for her. The good old Gentleman answer'd, that he would fulfil her Will as far as lay in his Power: And not long after, she departed this Life. Her Burial was very handsome and honourable. Half a Year was now expir'd since her Interment, when the old Counsellor began to plead his own Cause to young *Philadelphia*, reminding her that now the Death of *Gracelove* was out of Question; and that therefore she was as much at her Liberty to make her own Choice of an Husband as he was of a Wife; not forgetting, at the same Time, to let her know, that his Widow, (whoever had the good Fortune to be so) would be worth above thirty thousand Pounds in ready Money, besides a thousand a Year. But, above all, he urg'd his dying Lady's last Advice to him, that he would marry her; and hop'd she would see the Will of the Dead satisfy'd. The young Lady being broken in Sorrows, and having mortify'd all her Appetites to the Enjoyments of this World, and not knowing where to meet with so fair an Overture, tho'

at first, in Modesty, she seem'd to refuse it as too great
an Honour, yet yielded to less than a Quarter of an Hour's
Courtship. And the next Sunday marry'd they were,
with the Consent, and to the perfect Satisfaction of, his
Daughter, Madam *Eugenia;* who lov'd *Philadelphia* sincerely. They kept their Wedding very nobly for a Month,
at their own House in *Great Lincolns-Inn-Fields;* but the
Memory of the old Lady was still so fresh with the young
Lady *Fairlaw*, that she prevail'd with him to remove to
another, more convenient as she fancy'd, in *Covent-Garden*.
They had dwelt there not much more than four Months,
e're the good old Gentleman fell sick and dy'd. Whether
it were the Change of an old House for a new, or an old
Wife for a young, is yet uncertain, tho' his Physicians said,
and are still of Opinion, that, doubtless, it was the last.
'Tis past all Doubt, that she did really mourn for and
lament his Death ; for she lov'd him perfectly, and pay'd
him all the dutiful respect of a virtuous Wife, while she
liv'd within that State with him; which he rewarded as
I have said before. His Funeral was very sumptuous and
honourable indeed ! and as soon as it was over, *Eugenia*
desir'd her young beautiful Mother-in-Law to retreat a
little with her into the Country, to a pleasant House she
had, not twenty Miles distant from Town ; urging, That
she could by no Means enjoy her self under that Roof,
where her dear Father dy'd. The obliging Step-mother,
who might more properly have been call'd her Sister, being
exactly of the same Age with her, readily comply'd, and
she pass'd away all that Summer with *Eugenia*, at their
Country-Seat, and most Part of the Winter too; for
Eugenia could by no Means be prevail'd on to lie one
Night in her Mother's House ; 'twas with some Reluctancy
that she consented to dine there sometimes. At length
the whole Year of *Philadelphia's* Widowhood was expir'd;
during which, you can't but imagine that she was solicited
and address'd to by as many Lovers, or pretended Lovers,

as our dear King *Charles*, whom God grant long to reign, was lately by the Presbyterians, Independants, Anabaptists, and all those canting whiggish Brethren! But she had never lik'd any Man so well as to make him her Husband, by Inclination, unless it was *Gracelove*, devour'd by the greedy Inhabitants of the Sea.

Whilst her Fortune began to mend thus, her Brother's grew worse; but that was indeed the Effect of his Extravagancy: In less than two Years Time, he had spent eight thousand Pounds in *France*, whence he return'd to *England*, and pursuing his old profuse Manner of Living, contracted above 100*l.* Debts here, in less than four Months Time; which not being able to satisfy, he was arrested, and thrown into a Goal, whence he remov'd himself into the *King's Bench*, on that very Day that old *Fairlaw* dy'd. There, at first, for about a Month, he was entertain'd like a Gentleman; but finding no Money coming, nor having a Prospect of any, the Marshal and his Instruments turn'd him to the Common Side, where he learnt the Art of Peg-making, a Mystery to which he had been a Stranger all his Life long 'till then. 'Twas then he wish'd he might see his Sister, hoping that she was in a Condition to relieve him; which he was apt to believe, from the Discourse he had with *Gracelove* some Years past. Often he wish'd to see her, but in vain; however, the next *Easter* after the old Counsellor's Death, *Philadelphia*, according to his Custom, sent her Steward to relieve all the poor Prisoners about Town; among the rest he visited those in the common Side of the *King's Bench*, where he heard 'em call Sir *William Wilding* to partake of his Lady's Charity. The poor Prodigal was then feeding on the Relief of the Basket, not being yet able to get his Bread at his new Trade: To him the Steward gave a Crown, whereas the other had but Half a Crown apiece. Then he enquir'd of some of the unhappy Gentlemen, Sir *William's* Fellow-Collegians, of what Country Sir *William* was? How long

he had been there? And how much his Debts were? All
of which he receiv'd a satisfactory Account.   Upon his
Return to his Lady, he repeated the dismal News of her
Brother's Misfortunes to her; who immediately dispatch'd
him back again to the Prison, with Orders to give him
twenty Shillings more at present, and to get him remov'd
to the Master's Side, into a convenient Chamber, for the
Rent of which the Steward engag'd to pay; and promis'd
him, as she had commanded, twenty Shillings a Week, as
long as he stay'd there, on Condition that he would give the
Names of all his Creditors, and of all those to whom he
had engag'd any Part of his Estate; which the poor
Gentleman did most readily and faithfully: After which,
the Steward enquir'd for a Taylor, who came and took
Measure of *Philadelphia's* unkind Brother, and was order'd
to provide him Linnen, a Hat, Shoes, Stockings, and all
such Necessaries, not so much as omitting a Sword: With
all which he acquainted his Lady at his Return; who was
very much griev'd at her Brother's unhappy Circumstances,
and at the same Time extremely well pleas'd to find her
self in a Condition to relieve him.   The Steward went
constantly once a Week to pay him his Money; and Sir
William was continually very curious to know to whom
he was oblig'd for so many and great Favours; But he
was answer'd, That they came from a Lady who desir'd
to have her Name conceal'd. In less than a Year, *Philadelphia* had paid 25000*l.* and taken off the Mortgages on
2500*l. per Annum*, of her Brother's Estate; and coming
to Town from *Eugenia's* Country-House one Day, to
make the last Payment of two thousand Pounds, looking
out of her Coach on the Road, near *Dartford*, she saw a
Traveller on Foot, who seem'd to be tir'd with his Journey,
whose Face, she thought, she had formerly known: This
Thought invited her to look on him so long, that she, at
last, perswaded her self it was *Gracelove*, or his Ghost: For,
to say Truth, he was very pale and thin, his Complexion

swarthy, and his Cloaths (perhaps) as rotten as if he had been bury'd in 'em. However, unpleasant as it was, she could not forbear gazing after this miserable Spectacle; and the more she beheld it, the more she was confirm'd it was *Gracelove*, or something that had usurp'd his Figure. In short, she could not rest 'till she call'd to one of her Servants, who rode by the Coach, whom she strictly charg'd to go to that poor Traveller, and mount him on his Horse, 'till they came to *Dartford*; where she order'd him to take him to the same Inn where she baited, and refresh him with any Thing that he would eat or drink; and after that, to hire a Horse for him, to come to Town with them: That then he should be brought Home to her own House, and be carefully look'd after, 'till farther Orders from her. All which was most duly and punctually perform'd.

The next Morning early she sent for the Steward, whom she order'd to take the Stranger to a Sale-shop, and fit him with a Suit of good Cloaths, to buy him Shirts, and other Linnen, and all Necessaries, as he had provided for her Brother; and gave him Charge to use him as her particular Friend, during his Stay there, bidding him, withal, learn his Name and Circumstances, if possible, and to supply him with Money for his Pocket Expences: All which he most faithfully and discreetly perform'd, and brought his Lady an Account of his Sufferings by Sea, and Slavery among the *Turks*, as I have before related; adding, that his Name was *Gracelove*. This was the greatest Happiness, certainly, that ever yet the dear beautiful Creature was sensible of. On t'other Side, *Gracelove* could not but admire and praise his good Fortune, that had so miraculously and bountifully reliev'd him; and one Day having some private Discourse with the Steward, he could not forbear expressing the Sense he had of it; declaring, That he could not have expected such kind Treatment from any Body breathing, but from his Cousin, Counsellor *Fairlaw*, his Lady, or another young

Lady, whom he plac'd and left with his Cousins. Counsellor *Fairlaw!* (cry'd the Steward) why, Sir, my Lady is
the old Counsellor's Widow; she is very beautiful and
young too. What was her Name, Sir, before she marry'd
the Counsellor? (ask'd *Gracelove*) That I know not, (reply'd
t'other) for the old Steward dy'd presently after the old
Lady, which is not a Year and a Half since; in whose
Place I succeed; and I have never been so curious or inquisitive, as to pry into former Passages of the Family. Do
you know, Sir, (said *Gracelove*) whereabouts in Town they
liv'd before? Yes, Sir, (return'd the Steward, who was
taught how to answer) in *Great Lincolns-Inn-Fields*, I think,
Alas! (cry'd *Gracelove*) 'twas the same Gentleman to whom
I design'd to apply my self when I came to *England*. You
need not despair now, Sir, (said t'other) I dare say my Lady
will supply your Wants. O wonderful Goodness of a
Stranger! (cry'd *Gracelove*) uncommon and rare amongst
Relations and Friends! How have I, or how can I ever
merit this? Upon the End of their Conference, the Steward
went to *Philadelphia*, and repeated it almost *verbatim* to
her; who order'd *Gracelove* should be taken Measure of
by the best Taylor in *Covent-Garden;* that he should have
three of the most modish rich Suits made, that might become a private Gentleman of a Thousand Pounds a Year,
and Hats, Perukes, Linnen, Swords, and all Things suitable
to 'em, all to be got ready in less than a Month; in which
Time, she took all the Opportunity she could either find or
make to see him, and not to be seen by him: She oblig'd
her Steward to invite him to a Play, whither she follow'd
'em, and sate next to *Gracelove*, and talk'd with him; but
all the while masq'd. In this Month's Time she was daily
pester'd with the Visits of her Addressors; several there
were of 'em; but the chief were only a Lord of a very
small Estate, tho' of a pretty great Age; a young blustering
Knight, who had a Place of 500*l*. a Year at Court; and a
County Gentleman, of a very plentiful Estate, a Widower,

and of a middle Age. These three only of her Lovers she
invited to Dinner, on the first Day of the next Month :
In the mean while she sent a rich Suit, and Equipage
proportionable, to her Brother, with an Invitation to dine
with her on the same Day. Then she writ to *Eugenia* to
come and stay in Town, if not in the same House with
her, for two or three Days before; which her affectionate
Daughter obey'd; to whom *Philadelphia* related all her
Brother's past Extravagancies and what she had done for him
in redeeming most Part of his Estate; begging of her, that
if she could fancy his Person, she would take him into her
Mercy and marry him. Being assur'd, that such a virtuous
Wife as she would prove, must necessarily reclaim him, if
yet he were not perfectly convinc'd of his Follies; which,
she doubted not, his late long Sufferings had done. *Eugenia*
return'd, That she would wholly be directed and advis'd
by her in all Things; and that certainly she could not but
like the Brother, since she lov'd the Sister so perfectly and
truly.

The Day came, and just at Twelve, *Gracelove*, meeting
the Steward on the Stairs coming from his Lady, *Gracelove*
then told him, that he believ'd he might take the Opportunity of that Afternoon to go over to *Putney*, and take a
Game or two at Bowls. The Steward return'd, Very well,
Sir, I shall let my Lady know it, if she enquires for you.
Philadelphia, who overheard what they said, call'd the
Steward in Haste, and bid him call *Gracelove* back, and tell
him, she expected his Company at her Table to Day, and
that she desir'd he would appear like himself. The Steward
soon overtook him at the Door, just going out as *Eugenia*
came in, who look'd back on *Gracelove :* The poor Gentleman was strangely surpriz'd at the Sight of her, as she
was at his; but the Steward's Message did more amaze
and confound him. He went directly to his Chamber, to
dress himself in one of those rich Suits lately made for him;
but, the Distraction he was in, made him mistake his Coat

for his Wastcoat, and put the Coat on first; but, recalling his straggling Thoughts, he made Shift to get ready time enough to make his Appearance without a second Summons. *Philadelphia* was as pleasant at Dinner, as ever she had been all her Life; she look'd very obligingly on all the Sparks, and drank to every one of 'em particularly, beginning to the Lord — and ending to the Stranger, who durst hardly lift up his Eyes a second Time to her's, to confirm him that he knew her. Her Brother was so confounded, that he bow'd and continu'd his Head down 'till she had done drinking, not daring to encounter her Eyes, that would then have reproach'd him with his Villany to her.

After Dinner the Cloth was taken away; She began thus to her Lovers: My Lord! Sir *Thomas!* and Mr. *Fat-acres!* I doubt not, that it will be of some Satisfaction to you, to know whom I have made Choice for my next Husband; which now I am resolv'd no longer to defer.

The Person to whom I shall next drink, must be the Man who shall ever command me and my Fortune, were it ten times greater than it is; which I wish only for his Sake, since he deserves much more.—Here, (said she to one that waited) put Wine into two Glasses: Then she took the Diamond Ring from her Finger, and put it into one of 'em. My dear *Gracelove*, (cry'd she) I drank to thee; and send thee back thy own Ring, with *Philadelphia's* Heart. He startl'd, blush'd, and looked wildly; whilst all the Company stared on him. Nay, pledge me, (persu'd she) and return me the Ring: for it shall make us both one the next Morning. He bow'd, kiss'd, and return'd it, after he had taken off his Wine. The defeated Lovers knew not how to resent it? The Lord and Knight were for going, but the Country Gentleman oppos'd it, and told 'em, 'twas the greatest Argument of Folly, to be disturb'd at the Caprice of a Woman's Humour. They sate down again therefore, and she invited 'em to her Wedding on the Morrow.

And now, Brother, (said she) I have not quite forgotten you, tho' you have not been pleas'd to take Notice of me : I have a Dish in Reserve for you, which will be more grateful to your Fancy than all you have tasted to Day. Here! (cry'd she to the Steward) Mr. *Rightman*, do you serve up that Dish your self. *Rightman* then set a cover'd Dish on the Table. What! more Tricks yet? (cry'd my Lord and Sir *Thomas*) Come, Sir *William!* (said his Sister) uncover it! he did so; and cry'd out, O matchless Goodness of a virtuous Sister! here are the Mortgages of the best Part of my Estate! O! what a Villain! what a Monster have I been! no more, dear Brother; (said she, with Tears in her Eyes) I have yet a greater Happiness in Store for you : This Lady, this beautiful virtuous Lady, with twenty thousand Pounds, will make you happy in her Love. Saying this, she join'd their Hands; Sir *William* eagerly kiss'd *Eugenia's*, who blush'd, and said, Thus, Madam, I hope to shew how much I love and honour you. My Cousin *Eugenia!* (cry'd *Gracelove!*) The same, my dear lost dead Cousin *Gracelove!* (reply'd she) O! (said he in a Transport) my present Joys are greater than all my past Miseries! my Mistress and my Friend are found, and still are mine. Nay, (faith, said my Lord) this is pleasant enough to me, tho' I have been defeated of the Enjoyment of the Lady. The whole Company in general went away very well that Night, who return'd the next Morning, and saw the two happy Pair firmly united.

F I N I S .

THE FAIR JILT.

INTRODUCTION.

ALTHOUGH *The Fair Jilt* was published in 1688, it is interesting to note that ten years earlier, Michaelmas Term, 1678, there is advertised for R. Tonson *The Amorous Convert; being a true Relation of what happened in Holland*, which may very well be the first sketch of Mrs. Behn's maturer novel. The fact that she does not 'pretend here to entertain you with a feign'd story,' but on the contrary, 'every circumstance to a tittle is truth', and that she expressly asserts, ' To a great part of the main I myself was an eye-witness', aroused considerable suspicion in Bernbaum as to the veracity of her narration, a suspicion which, when he gravely discovers history to know no such person as her 'Prince Tarpuin of the race of the last Kings of Rome', is resolved into a certainty that she is romancing fully and freely throughout. It is surely obvious that such a point does not so much demonstrate Mrs. Behn's untruthfulness as her consummate art. With all the nice skill of a born novelist she has so mingled fact and fancy, what did occur and what might have been, that any attempt to disentangle the twain would be idle indeed. The passages where she is most insistent upon the due sequence of events, most detailed in observation are not impossibly purely fictional, the incidents related without stress or emphatic assertions are probably enough the plain unvarnished happenings as she witnessed them. That the history is mainly true admits of little question; that Mrs. Behn has heightened and coloured the interest is equally certain.

The Fair Jilt must be allowed to stand in the very first rank amongst her novels. It has been aptly compared to a novella by Bandello, and is indeed more than worthy of the pen of the good Dominican Bishop of Agen. In all its incidents and motives the story is eternally true. The fateful beauty, playing now the part of Potiphar's wife, and now the yet commoner rôle of an enchantress whose charms drive men to madness and crime, men who adore her even from their prison cell and are glad to go to a shameful death for her sake, appears in all history, in all literature, nay, in the very newspaper scandals and police courts of to-day. As a picture of untrammelled passion, culpable and corrupt, but yet terribly fascinating in her very recklessness and abandon, Miranda is indeed a powerful study. Always guilty, she is always excused, or if punished but sparingly and little, whilst the friar languishes in a foul dungeon, the page-boy is hanged, her husband stands upon the public scaffold. And then in the end, 'very penitent for her life past', she is received with open arms by Tarquin's old father, who looks upon her as a very angel, and retiring to the tranquility of a country-house she passes her days in ' as perfect a state of happiness as this troublesome world can afford'.

TO

HENRY PAIN, ESQ;

Sir,

DEDICATIONS are like Love, and no Man of Wit or Eminence escapes them; early or late, the Affliction of the Poet's Complement falls upon him; and Men are oblig'd to receive 'em as they do their Wives; *For better, for worse;* at lest with a feign'd Civility.

It was not Want of Respect, but Fear, that has hitherto made us keep clear of your Judgment, too piercing to be favourable to what is not nicely valuable. We durst not awaken your Criticism; and by begging your Protection in the Front of a Book, give you an Occasion to find nothing to deserve it. Nor can this little History lay a better Claim to that Honour, than those that have not pretended to it; which has but this Merit to recommend it, That it is Truth: Truth, which you so much admire. But 'tis a Truth that entertains you with so many Accidents diverting and moving, that they will need both a Patron, and an Assertor in this incredulous World. For however it may be imagin'd that Poetry (my Talent) has so greatly the Ascendant over me, that all I write must pass for Fiction, I now desire to have it understood that this is Reality, and Matter of Fact, and acted in this our latter Age: And that in the person of *Tarquin,* I bring a Prince to kiss your Hands, who own'd himself, and was receiv'd, as the last of the Race of the *Roman* Kings; whom I have often seen, and you have heard of; and whose Story is so well known to your self, and many Hundreds more: Part of which I had from the Mouth of this unhappy great Man, and was an Eye-Witness to the rest.

'Tis true, Sir, I present you with a Prince unfortunate, but still the more noble Object for your Goodness and Pity; who never valu'd a brave Man the less for being unhappy. And whither shou'd the Afflicted flee for Refuge but to the Generous? Amongst all the Race, he cannot find a better Man, or more certain Friend: Nor amongst all his Ancestors, match your greater Soul, and Magnificence of Mind. He will behold in one *English* Subject, a Spirit as illustrious, a Heart as fearless, a Wit and Eloquence as excellent, as *Rome* it self cou'd produce. Its Senate scarce boasted of a better States-man, nor Augustus of a more faithful Subject; as your Imprisonment and Sufferings, through all the Course of our late National Distractions, have sufficiently manifested: But nothing cou'd press or deject your great Heart; you were the same Man still, unmov'd in all Turns, easie and innocent; no Persecution being able to abate your constant good Humour, or wonted Gallantry.

If, Sir, you find here a Prince of less Fortitude and Vertue than your self, charge his Miscarriages on Love : a Weakness of that Nature you will easily excuse, (being so great a Friend to the Fair;) though possibly, he gave a Proof of it too Fatal to his Honour. Had I been to have form'd his Character, perhaps I had made him something more worthy of the Honour of your Protection : But I was oblig'd to pursue the Matter of Fact, and give a just Relation of that part of his Life which, possibly, was the only reproachful part of it. If he be so happy, as to entertain a Man of Wit and Business, I shall not fear his Welcome to the rest of the World : And 'tis only with your Passport he can hope to be so.

The particular Obligations I have to your Bounty and Goodness, O Noble Friend, and Patron of the *Muses!* I do not so much as pretend to acknowledge in this little Present; those being above the Poet's Pay, which is a sort of Coin, not currant in this Age : though perhaps may be esteem'd as Medals in the Cabinets of Men of Wit. If this be so happy to be of that Number, I desire no more lasting a Fame, that it may bear this Inscription, that I am,

SIR,

Your most Obliged, and

Most Humble Servant,

A. BEHN.

THE *FAIR JILT*:

or,

The Amours of Prince *Tarquin* and *Miranda*.

As Love is the most noble and divine Passion of the Soul, so it is that to which we may justly attribute all the real Satisfactions of Life; and without it Man is unfinish'd and unhappy.

There are a thousand things to be said of the Advantages this generous Passion brings to those, whose Hearts are capable of receiving its soft Impressions; for 'tis not every one that can be sensible of its tender Touches. How many Examples, from History and Observation, could I give of its wondrous Power; nay, even to a Degree of Transmigration! How many Idiots has it made wise! How many Fools eloquent! How many home-bred Squires accomplish'd! How many Cowards brave! And there is no sort of Species of Mankind on whom it cannot work some Change and Miracle, if it be a noble well-grounded Passion, except on the Fop in Fashion, the harden'd incorrigible Fop; so often wounded, but never reclaim'd: For still, by a dire Mistake, conducted by vast Opiniatrety, and a greater Portion of Self-love, than the rest of the Race of Man, he believes that Affectation in his Mein and Dress, that Mathematical Movement, that Formality in every Action, that a Face manag'd with Care, and soften'd into Ridicule, the languishing Turn, the Toss, and the Back-shake of the Periwig, is the direct Way to the Heart of the fine Person he adores; and instead of curing Love in his Soul, serves only to advance his Folly; and the more he is enamour'd, the more industriously he assumes (every Hour) the Coxcomb. These are Love's Play-things, a sort of Animals with whom he sports; and whom he never wounds, but when he is in good Humour, and always shoots laughing. 'Tis the Diversion of the little God, to see what a Fluttering and Bustle one of these Sparks, new-wounded, makes; to what fantastick Fooleries he has Recourse: The Glass is every Moment call'd to counsel, the Valet consulted and plagu'd for new Invention of Dress, the Footman and Scrutore perpetually employ'd; *Billet-doux* and *Madrigals* take up all his Mornings, till Play-time in dressing, till Night in gazing; still, like a Sun-flower, turn'd towards the Beams of the fair Eyes of his *Cælia*, adjusting himself in the most amorous Posture he can assume, his Hat under his Arm, while the other Hand is put carelesly into his Bosom, as if laid upon his panting Heart; his Head a little bent to one Side, supported with a World of Cravat-string, which he takes mighty Care not to put into Disorder; as one may guess by a never-failing and horrid Stiffness in his Neck; and if he had any Occasion to look aside, his whole Body turns at the same Time, for Fear the Motion of the Head alone should incommode the Cravat or Periwig: And sometimes the Glove is well manag'd, and the white Hand display'd. Thus, with a thousand other little Motions and Formalities, all in the common Place or Road of Foppery, he takes infinite Pains to shew himself to the Pit and Boxes, a most accomplish'd Ass. This is he, of all human Kind, on whom Love can do no Miracles, and who can no where, and upon no Occasion, quit one Grain of his refin'd Foppery, unless in a Duel, or a Battle, if ever his Stars should be so severe and ill-manner'd, to reduce him to the Necessity of either: Fear then would ruffle that fine Form he had so long preserv'd in nicest Order, with Grief considering, that an unlucky Chance-wound in his Face, if such a dire Misfortune should befal him, would spoil the Sale of it for ever.

Perhaps it will be urg'd, that since no Metamorphosis can be made in a Fop by Love, you must consider him one of those that only talks of Love, and thinks himself that happy Thing, a Lover; and wanting fine Sense enough for the real Passion, believes what he feels to be it. There are in the Quiver of the God a great many different Darts; some that wound for a Day, and others for a Year; they are all fine, painted, glittering Darts, and shew as well as those made of the noblest Metal; but the Wounds they make reach the Desire only, and are cur'd by possessing, while the short-liv'd Passion betrays the Cheat. But 'tis that refin'd and illustrious Passion of the Soul, whose Aim is Virtue, and whose end is Honour, that has the Power of changing Nature, and is capable of performing all those heroick Things, of which History is full.

How far distant Passions may be from one another, I shall be able to make appear in these following Rules. I'll prove to you the strong Effects of Love in some unguarded and ungovern'd Hearts; where it rages beyond the Inspirations of *a God all soft and gentle*, and reigns more like *a Fury from Hell*.

I do not pretend here to entertain you with a feign'd Story, or any Thing piec'd together with romantick Accidents; but every Circumstance, to a Tittle, is Truth. To a great Part of the Main I myself was an Eye-witness; and what I did not see, I was confirm'd of by Actors in the Intrigue, Holy Men, of the Order of St. *Francis*: But for the Sake of some of her Relations, I shall give my *Fair Jilt* a feign'd Name, that of *Miranda*; but my Hero must retain his own, it being too illustrious to be conceal'd.

You are to understand, that in all the Catholick Countries, where Holy Orders are establish'd, there are abundance of differing Kinds of Religious, both of Men and Women. Amongst the Women, there are those we call *Nuns*, that make solemn Vows of perpetual Chastity; There are others who make but a simple Vow, as for five or ten Years, or

more or less; and that time expir'd, they may contract anew
for longer time, or marry, or dispose of themselves as they
shall see good; and these are ordinarily call'd *Galloping
Nuns*: Of these there are several Orders; as *Canonesses*,
Begines, *Quests*, *Swart-Sisters*, and *Jesuitesses*, with several
others I have forgot. Of those of the *Begines* was our *Fair
Votress*.

These Orders are taken up by the best Persons of the
Town, young Maids of Fortune, who live together, not
inclos'd, but in Palaces that will hold about fifteen hundred
or two thousand of these *Filles Devotes;* where they have
a regulated Government, under a sort of *Abbess*, or *Prioress*,
or rather a *Governante*. They are oblig'd to a Method of
Devotion, and are under a sort of Obedience. They wear
a Habit much like our Widows of Quality in *England*,
only without a *Bando;* and their Veil is of a thicker Crape
than what we have here, thro' which one cannot see the
Face; for when they go abroad, they cover themselves all
over with it; but they put 'em up in the Churches, and
lay 'em by in the Houses. Every one of these have a
Confessor, who is to 'em a sort of Steward : For, you must
know, they that go into these Places, have the Management of their own Fortunes, and what their Parents design
'em. Without the Advice of this Confessor, they act
nothing, nor admit of a Lover that he shall not approve;
at least, this Method ought to be taken, and is by almost
all of 'em; tho' *Miranda* thought her Wit above it, as
her Spirit was.

But as these Women are, as I said, of the best Quality,
and live with the Reputation of being retir'd from the
World a little more than ordinary, and because there is a
sort of Difficulty to approach 'em, they are the People the
most courted, and liable to the greatest Temptations; for
as difficult as it seems to be, they receive Visits from all
the Men of the best Quality, especially Strangers. All the
Men of Wit and Conversation meet at the Apartments of

these fair *Filles Devotes*, where all Manner of Gallantries are perform'd, while all the Study of these Maids is to accomplish themselves for these noble Conversations. They receive Presents, Balls, Serenades, and Billets ; All the News, Wit, Verses, Songs, Novels, Musick, Gaming, and all fine Diversion, is in their Apartments, they themselves being of the best Quality and Fortune. So that to manage these Gallantries, there is no sort of Female Arts they are not practis'd in, no Intrigue they are ignorant of, and no Management of which they are not capable.

Of this happy Number was the fair *Miranda*, whose Parents being dead, and a vast Estate divided between her self and a young Sister, (who liv'd with an unmarry'd old Uncle, whose Estate afterwards was all divided between 'em) she put her self into this uninclos'd religious House; but her Beauty, which had all the Charms that ever Nature gave, became the Envy of the whole *Sisterhood*. She was tall, and admirably shaped ; she had a bright Hair, and Hazle-Eyes, all full of Love and Sweetness : No Art could make a Face so fair as hers by Nature, which every Feature adorn'd with a Grace that Imagination cannot reach : Every Look, every Motion charm'd, and her black Dress shew'd the Lustre of her Face and Neck. She had an Air, though gay as so much Youth could inspire, yet so modest, so nobly reserv'd, without Formality, or Stiffness, that one who look'd on her would have imagin'd her Soul the Twin-Angel of her Body ; and both together made her appear something divine. To this she had a great deal of Wit, read much, and retain'd all that serv'd her Purpose. She sung delicately, and danc'd well, and play'd on the Lute to a Miracle. She spoke several Languages naturally ; for being Co-heiress to so great a Fortune, she was bred with the nicest Care, in all the finest Manners or Education ; and was now arriv'd to her Eighteenth Year.

'Twere needless to tell you how great a Noise the Fame of this young Beauty, with so considerable a Fortune, made in the World: I may say, the World, rather than confine her Fame to the scanty Limits of a Town; it reach'd to many others: And there was not a Man of any Quality that came to *Antwerp*, or pass'd thro' the City, but made it his Business to see the lovely *Miranda*, who was universally ador'd: Her Youth and Beauty, her Shape, and Majesty of Mein, and Air of Greatness, charm'd all her Beholders; and thousands of People were dying by her Eyes, while she was vain enough to glory in her Conquests, and make it her Business to wound. She lov'd nothing so much as to behold sighing Slaves at her Feet, of the greatest Quality; and treated them all with an Affability that gave them Hope. Continual Musick, as soon as it was dark, and Songs of dying Lovers, were sung under her Windows; and she might well have made herself a great Fortune (if she had not been so already) by the rich Presents that were hourly made her; and every body daily expected when she would make some one happy, by suffering her self to be conquer'd by Love and Honour, by the Assiduities and Vows of some one of her Adorers. But *Miranda* accepted their Presents, heard their Vows with Pleasure, and willingly admitted all their soft Addresses; but would not yield her Heart, or give away that lovely Person to the Possession of one, who could please it self with so many. She was naturally amorous, but extremely inconstant: She lov'd one for his Wit, another for his Face, and a third for his Mein; but above all, she admir'd Quality: Quality alone had the Power to attach her entirely; yet not to one Man, but that Virtue was still admir'd by her in all: Where-ever she found that, she lov'd, or at least acted the Lover with such Art, that (deceiving well) she fail'd not to compleat her Conquest; and yet she never durst trust her fickle Humour with Marriage. She knew the Strength of her own Heart, and that it could not suffer itself to be confin'd to one Man, and wisely avoided those Inquietudes, and that Uneasiness of Life she was sure to find in that married

State, which would, against her Nature, oblige her to the Embraces of one, whose Humour was, to love all the Young and the Gay. But Love, who had hitherto only play'd with her Heart, and given it nought but pleasing wanton Wounds, such as afforded only soft Joys, and not Pains, resolv'd, either out of Revenge to those Numbers she had abandon'd, and who had sigh'd so long in vain, or to try what Power he had upon so fickle a Heart, to send an Arrow dipp'd in the most tormenting Flames that rage in Hearts most sensible. He struck it home and deep, with all the Malice of an angry God.

There was a Church belonging to the *Cordeliers*, whither *Miranda* often repair'd to her Devotion ; and being there one Day, accompany'd with a young Sister of the Order, after the Mass was ended, as 'tis the Custom, some one of the Fathers goes about the Church with a Box for Contribution, or Charity-Money : It happen'd that Day, that a young Father, newly initiated, carried the Box about, which, in his Turn, he brought to *Miranda*. She had no sooner cast her Eyes on this young Friar, but her Face was overspread with Blushes of Surprize : She beheld him stedfastly, and saw in his Face all the Charms of Youth, Wit, and Beauty ; he wanted no one Grace that could form him for Love, he appear'd all that is adorable to the Fair Sex, nor could the mis-shapen Habit hide from her the lovely Shape it endeavour'd to cover, nor those delicate Hands that approach'd her too near with the Box. Besides the Beauty of his Face and Shape, he had an Air altogether great, in spite of his profess'd Poverty, it betray'd the Man of Quality ; and that Thought weigh'd greatly with *Miranda*. But Love, who did not design she should now feel any sort of those easy Flames, with which she had heretofore burnt, made her soon lay all those Considerations aside, which us'd to invite her to love, and now lov'd she knew not why.

She gaz'd upon him, while he bow'd before her, and

waited for her Charity, till she perceiv'd the lovely Friar to
blush, and cast his Eyes to the Ground. This awaken'd
her Shame, and she put her Hand into her Pocket, and was
a good while in searching for her Purse, as if she thought
of nothing less than what she was about; at last she drew
it out, and gave him a Pistole; but with so much Delibera-
tion and Leisure, as easily betray'd the Satisfaction she took
in looking on him; while the good Man, having receiv'd
her Bounty, after a very low Obeysance, proceeded to the
rest; and *Miranda* casting after him a Look all languishing,
as long as he remain'd in the Church, departed with a Sigh
as soon as she saw him go out, and returned to her Apartment without speaking one Word all the Way to the young
Fille Devote, who attended her; so absolutely was her Soul
employ'd with this young Holy Man. *Cornelia* (so was
this Maid call'd who was with her) perceiving she was so
silent, who us'd to be all Wit and good Humour, and
observing her little Disorder at the Sight of the young
Father, tho' she was far from imagining it to be Love,
took an Occasion, when she was come home, to speak of
him. 'Madam, *said she*, did you not observe that fine young
Cordelier, who brought the Box?' At a Question that
nam'd that Object of her Thoughts, *Miranda* blush'd;
and she finding she did so, redoubled her Confusion, and
she had scarce Courage enough to say,—*Yes, I did observe
him*: And then, forcing herself to smile a little, continu'd,
'And I wonder'd to see so jolly a young Friar of an Order
so severe and mortify'd.—Madam, (*reply'd* Cornelia) when
you know his *Story*, you will not wonder.' *Miranda*, who
was impatient to know all that concern'd her new Conqueror, obliged her to tell his Story; and *Cornelia* obey'd,
and proceeded.

The Story of Prince Henrick.

'You must know, Madam, that this young Holy Man is a Prince of *Germany*, of the House of—, whose Fate it was, to fall most passionately in Love with a fair young Lady, who lov'd him with an Ardour equal to what he vow'd her. Sure of her Heart, and wanting only the Approbation of her Parents, and his own, which her Quality did not suffer him to despair of, he boasted of his Happiness to a young Prince, his elder Brother, a Youth amorous and fierce, impatient of Joys, and sensible of Beauty, taking Fire with all fair Eyes: He was his Father's Darling, and Delight of his fond Mother; and, by an Ascendant over both their Hearts, rul'd their Wills.

'This young Prince no sooner saw, but lov'd the fair Mistress of his Brother; and with an Authority of a Sovereign, rather than the Advice of a Friend, warn'd his Brother *Henrick* (this now young Friar) to approach no more this Lady, whom he had seen; and seeing, lov'd.

'In vain the poor surpriz'd Prince pleads his Right of Love, his Exchange of Vows, and Assurance of a Heart that could never be but for himself. In vain he urges his Nearness of Blood, his Friendship, his Passion, or his Life, which so entirely depended on the Possession of the charming Maid. All his Pleading serv'd but to blow his Brother's Flame; and the more he implores, the more the other burns; and while *Henrick* follows him, on his Knees, with humble Submissions, the other flies from him in Rages of transported Love; nor could his Tears, that pursu'd his Brother's Steps, move him to Pity: Hot-headed, vain-conceited of his Beauty, and greater Quality as elder Brother, he doubts not of Success, and resolv'd to sacrifice all to the Violence of his new-born Passion.

'In short, he speaks of his Design to his Mother, who promis'd him her Assistance; and accordingly proposing

it first to the Prince her Husband, urging the Languishment of her Son, she soon wrought so on him, that a
Match being concluded between the Parents of this young
Beauty, and *Henrick's* Brother, the Hour was appointed
before she knew of the Sacrifice she was to be made. And
while this was in Agitation, *Henrick* was sent on some
great Affairs, up into *Germany*, far out of the Way ; not
but his boding Heart, with perpetual Sighs and Throbs,
eternally foretold him his Fate.

‘ All the Letters he wrote were intercepted, as well as
those she wrote to him. She finds herself every Day perplex'd with the Addresses of the Prince she hated ; he was
ever sighing at her Feet. In vain were all her reproaches,
and all her Coldness, he was on the surer Side; for what he
found Love would not do, Force of Parents would.

She complains, in her Heart, of young *Henrick*, from
whom she could never receive one Letter ; and at last
could not forbear bursting into Tears, in spite of all her
Force, and feign'd Courage, when, on a Day, the Prince
told her, that *Henrick* was withdrawn to give him Time
to court her ; to whom he said, he confess'd he had made
some Vows, but did repent of 'em, knowing himself too
young to make 'em good : That it was for that Reason
he brought him first to see her ; and for that Reason, that
after that, he never saw her more, nor so much as took
Leave of her ; when, indeed, his Death lay upon the next
Visit, his Brother having sworn to murder him ; and to that
End, put a Guard upon him, till he was sent into *Germany*.

‘ All this he utter'd with so many passionate Asseverations, Vows, and seeming Pity for her being so inhumanly
abandon'd, that she almost gave Credit to all he had said,
and had much ado to keep herself within the Bounds of
Moderation, and silent Grief. Her Heart was breaking,
her Eyes languish'd, and her Cheeks grew pale, and she
had like to have fallen dead into the treacherous Arms of
him that had reduc'd her to this Discovery ; but she did

what she could to assume her Courage, and to shew as little Resentment as possible for a Heart, like hers, oppress'd with Love, and now abandon'd by the dear Subject of its Joys and Pains.

'But, Madam, not to tire you with this Adventure, the Day arriv'd wherein our still weeping Fair Unfortunate was to be sacrific'd to the Capriciousness of Love; and she was carry'd to Court by her Parents, without knowing to what End, where she was even compell'd to marry the Prince.

'*Henrick*, who all this While knew no more of his Unhappiness, than what his Fears suggested, returns, and passes even to the Presence of his Father, before he knew any Thing of his Fortune; where he beheld his Mistress and his Brother, with his Father, in such a Familiarity, as he no longer doubted his Destiny. 'Tis hard to judge, whether the Lady, or himself, was most surpriz'd; she was all pale and unmoveable in her Chair, and *Henrick* fix'd like a Statue; at last Grief and Rage took Place of Amazement, and he could not forbear crying out, *Ah, Traytor! Is it thus you have treated a Friend and Brother? And you, O perjur'd Charmer! Is it thus you have rewarded all my Vows?* He could say no more; but reeling against the Door, had fallen in a Swoon upon the Floor, had not his Page caught him in his Arms, who was entring with him. The good old Prince, the Father, who knew not what all this meant, was soon inform'd by the young weeping Princess; who, in relating the Story of her Amour with *Henrick*, told her Tale in so moving a Manner, as brought Tears to the Old Man's Eyes, and Rage to those of her Husband; he immediately grew jealous to the last Degree: He finds himself in Possession ('tis true) of the Beauty he ador'd, but the Beauty adoring another; a Prince young and charming as the Light, soft, witty, and raging with an equal Passion. He finds this dreaded Rival in the same House with him, with an Authority equal to his own; and

fancies, where two Hearts are so entirely agreed, and have
so good an Understanding, it would not be impossible to
find Opportunities to satisfy and ease that mutual Flame,
that burnt so equally in both ; he therefore resolved to send
him out of the World, and to establish his own Repose
by a Deed, wicked, cruel, and unnatural, to have him
assassinated the first Opportunity he could find. This
Resolution set him a little at Ease, and he strove to dissemble Kindness to *Henrick*, with all the Art he was
capable of, suffering him to come often to the Apartment
of the Princess, and to entertain her oftentimes with
Discourse, when he was not near enough to hear what
he spoke ; but still watching their Eyes, he found those of
Henrick full of Tears, ready to flow, but restrain'd, looking
all dying, and yet reproaching, while those of the Princess
were ever bent to the Earth, and she as much as possible,
shunning his Conversation. Yet this did not satisfy the
jealous Husband ; 'twas not her Complaisance that could
appease him ; he found her Heart was panting within,
whenever *Henrick* approach'd her, and every Visit more
and more confirmed his Death.

‘ The Father often found the Disorders of the Sons ;
the Softness and Address of the one gave him as much
Fear, as the angry Blushings, the fierce Looks, and broken
Replies of the other, whenever he beheld *Henrick* approach
his Wife ; so that the Father, fearing some ill Consequence
of this, besought *Henrick* to withdraw to some other
Country, or travel into *Italy*, he being now of an Age
that required a View of the World. He told his Father,
That he would obey his Commands, tho' he was certain,
that Moment he was to be separated from the Sight of
the fair Princess, his Sister, would be the last of his Life ;
and, in fine, made so pitiful a Story of his suffering Love,
as almost moved the old Prince to compassionate him so
far, as to permit him to stay ; but he saw inevitable Danger
in that, and therefore bid him prepare for his Journey.

'That which pass'd between the Father and *Henrick*, being a Secret, none talked of his departing from Court; so that the Design the Brother had went on ; and making a Hunting-Match one Day, where most young People of Quality were, he order'd some whom he had hired to follow his Brother, so as if he chanced to go out of the Way, to dispatch him ; and accordingly, Fortune gave 'em an Opportunity ; for he lagg'd behind the Company, and turn'd aside into a pleasant Thicket of Hazles, where alighting, he walk'd on Foot in the most pleasant Part of it, full of Thought, how to divide his Soul between Love and Obedience.   He was sensible that he ought not to stay ; that he was but an Affliction to the young Princess, whose Honour could never permit her to ease any Part of his Flame ; nor was he so vicious to entertain a Thought that should stain her Virtue.   He beheld her now as his Brother's Wife, and that secured his Flame from all loose Desires, if her native Modesty had not been sufficient or itself to have done it, as well as that profound Respect he paid her ; and he consider'd, in obeying his Father, he left her at Ease, and his Brother freed of a thousand Fears; he went to seek a Cure, which if he could not find, at last he could but die ; and so he must, even at her Feet: However, that it was more noble to seek a Remedy for his Disease, than expect a certain Death by staying.   After a thousand Reflections on his hard Fate, and bemoaning himself, and blaming his cruel Stars, that had doom'd him to die so young, after an Infinity of Sighs and Tears, Resolvings and Unresolvings, he, on the sudden, was interrupted by the trampling of some Horses he heard, and their rushing through the Boughs, and saw four Men make towards him : He had not time to mount, being walk'd some Paces from his Horse.   One of the Men advanced, and cry'd, *Prince, you must die—I do believe thee*, (reply'd *Henrick*) *but not by a Hand so base as thine* :   And at the same Time drawing his Sword, run him into the Groin.

When the Fellow found himself so wounded, he wheel'd off and cry'd, *Thou art a Prophet, and hast rewarded my Treachery with Death.* The rest came up, and one shot at the Prince, and shot him in the Shoulder; the other two hastily laying hold (but too late) on the Hand of the Murderer, cry'd, *Hold, Traytor; we relent, and he shall not die.* He reply'd, *'Tis too late, he is shot; and see, he lies dead. Let us provide for ourselves, and tell the Prince, we have done the Work; for you are as guilty as I am.* At that they all fled, and left the Prince lying under a Tree, weltering in his Blood.

'About the Evening, the Forester going his Walks, saw the Horse, richly caparison'd, without a Rider, at the Entrance of the Wood; and going farther, to see if he could find its Owner, found there the Prince almost dead; he immediately mounts him on the Horse, and himself behind, bore him up, and carry'd him to the Lodge; where he had only one old Man, his Father, well skilled in Surgery, and a Boy. They put him to Bed; and the old Forester, with what Art he had, dress'd his Wounds, and in the Morning sent for an abler Surgeon, to whom the Prince enjoin'd Secrecy, because he knew him. The Man was faithful, and the Prince in Time was recover'd of his Wound; and as soon as he was well, he came to *Flanders*, in the Habit of a Pilgrim, and after some Time took the Order of St. *Francis*, none knowing what became of him, till he was profess'd; and then he wrote his own Story to the Prince his Father, to his Mistress, and his ungrateful Brother. The young Princess did not long survive his Loss, she languished from the Moment of his Departure; and he had this to confirm his devout Life, to know she dy'd for him.

'My Brother, Madam, was an Officer under the Prince his Father, and knew his Story perfectly well; from whose Mouth I had it.

What! (reply'd *Miranda* then) *is Father* Henrick *a Man of Quality?* *Yes, Madam,* (said *Cornelia*) *and has changed his Name to* Francisco. But *Miranda,* fearing to betray the Sentiments of her Heart, by asking any more Questions about him, turned the Discourse; and some Persons of Quality came in to visit her (for her Apartment was about six o'Clock, like the Presence-Chamber of a Queen, always filled with the greatest People): There meet all the *Beaux Esprits,* and all the Beauties. But it was visible *Miranda* was not so gay as she used to be; but pensive, and answering *mal a propos* to all that was said to her. She was a thousand times going to speak, against her Will, something of the charming Friar, who was never from her Thoughts; and she imagined, if he could inspire Love in a coarse, grey, ill-made Habit, a shorn Crown, a Hair-cord about his Waist, bare-legg'd, in Sandals instead of Shoes; what must he do, when looking back on Time, she beholds him in a Prospect of Glory, with all that Youth, and illustrious Beauty, set off by the Advantage of Dress and Equipage? She frames an Idea of him all gay and splendid, and looks on his present Habit as some Disguise proper for the Stealths of Love; some feigned put-on Shape, with the more Security to approach a Mistress, and make himself happy; and that the Robe laid by, she has the Lover in his proper Beauty, the same he would have been, if any other Habit (though ever so rich) were put off: In the Bed, the silent gloomy Night, and the soft Embraces of her Arms, he loses all the Friar, and assumes all the Prince; and that aweful Reverence, due alone to his Holy Habit, he exchanges for a thousand Dalliances, for which his Youth was made; for Love, for tender Embraces, and all the Happiness of Life. Some Moments she fancies him a Lover, and that the fair Object that takes up all his Heart, has left no Room for her there; but that was a Thought that did not long perplex her, and which, almost as soon as born, she turned to her Advantage. She beholds him a Lover, and therefore finds he has a Heart sensible and tender; he had Youth to be fir'd, as well as

to inspire; he was far from the loved Object, and totally
without Hope; and she reasonably consider'd, that Flame
would of itself soon die, that had only Despair to feed on.
She beheld her own Charms; and Experience, as well as
her Glass, told her, they never failed of Conquest, especially
where they designed it: And she believed *Henrick* would
be glad, at least, to quench that Flame in himself, by an
Amour with her, which was kindled by the young Princess
of — his Sister.

These, and a thousand other Self-flatteries, all vain and
indiscreet, took up her waking Nights, and now more retired Days; while Love, to make her truly wretched,
suffered her to sooth herself with fond Imaginations; not
so much as permitting her Reason to plead one Moment
to save her from undoing: She would not suffer it to tell
her, he had taken Holy Orders, made sacred and solemn
Vows of everlasting Chastity, that it was impossible he
could marry her, or lay before her any Argument that
might prevent her Ruin; but Love, mad malicious Love,
was always called to Counsel, and, like easy Monarchs,
she had no Ears, but for Flatterers.

Well then, she is resolv'd to love, without considering
to what End, and what must be the Consequence of such
an Amour. She now miss'd no Day of being at that little
Church, where she had the Happiness, or rather the Misfortune (so Love ordained) to see this Ravisher of her
Heart and Soul; and every Day she took new Fire from
his lovely Eyes. Unawares, unknown, and unwillingly,
he gave her Wounds, and the Difficulty of her Cure made
her rage the more: She burnt, she languish'd, and died
for the young Innocent, who knew not he was the Author
of so much Mischief.

Now she resolves a thousand Ways in her tortur'd
Mind, to let him know her Anguish, and at last pitch'd
upon that of writing to him soft Billets, which she had learn'd
the Art of doing; or if she had not, she had now Fire

enough to inspire her with all that could charm and move. These she deliver'd to a young Wench, who waited on her, and whom she had entirely subdu'd to her Interest, to give to a certain Lay-Brother of the Order, who was a very simple harmless Wretch, and who served in the Kitchen, in the Nature of a Cook, in the Monastery of *Cordeliers*. She gave him Gold to secure his Faith and Service; and not knowing from whence they came (with so good Credentials) he undertook to deliver the Letters to Father *Francisco*; which Letters were all afterwards, as you shall hear, produced in open Court. These Letters failed not to come every Day; and the Sense of the first was, to tell him, that a very beautiful young Lady, of a great Fortune, was in love with him, without naming her; but it came as from a third Person, to let him know the Secret, that she desir'd he would let her know whether she might hope any Return from him; assuring him, he needed but only see the fair Languisher, to confess himself her Slave.

This Letter being deliver'd him, he read by himself, and was surpriz'd to receive Words of this Nature, being so great a Stranger in that Place; and could not imagine or would not give himself the Trouble of guessing who this should be, because he never designed to make Returns.

The next Day, *Miranda*, finding no Advantage from her Messenger of Love, in the Evening sends another (impatient of Delay) confessing that she who suffer'd the Shame of writing and imploring, was the Person herself who ador'd him. 'Twas there her raging Love made her say all Things that discover'd the Nature of its Flame, and propose to flee with him to any Part of the World, if he would quit the Convent; that she had a Fortune considerable enough to make him happy; and that his Youth and Quality were not given him to so unprofitable an End as to lose themselves in a Convent, where Poverty and Ease was all the Business. In fine, she leaves nothing unurg'd that might debauch and invite him; not forgetting

to send him her own Character of Beauty, and left him
to judge of her Wit and Spirit by her Writing, and her
Love by the Extremity of Passion she profess'd. To all
which the lovely Friar made no Return, as believing a
gentle Capitulation or Exhortation to her would but
inflame her the more, and give new Occasions for her
continuing to write. All her Reasonings, false and vicious,
he despis'd, pity'd the Error of her Love, and was Proof
against all she could plead. Yet notwithstanding his
Silence, which left her in Doubt, and more tormented
her, she ceas'd not to pursue him with her Letters, varying her Style; sometimes all wanton, loose and raving;
sometimes feigning a Virgin-Modesty all over, accusing
her self, blaming her Conduct, and sighing her Destiny,
as one compell'd to the shameful Discovery by the Austerity
of his Vow and Habit, asking his Pity and Forgiveness;
urging him in Charity to use his Fatherly Care to persuade
and reason with her wild Desires, and by his Counsel
drive the God from her Heart, whose Tyranny was worse
than that of a Fiend; and he did not know what his pious
Advice might do. But still she writes in vain, in vain she
varies her Style, by a Cunning, peculiar to a Maid possess'd
with such a sort of Passion.

This cold Neglect was still Oil to the burning Lamp,
and she tries yet more Arts, which for want of right
Thinking were as fruitless. She has Recourse to Presents;
her Letters came loaded with Rings of great Price, and
Jewels, which Fops of Quality had given her. Many of
this Sort he receiv'd, before he knew where to return 'em,
or how; and on this Occasion alone he sent her a Letter,
and restor'd her Trifles, as he call'd them: But his Habit
having not made him forget his Quality and Education,
he wrote to her with all the profound Respect imaginable;
believing by her Presents, and the Liberality with which
she parted with 'em, that she was of Quality. But the
whole Letter, as he told me afterwards, was to persuade

her from the Honour she did him, by loving him; urging
a thousand Reasons, solid and pious, and assuring her,
he had wholly devoted the rest of his Days to Heaven,
and had no Need of those gay Trifles she had sent him,
which were only fit to adorn Ladies so fair as herself, and
who had Business with this glittering World, which he
disdain'd, and had for ever abandon'd. He sent her a
thousand Blessings, and told her, she should be ever in
his Prayers, tho' not in his Heart, as she desir'd: And
abundance of Goodness more he express'd, and Counsel
he gave her, which had the same Effect with his Silence;
it made her love but the more, and the more impatient
she grew. She now had a new Occasion to write, she now
is charm'd with his Wit; this was the new Subject. She
rallies his Resolution, and endeavours to re-call him to the
World, by all the Arguments that human Invention is
capable of.

But when she had above four Months languish'd thus
in vain, not missing one Day, wherein she went not to see
him, without discovering herself to him; she resolv'd, as
her last Effort, to shew her Person, and see what that,
assisted by her Tears, and soft Words from her Mouth,
could do, to prevail upon him.

It happen'd to be on the Eve of that Day when she
was to receive the Sacrament, that she, covering herself
with her Veil, came to *Vespers*, purposing to make Choice
of the conquering Friar for her Confessor.

She approach'd him; and as she did so, she trembled
with Love. At last she cry'd, *Father, my Confessor is gone
for some Time from the Town, and I am oblig'd To-morrow
to receive, and beg you will be pleas'd to take my Confession.*

He could not refuse her; and let her into the *Sacristy*,
where there is a Confession-Chair, in which he seated
himself; and on one Side of him she kneel'd down, over-
against a little Altar, where the Priests Robes lye, on which
were plac'd some lighted Wax-Candles, that made the

little Place very light and splendid, which shone full upon *Miranda*.

After the little Preparation usual in Confession, she turn'd up her Veil, and discover'd to his View the most wondrous Object of Beauty he had ever seen, dress'd in all the Glory of a young Bride; her Hair and Stomacher full of Diamonds, that gave a Lustre all dazling to her brighter Face and Eyes. He was surpriz'd at her amazing Beauty, and question'd whether he saw a Woman, or an Angel at his Feet. Her Hands, which were elevated, as if in Prayer, seem'd to be form'd of polish'd Alabaster; and he confess'd, he had never seen any Thing in Nature so perfect and so admirable.

He had some Pain to compose himself to hear her Confession, and was oblig'd to turn away his Eyes, that his Mind might not be perplex'd with an Object so diverting; when *Miranda*, opening the finest Mouth in the World, and discovering new Charms, began her Confession.

' Holy Father *(said she)* amongst the Number of my vile Offences, that which afflicts me to the greatest Degree, is, that I am in love: Not *(continued she)* that I believe simple and virtuous Love a Sin, when 'tis plac'd on an Object proper and suitable; but, my dear Father, *(said she, and wept)* I love with a Violence which cannot be contain'd within the Bounds of Reason, Moderation, or Virtue. I love a Man whom I cannot possess without a Crime, and a Man who cannot make me happy without being perjur'd. Is he marry'd? *(reply'd the Father.)* No; *(answer'd* Miranda.) Are you so? *(continued he.)* Neither, *(said she.)* Is he too near ally'd to you? *(said* Francisco:) a Brother, or Relation? Neither of these, *(said she.)* He is unenjoy'd, unpromis'd; and so am I: Nothing opposes our Happiness, or makes my Love a Vice, but you—'Tis you deny me Life: 'Tis you that forbid my Flame: 'Tis you will have me die, and seek my Remedy in my Grave, when I complain of Tortures, Wounds, and Flames. O cruel Charmer! 'tis for you I languish; and here, at your Feet, implore that Pity, which all my Addresses have fail'd of procuring me.'—

With that, perceiving he was about to rise from his Seat, she held him by his Habit, and vow'd she would in that Posture follow him, where-ever he flew from her. She elevated her Voice so loud, he was afraid she might be heard, and therefore suffer'd her to force him into his Chair again; where being seated, he began, in the most passionate Terms imaginable, to dissuade her; but finding she the more persisted in Eagerness of Passion, he us'd all the tender Assurance that he could force from himself, that he would have for her all the Respect, Esteem and Friendship that he was capable of paying; that he had a real Compassion for her: and at last she prevail'd so far with him, by her Sighs and Tears, as to own he had a Tenderness for her, and that he could not behold so many Charms, without being sensibly touch'd by 'em, and finding all those Effects, that a Maid so fair and young causes in the Souls of Men of Youth and Sense: But that, as he was assured, he could never be so happy to marry her, and as certain he could not grant any Thing but honourable Passion, he humbly besought her not to expect more from him than such. And then began to tell her how short Life was, and transitory its Joys; how soon she would grow weary of Vice, and how often change to find real Repose in it, but never arrive to it. He made an End, by new Assurance of his eternal Friendship, but utterly forbad her to hope.

Behold her now deny'd, refus'd and defeated, with all her pleading Youth, Beauty, Tears, and Knees, imploring, as she lay, holding fast his *Scapular*, and embracing his Feet. What shall she do? She swells with Pride, Love, Indignation and Desire; her burning Heart is bursting with Despair, her Eyes grow fierce, and from Grief she rises to a Storm; and in her Agony of Passion, with Looks all disdainful, haughty, and full of Rage, she began to revile him, as the poorest of Animals; tells him his Soul was dwindled to the Meanness of his Habit, and his Vows of Poverty were suited to his degenerate Mind. 'And *(said she)* since all my nobler Ways have fail'd me; and that, for a little Hypocritical Devotion, you resolve to lose the greatest Blessings of Life, and to sacrifice me to your Religious Pride and Vanity, I will either force you to abandon that dull Dissimulation, or you shall die, to prove your Sanctity real. Therefore answer me immediately, answer my Flame, my raging Fire, which your Eyes have kindled; or here, in this very Moment, I will ruin thee; and make no Scruple of revenging the Pains I suffer, by that which shall take away your Life and Honour.'

The trembling young Man, who, all this While, with extreme Anguish of Mind, and Fear of the dire Result, had listen'd to her Ravings, full of Dread, demanded what she would have him do? When she reply'd—'Do that which thy Youth and Beauty were ordain'd to do:— this Place is private, a sacred Silence reigns here, and no one dares to pry into the Secrets of this Holy Place: We are as secure from Fears and Interruption, as in Desarts uninhabited, or Caves forsaken by wild Beasts. The Tapers too shall veil their Lights, and only that glimmering Lamp shall be Witness of our dear Stealths of Love— Come to my Arms, my trembling, longing Arms; and curse the Folly of thy Bigotry, that has made thee so long lose a Blessing, for which so many Princes sigh in vain.'

At these Words she rose from his Feet, and snatching him in her Arms, he could not defend himself from receiving a thousand Kisses from the lovely Mouth of the charming Wanton; after which, she ran herself, and in an Instant put out the Candles. But he cry'd to her, 'In vain, O too indiscreet Fair One, in vain you put out the Light; for Heaven still has Eyes, and will look down upon my broken Vows. I own your Power, I own I have all the

Sense in the World of your charming Touches; I am
frail Flesh and Blood, but—yet—yet I can resist; and I
prefer my Vows to all your powerful Temptations.—
I will be deaf and blind, and guard my Heart with Walls
of Ice, and make you know, that when the Flames of true
Devotion are kindled in a Heart, it puts out all other Fires;
which are as ineffectual, as Candles lighted in the Face of
the Sun.—Go, vain Wanton, and repent, and mortify
that Blood which has so shamefully betray'd thee, and
which will one Day ruin both thy Soul and Body.'—

At these Words *Miranda*, more enrag'd, the nearer
she imagin'd her self to Happiness, made no Reply; but
throwing her self, in that Instant, into the Confessing-
Chair, and violently pulling the young Friar into her Lap,
she elevated her Voice to such a Degree, in crying out,
Help, Help! A Rape! Help, Help! that she was heard
all over the Church, which was full of People at the Evening's Devotion; who flock'd about the Door of the *Sacristy*,
which was shut with a Spring-Lock on the Inside, but
they durst not open the Door.

'Tis easily to be imagin'd, in what Condition our young
Friar was, at this last devilish Stratagem of his wicked
Mistress. He strove to break from those Arms that held
him so fast; and his Bustling to get away, and her's to
retain him, disorder'd her Hair and Habit to such a Degree,
as gave the more Credit to her false Accusation.

The Fathers had a Door on the other Side, by which
they usually enter'd, to dress in this little Room; and at
the Report that was in an Instant made 'em, they hasted
thither, and found *Miranda* and the good Father very
indecently struggling; which they mis-interpreted, as
Miranda desir'd; who, all in Tears, immediately threw
her self at the Feet of the Provincial, who was one of
those that enter'd; and cry'd, 'O holy Father! revenge
an innocent Maid, undone and lost to Fame and Honour,
by that vile Monster, born of Goats, nurs'd by Tygers,

and bred up on savage Mountains, where Humanity and Religion are Strangers. For, O holy Father, could it have enter'd into the Heart of Man, to have done so barbarous and horrid a Deed, as to attempt the Virgin-Honour of an unspotted Maid, and one of my Degree, even in the Moment of my Confession, in that holy Time, when I was prostrate before him and Heaven, confessing those Sins that press'd my tender Conscience; even then to load my Soul with the blackest of Infamies, to add to my Number a Weight that must sink me to Hell? Alas! under the Security of his innocent Looks, his holy Habit, and his aweful Function, I was led into this Room to make my Confession; where, he locking the Door, I had no sooner began, but he gazing on me, took fire at my fatal Beauty; and starting up, put out the Candles and caught me in his Arms; and raising me from the Pavement, set me in the Confession-Chair; and then—Oh, spare me the rest.'

With that a Shower of Tears burst from her fair dissembling Eyes, and Sobs so naturally acted, and so well manag'd, as left no doubt upon the good Men, but all she had spoken was Truth.

'— At first, *(proceeded she)* I was unwilling to bring so great a Scandal on his Order, to cry out; but struggled as long as I had Breath; pleaded the Heinousness of the Crime, urging my Quality, and the Danger of the Attempt. But he, deaf as the Winds, and ruffling as a Storm, pursu'd his wild Design with so much Force and Insolence, as I at last, unable to resist, was wholly vanquish'd, robb'd of my native Purity. With what Life and Breath I had, I call'd for Assistance, both from Men and Heaven; but oh, alas! your Succours came too late:—You find me here a wretched, undone, and ravish'd Maid. Revenge me, Fathers; revenge me on the perfidious Hypocrite, or else give me a Death that may secure your Cruelty and Injustice from ever being proclaim'd over the World; or my

Tongue will be eternally reproaching you, and cursing the wicked Author of my Infamy.'

She ended as she began, with a thousand Sighs and Tears; and received from the Provincial all Assurances of Revenge.

The innocent betray'd Victim, all the while she was speaking, heard her with an Astonishment that may easily be imagined; yet shew'd no extravagant Signs of it, as those would do, who feign it, to be thought innocent; but being really so, he bore with an humble, modest, and blushing Countenance, all her Accusations; which silent Shame they mistook for evident Signs of his Guilt.

When the Provincial demanded, with an unwonted Severity in his Eyes and Voice, what he could answer for himself? calling him Profaner of his Sacred Vows, and Infamy to the Holy Order; the injur'd, but innocently accus'd, only reply'd: 'May Heaven forgive that bad Woman, and bring her to Repentance! For his Part, he was not so much in Love with Life, as to use many arguments to justify his Innocence; unless it were to free that Order from a Scandal, of which he had the Honour to be profess'd. But as for himself, Life or Death were Things indifferent to him, who heartily despis'd the World.'

He said no more, and suffer'd himself to be led before the Magistrate; who committed him to Prison, upon the Accusation of this implacable Beauty; who, with so much feign'd Sorrow, prosecuted the Matter, even to his Tryal and Condemnation; where he refus'd to make any great Defence for himself. But being daily visited by all the Religious, both of his own and other Orders, they oblig'd him (some of 'em knowing the Austerity of his Life, others his Cause of Griefs that first brought him into Orders, and others pretending a nearer Knowledge, even of his Soul it self) to stand upon his Justification, and discover what he knew of that wicked Woman; whose Life had not been so exemplary for Virtue, not to have given the World a thousand Suspicions of her Lewdness and Prostitutions.

The daily Importunities of these Fathers made him produce her Letters : But as he had all the Gown-men on his Side, she had all the Hats and Feathers on her's; all the Men of Quality taking her Part, and all the Church-men his. They heard his daily Protestations and Vows, but not a Word of what passed at Confession was yet discover'd : He held that as a Secret sacred on his Part; and what was said in Nature of a Confession, was not to be revealed, though his Life depended on the Discovery. But as to the Letters, they were forc'd from him, and expos'd; however, Matters were carry'd with so high a Hand against him, that they serv'd for no Proof at all of his Innocence, and he was at last condemn'd to be burn'd at the Market-Place.

After his Sentence was pass'd, the whole Body of Priests made their Addresses to the Marquis *Castel Roderigo*, the then Governor of *Flanders*, for a Reprieve; which, after much ado, was granted him for some Weeks, but with an absolute Denial of Pardon : So prevailing were the young Cavaliers of his Court, who were all Adorers of this Fair Jilt.

About this time, while the poor innocent young *Henrick* was thus languishing in Prison, in a dark and dismal Dungeon, and *Miranda*, cured of her Love, was triumphing in her Revenge, expecting and daily giving new Conquests; and who, by this time, had re-assum'd all her wonted Gaiety; there was a great Noise about the Town, that a Prince of mighty Name, and fam'd for all the Excellencies of his Sex, was arriv'd; a Prince young, and gloriously attended, call'd Prince *Tarquin*.

We had often heard of this great Man, and that he was making his Travels in *France* and *Germany* : And we had also heard, that some Years before, he being about Eighteen Years of Age, in the Time when our King *Charles*, of blessed Memory, was in *Brussels*, in the last Year of his Banishment, that all on a sudden, this young Man rose up upon 'em like the Sun, all glorious and dazling, demanding

Place of all the Princes in that Court. And when his Pretence was demanded, he own'd himself Prince *Tarquin*, of the Race of the last Kings of *Rome*, made good his Title, and took his Place accordingly. After that he travell'd for about six Years up and down the World, and then arriv'd at *Antwerp*, about the Time of my being sent thither by King *Charles*.

Perhaps there could be nothing seen so magnificent as this Prince: He was, as I said, extremely handsome, from Head to Foot exactly form'd, and he wanted nothing that might adorn that native Beauty to the best Advantage. His Parts were suitable to the rest: He had an Accomplishment fit for a Prince, an Air haughty, but a Carriage affable, easy in Conversation, and very entertaining, liberal and good-natur'd, brave and inoffensive. I have seen him pass the Streets with twelve Footmen, and four Pages; the Pages all in green Velvet Coats lac'd with Gold, and white Velvet Tunicks; the Men in Cloth, richly lac'd with Gold; his Coaches, and all other Officers, suitable to a great Man.

He was all the Discourse of the Town; some laughing at his Title, others reverencing it: Some cry'd, that he was an Imposter; others, that he had made his Title as plain, as if *Tarquin* had reign'd but a Year ago. Some made Friendships with him, others would have nothing to say to him: But all wonder'd where his Revenue was, that supported this Grandeur; and believ'd, tho' he could make his Descent from the *Roman* Kings very well out, that he could not lay so good a Claim to the *Roman* Land. Thus every body meddled with what they had nothing to do; and, as in other Places, thought themselves on the surer Side, if, in these doubtful Cases, they imagin'd the worst.

But the Men might be of what Opinion they pleas'd concerning him; the Ladies were all agreed that he was a Prince, and a young handsome Prince, and a Prince not to be resisted : He had all their Wishes, all their Eyes, and all their Hearts. They now dress'd only for him ; and what Church he grac'd, was sure, that Day, to have the Beauties, and all that thought themselves so.

You may believe, our amorous *Miranda* was not the least Conquest he made. She no sooner heard of him, which was as soon as he arriv'd, but she fell in love with his very Name. *Jesu!*—A young King of *Rome!* Oh, it was so novel, that she doated on the Title ; and had not car'd whether the rest had been Man or Monkey almost : She was resolved to be the *Lucretia* that this young *Tarquin* should ravish.

To this End, she was no sooner up the next Day, but she sent him a *Billet Doux*, assuring him how much she admired his Fame ; and that being a Stranger in the Town, she begged the Honour of introducing him to all the *Belle* Conversations, *&c.* which he took for the Invitation of some Coquet, who had Interest in fair Ladies ; and civilly return'd her an Answer, that he would wait on her. She had him that Day watched to Church ; and impatient to see what she heard so many People flock to see, she went also to the same Church ; those sanctified Abodes being too often profaned by such Devotees, whose Business is to ogle and ensnare.

But what a Noise and Humming was heard all over the Church, when *Tarquin* enter'd ! His Grace, his Mein, his Fashion, his Beauty, his Dress, and his Equipage surprized all that were present : And by the good Management and Care of *Miranda*, she got to kneel at the Side of the Altar, just over against the Prince, so that, if he would, he could not avoid looking full upon her. She had turned up her Veil, and all her Face and Shape appear'd such, and so inchanting, as I have described ; and her Beauty heighten'd with Blushes, and her Eyes full of Spirit and Fire, with Joy, to find the young *Roman* Monarch so charming, she appear'd like something more than mortal, and compelled

his Eyes to a fixed gazing on her Face : She never glanc'd
that Way, but she met them ; and then would feign so
modest a Shame, and cast her Eyes downwards with such
inviting Art, that he was wholly ravished and charmed,
and she over-joy'd to find he was so.

The Ceremony being ended, he sent a Page to follow
that Lady Home, himself pursuing her to the Door of the
Church, where he took some holy Water, and threw upon
her, and made her a profound Reverence. She forc'd an
innocent Look, and a modest Gratitude in her Face, and
bow'd, and passed forward, half assur'd of her Conquest;
leaving her, to go home to his Lodging, and impatiently
wait the Return of his Page. And all the Ladies who saw
this first Beginning between the Prince and *Miranda*,
began to curse and envy her Charms, who had deprived
them of half their Hopes.

After this, I need not tell you, he made *Miranda* a
Visit ; and from that Day never left her Apartment, but
when he went home at Nights, or unless he had Business ;
so entirely was he conquer'd by this Fair One. But the
Bishop, and several Men of Quality, in Orders, that
profess'd Friendship to him, advised him from her Company ;
and spoke several Things to him, that might (if Love had
not made him blind) have reclaimed him from the Pursuit
of his Ruin. But whatever they trusted him with, she
had the Art to wind herself about his Heart, and make
him unravel all his Secrets ; and then knew as well, by
feign'd Sighs and Tears, to make him disbelieve all ; so
that he had no Faith but for her ; and was wholly inchanted
and bewitch'd by her. At last, in spite of all that would
have opposed it, he marry'd this famous Woman, possess'd
by so many great Men and Strangers before, while all the
World was pitying his Shame and Misfortunes.

Being marry'd, they took a great House ; and as she
was indeed a great Fortune, and now a great Princess,
there was nothing wanting that was agreeable to their

Quality; all was splendid and magnificent. But all this would not acquire them the World's Esteem; they had an Abhorrence for her former Life, and despised her; and for his espousing a Woman so infamous, they despised him. So that though they admir'd, and gazed upon their Equipage, and glorious Dress, they foresaw the Ruin that attended it, and paid her Quality little Respect.

She was no sooner married, but her Uncle died; and dividing his Fortune between *Miranda* and her Sister, leaves the young Heiress, and all her Fortune, entirely in the Hands of the Princess.

We will call this Sister *Alcidiana*; she was about fourteen Years of Age, and now had chosen her Brother, the Prince, for her Guardian. If *Alcidiana* were not altogether so great a Beauty as her Sister, she had Charms sufficient to procure her a great many Lovers, though her Fortune had not been so considerable as it was; but with that Addition, you may believe, she wanted no Courtships from those of the best Quality; tho' every body deplor'd her being under the Tutorage of a Lady so expert in all the Vices of her Sex, and so cunning a Manager of Sin, as was the Princess; who, on her Part, failed not, by all the Caresses, and obliging Endearments, to engage the Mind of this young Maid, and to subdue her wholly to her Government. All her Senses were eternally regaled with the most bewitching Pleasures they were capable of: She saw nothing but Glory and Magnificence, heard nothing but Musick of the sweetest Sounds; the richest Perfumes employ'd her Smelling; and all she eat and touch'd was delicate and inviting; and being too young to consider how this State and Grandeur was to be continu'd, little imagined her vast Fortune was every Day diminishing, towards its needless Support.

When the Princess went to Church, she had her Gentleman bare before her, carrying a great Velvet Cushion, with great Golden Tassels, for her to kneel on, and her

Train borne up a most prodigious Length, led by a Gentleman Usher, bare; follow'd by innumerable Footmen,
Pages, and Women. And in this State she would walk in
the Streets, as in those Countries it is the Fashion for the
great Ladies to do, who are well; and in her Train two
or three Coaches, and perhaps a rich Velvet Chair embroider'd, would follow in State.

It was thus for some time they liv'd, and the Princess was
daily press'd by young sighing Lovers, for her Consent to
marry *Alcidiana*; but she had still one Art or other to put
them off, and so continually broke all the great Matches
that were proposed to her, notwithstanding their Kindred
and other Friends had industriously endeavour'd to make
several great Matches for her; but the Princess was still
positive in her Denial, and one Way or other broke all.
At last it happened, there was one proposed, yet more
advantageous, a young Count, with whom the young
Maid grew passionately in Love, and besought her Sister
to consent that she might have him, and got the Prince
to speak in her Behalf; but he had no sooner heard the
secret Reasons *Miranda* gave him, but (entirely her Slave)
he chang'd his Mind, and suited it to hers, and she, as
before, broke off that Amour: Which so extremely incensed *Alcidiana*, the she, taking an Opportunity, got from
her Guard, and ran away, putting her self into the Hands
of a wealty Merchant, her Kinsman, and one who bore
the greatest Authority in the City; him she chuses for her
Guardian, resolving to be no longer a Slave to the Tyranny
of her Sister. And so well she ordered Matters, that she
writ this young Cavalier, her last Lover, and retrieved
him; who came back to *Antwerp* again, to renew his
Courtship.

Both Parties being agreed, it was no hard Matter to
persuade all but the Princess. But though she opposed it,
it was resolved on, and the Day appointed for Marriage,
and the Portion demanded; demanded only, but never

to be paid, the best Part of it being spent. However, she put them off from Day to Day, by a thousand frivolous Delays; and when she saw they would have Recourse to Force, and all that her Magnificence would be at an End, if the Law should prevail against her; and that without this Sister's Fortune, she could not long support her Grandeur; she bethought herself of a Means to make it all her own, by getting her Sister made away; but she being out of her Tuition, she was not able to accomplish so great a Deed of Darkness. But since it was resolved it must be done, she contrives a thousand Stratagems; and at last pitches upon an effectual one.

She had a Page call'd *Van Brune*, a Youth of great Address and Wit, and one she had long managed for her Purpose. This Youth was about seventeen Years of Age, and extremely beautiful; and in the Time when *Alcidiana* lived with the Princess, she was a little in Love with this handsome Boy; but it was checked in its Infancy, and never grew up to a Flame: Nevertheless, *Alcidiana* retained still a sort of Tenderness for him, while he burn'd in good Earnest with Love for the Princess.

The Princess one Day ordering this Page to wait on her in her Closet, she shut the Door; and after a thousand Questions of what he would undertake to serve her, the amorous Boy finding himself alone, and caress'd by the fair Person he ador'd, with joyful Blushes that beautify'd his Face, told her, 'There was nothing upon Earth, he would not do, to obey her least Commands.' She grew more familiar with him, to oblige him; and seeing Love dance in his Eyes, of which she was so good a Judge, she treated him more like a Lover, than a Servant; till at last the ravished Youth, wholly transported out of himself, fell at her Feet, and impatiently implor'd to receive her Commands quickly, that he might fly to execute them; for he was not able to bear her charming Words, Looks, and Touches, and retain his Duty. At this she smil'd, and told him, the Work was of such a Nature, as would mortify all Flames about him; and he would have more Need of Rage, Envy, and Malice, than the Aids of a Passion so soft as what she now found him capable of. He assur'd her, he would stick at nothing, tho' even against his Nature, to recompense for the Boldness he now, through his Indiscretion, had discover'd. She smiling, told him, he had committed no Fault; and that possibly, the Pay he should receive for the Service she required at his Hands, should be—what he most wish'd for in the World. At this he bow'd to the Earth; and kissing her Feet, bad her command: And then she boldly told him, *'Twas to kill her Sister* Alcidiana. The Youth, without so much as starting or pausing upon the Matter, told her, *It should be done;* and bowing low, immediately went out of the Closet. She call'd him back, and would have given him some Instruction; but he refused it, and said, 'The Action and the Contrivance should be all his own.' And offering to go again, she—again recalled him; putting into his Hand a Purse of a hundred Pistoles, which he took, and with a low Bow departed.

He no sooner left her Presence, but he goes directly, and buys a Dose of Poison, and went immediately to the House where *Alcidiana* lived; where desiring to be brought to her Presence, he fell a weeping; and told her, his Lady had fallen out with him, and dismissed him her Service, and since from a Child he had been brought up in the Family, he humbly besought *Alcidiana* to receive him into hers, she being in a few Days to be marry'd. There needed not much Intreaty to a Thing that pleased her so well, and she immediately received him to Pension: And he waited some Days on her, before he could get an Opportunity to administer his devilish Potion. But one Night, when she drank Wine with roasted Apples, which was usual with her; instead of Sugar, or with the Sugar, the baneful Drug was mixed, and she drank it down.

About this Time, there was a great Talk of this Page's coming from one Sister, to go to the other. And Prince *Tarquin*, who was ignorant of the Design from the Beginning to the End, hearing some Men of Quality at his Table speaking of *Van Brune's* Change of Place (the Princess then keeping her Chamber upon some trifling Indisposition) he answer'd, 'That surely they were mistaken, that he was not dismissed from the Princess's Service:' And calling some of his Servants, he asked for *Van Brune*; and whether any Thing had happen'd between her Highness and him, that had occasion'd his being turned off. They all seem'd ignorant of this Matter; and those who had spoken of it, began to fancy there was some Juggle in the Case, which Time would bring to Light.

The ensuing Day 'twas all about the Town, that *Alcidiana* was poison'd; and though not dead, yet very near it; and that the Doctors said, she had taken Mercury. So that there was never so formidable a Sight as this fair young Creature; her Head and Body swoln, her Eyes starting out, her Face black, and all deformed: So that diligent Search was made, who it should be that did this; who gave her Drink and Meat. The Cook and Butler were examined, the Footman called to an Account; but all concluded, she received nothing but from the Hand of her new Page, since he came into her Service. He was examined, and shew'd a thousand guilty Looks: And the Apothecary, then attending among the Doctors, proved he had bought Mercury of him three or four Days before; which he could not deny; and making many Excuses for his buying it, betray'd him the more; so ill he chanced to dissemble. He was immediately sent to be examined by the Margrave or Justice, who made his *Mittimus*, and sent him to Prison.

'Tis easy to imagine, in what Fears and Confusion the Princess was at this News: She took her Chamber upon it, more to hide her guilty Face, than for any Indisposition.

And the Doctors apply'd such Remedies to *Alcidiana*, such Antidotes against the Poison, that in a short Time she recover'd; but lost the finest Hair in the World, and the Complexion of her Face ever after.

It was not long before the Trials for Criminals came on; and the Day being arrived, *Van Brune* was try'd the first of all; every Body having already read his Destiny, according as they wished it; and none would believe, but just indeed as it was: So that for the Revenge they hoped to see fall upon the Princess, every one wished he might find no Mercy, that she might share of his Shame and Misery.

The Sessions-House was filled that Day with all the Ladies, and chief of the Town, to hear the Result of his Trial; and the sad Youth was brought, loaded with Chains, and pale as Death; where every Circumstance being sufficiently proved against him, and he making but a weak Defence for himself, he was convicted, and sent back to Prison, to receive his Sentence of Death on the Morrow; where he owned all, and who set him on to do it. He own'd 'twas not Reward of Gain he did it for, but Hope he should command at his Pleasure the Possession of his Mistress, the Princess, who should deny him nothing, after having entrusted him with so great a Secret; and that besides, she had elevated him with the Promise of that glorious Reward, and had dazzled his young Heart with so charming a Prospect, that blind and mad with Joy, he rushed forward to gain the desired Prize, and thought on nothing but his coming Happiness: That he saw too late the Follies of his presumptuous Flame, and cursed the deluding Flatteries of the fair Hypocrite, who had soothed him to his Undoing: That he was a miserable Victim to her Wickedness; and hoped he should warn all young Men, by his Fall, to avoid the Dissimulation of the deceiving Fair: That he hoped they would have Pity on his Youth, and attribute his Crime to the subtle Persuasions alone of his Mistress the Princess: And that since *Alcidiana* was

not dead, they would grant him Mercy, and permit him
to live to repent of his grievous Crime, in some Part of
the World, whither they might banish him.

He ended with Tears, that fell in abundance from his
Eyes; and immediately the Princess was apprehended,
and brought to Prison, to the same Prison where yet the
poor young Father *Francisco* was languishing, he having
been from Week to Week reprieved, by the Intercession
of the Fathers; and possibly she there had Time to make
some Reflections.

You may imagine *Tarquin* left no Means unessay'd, to
prevent the Imprisonment of the Princess, and the publick
Shame and Infamy she was likely to undergo in this
Affair: But the whole City being over-joy'd that she
should be punished, as an Author of all this Mischief, were
generally bent against her, both Priests, Magistrates and
People; the whole Force of the Stream running that Way,
she found no more Favour than the meanest Criminal.
The Prince therefore, when he saw 'twas impossible to
rescue her from the Hands of Justice, suffer'd with Grief
unspeakable, what he could not prevent, and led her
himself to the Prison, follow'd by all his People, in as much
State as if he had been going to his Marriage; where, when
she came, she was as well attended and served as before,
he never stirring one Moment from her.

The next Day, she was tried in open and common
Court; where she appeared in Glory, led by *Tarquin*, and
attended according to her Quality: And she could not
deny all the Page had alledged against her, who was
brought thither also in Chains; and after a great many
Circumstances, she was found Guilty, and both received
Sentence; the Page to be hanged till he was dead, on a
Gibbet in the Market-Place; and the Princess to stand
under the Gibbet, with a Rope about her Neck, the other
End of which was to be fastned to the Gibbet where the
Page was hanging; and to have an Inscription, in large

Characters, upon her Back and Breast, of the Cause why; where she was to stand from ten in the Morning to twelve.

This Sentence, the People with one Accord, believed too favourable for so ill a Woman, whose Crimes deserved Death, equal to that of *Van Brune*. Nevertheless, there were some who said, it was infinitely more severe than Death it self.

The following *Friday* was the Day of Execution, and one need not tell of the Abundance of People, who were flocked together in the Market-Place: And all the Windows were taken down, and filled with Spectators, and the Tops of Houses; when at the Hour appointed, the fatal Beauty appear'd. She was dress'd in a black Velvet Gown, with a rich Row of Diamonds all down the fore Part of her Breast, and a great Knot of Diamonds at the Peak behind; and a Petticoat of flower'd Gold, very rich, and laced; with all Things else suitable. A Gentleman carry'd her great Velvet Cushion before her, on which her Prayer-Book, embroider'd, was laid; her Train was borne up by a Page, and the Prince led her, bare; followed by his Footmen, Pages, and other Officers of his House.

When they arrived at the Place of Execution, the Cushion was laid on the Ground, upon a *Portugal* Mat, spread there for that Purpose; and the Princess stood on the Cushion, with her Prayer-Book in her Hand, and a Priest by her Side; and was accordingly tied up to the Gibbet.

She had not stood there ten Minutes, but she had the Mortification (at least one would think it so to her) to see her sad Page, *Van Brune*, approach, fair as an Angel, but languishing and pale. That Sight moved all the Beholders with as much Pity, as that of the Princess did with Disdain and Pleasure.

He was dressed all in Mourning, and very fine Linen, bare-headed, with his own Hair, the fairest that could be seen, hanging all in Curls on his Back and Shoulders, very long. He had a Prayer-Book of black Velvet in his Hand, and behaved himself with much Penitence and Devotion.

When he came under the Gibbet, he seeing his Mistress in that Condition, shew'd an infinite Concern, and his fair Face was cover'd over with Blushes; and falling at her Feet, he humbly ask'd her Pardon for having been the Occasion of so great an Infamy to her, by a weak Confession, which the Fears of Youth, and Hopes of Life, had obliged him to make, so greatly to her Dishonour; for indeed he wanted that manly Strength, to bear the Efforts of dying, as he ought, in Silence, rather than of commiting so great a Crime against his Duty, and Honour itself; and that he could not die in Peace, unless she would forgive him. The Princess only nodded her Head, and cried, *I do*—

And after having spoken a little to his Father-Confessor, who was with him, he chearfully mounted the Ladder, and in Sight of the Princess he was turned off, while a loud Cry was heard thro' all the Market-Place, especially from the Fair Sex; he hanged there till the Time the Princess was to depart; and then she was put into a rich embroider'd Chair, and carry'd away, *Tarquin* going into his, for he had all that Time stood supporting the Princess under the Gallows, and was very weary. She was sent back, till her Releasement came, which was that Night about seven o'Clock; and then she was conducted to her own House in great State, with a Dozen White Wax Flambeaux about her Chair.

If the Guardian of *Alcidiana*, and her Friends, before were impatient of having the Portion out of the Hands of these Extravagants, it is not to be imagined, but they were now much more so; and the next Day they sent an Officer, according to Law, to demand it, or to summon the Prince to give Reasons why he would not pay it. The Officer received for Answer, That the Money should be call'd in, and paid in such a Time, setting a certain

Time, which I have not been so curious as to retain, or put in my Journal-Observations; but I am sure it was not long, as may be easily imagin'd, for they every Moment suspected the Prince would pack up, and be gone, some time or other, on the sudden; and for that Reason they would not trust him without Bail, or two Officers to remain in his House, to watch that nothing should be remov'd or touch'd. As for Bail, or Security, he could give none; every one slunk their Heads out of the Collar, when it came to that: So that he was oblig'd, at his own Expence, to maintain Officers in his House.

The Princess finding her self reduced to the last Extremity, and that she must either produce the Value of a hundred thousand Crowns, or see the Prince her Husband lodged for ever in a Prison, and all their Glory vanish; and that it was impossible to fly, since guarded; she had Recourse to an Extremity, worse than the Affair of *Van Brune*. And in order to this, she first puts on a world of Sorrow and Concern, for what she feared might arrive to the Prince: And indeed, if ever she shed Tears which she did not dissemble, it was upon this Occasion. But here she almost over-acted: She stirred not from her Bed, and refused to eat, or sleep, or see the Light; so that the Day being shut out of her Chamber, she lived by Wax-lights, and refus'd all Comfort and Consolation.

The Prince, all raving with Love, tender Compassion and Grief, never stirred from her Bed-side, nor ceas'd to implore, that she would suffer herself to live. But she, who was not now so passionately in Love with *Tarquin*, as she was with the Prince; nor so fond of the Man as his Titles, and of Glory; foresaw the total Ruin of the last, if not prevented by avoiding the Payment of this great Sum; which could not otherwise be, than by the Death of *Alcidiana*: And therefore, without ceasing, she wept, and cry'd out, 'She could not live, unless *Alcidiana* died. This *Alcidiana (continued she)* who has been the Author of my

Shame; who has expos'd me under a Gibbet, in the Publick Market-Place—Oh!—I am deaf to all Reason, blind to natural Affection. I renounce her, I hate her as my mortal Foe, my Stop to Glory, and the Finisher of my Days, e'er half my Race of Life be run.'

Then throwing her false, but snowy, charming Arms about the Neck her Heart-breaking Lord, and Lover, who lay sighing, and listening by her Side, he was charmed and bewitch'd into saying all Things that appeased her; and lastly, told her, 'Alcidiana should be no longer any Obstacle to her Repose; but that, if she would look up, and cast her Eyes of Sweetness and Love upon him, as heretofore; forget her Sorrow, and redeem her lost Health; he would take what Measures she should propose to dispatch this fatal Stop to her Happiness, out of the Way.'

These Words failed not to make her caress him in the most endearing Manner that Love and Flattery could invent; and she kiss'd him to an Oath, a solemn Oath, to perform what he had promised; and he vow'd liberally. And she assumed in an Instant her Good-Humour, and suffer'd a Supper to be prepared, and did eat; which in many Days before she had not done: So obstinate and powerful was she in dissembling well.

The next Thing to be consider'd was, which Way this Deed was to be done; for they doubted not, but when it was done, all the World would lay it upon the Princess, as done by her Command: But she urged, Suspicion was no Proof; and that they never put to Death any one, but when they had great and certain Evidence who were the Offenders. She was sure of her own Constancy, that Racks and Tortures should never get the Secret from her Breast; and if he were as confident on his Part, there was no Danger. Yet this Preparation she made towards laying the Fact on others, that she caused several Letters to be wrote from Germany, as from the Relations of Van Brune, who threaten'd Alcidiana with Death, for depriving their

Kinsman (who was a Gentleman) of his Life, though he had not taken away hers. And it was the Report of the Town, how this young Maid was threaten'd. And indeed, the Death of the Page had so afflicted a great many, that *Alcidiana* had procured her self abundance of Enemies upon that Account, because she might have saved him if she had pleased; but, on the contrary, she was a Spectator, and in full Health and Vigour, at his Execution: And People were not so much concerned for her at this Report, as they would have been.

The Prince, who now had, by reasoning the Matter soberly with *Miranda*, found it absolutely necessary to dispatch *Alcidiana*, resolved himself, and with his own Hand, to execute it; not daring to trust to any of his most favourite Servants, though he had many, who possibly would have obey'd him; for they loved him as he deserved, and so would all the World, had he not been so purely deluded by this fair Enchantress. He therefore, as I said, resolved to keep this great Secret to himself; and taking a Pistol, charged well with two Bullets, he watch'd an Opportunity to shoot her as she should go out or into her House, or Coach, some Evening.

To this End he waited several Nights near her Lodgings, but still, either she went not out, or when she return'd, she was so guarded with Friends, her Lover, and Flambeaux, that he could not aim at her without endangering the Life of some other. But one Night above the rest, upon a *Sunday*, when he knew she would be at the Theatre, for she never missed that Day seeing the Play, he waited at the Corner of the Stadt-House, near the Theatre, with his Cloak cast over his Face, and a black Periwig, all alone, with his Pistol ready cock'd; and remain'd not very long but he saw her Kinsman's Coach come along; 'twas almost dark, Day was just shutting up her Beauties, and left such a Light to govern the World, as serv'd only just to distinguish one Object from another, and a convenient Help to

Mischief. He saw alight out of the Coach only one young Lady, the Lover, and then the destin'd Victim; which he (drawing near) knew rather by her Tongue than Shape. The Lady ran into the Play-House, and left *Alcidiana* to be conducted by her Lover into it: Who led her to the Door, and went to give some Order to the Coachman; so that the Lover was about twenty Yards from *Alcidiana*; when she stood the fairest Mark in the World, on the Threshold of the Entrance of the Theatre, there being many Coaches about the Door, so that hers could not come so near. *Tarquin* was resolved not to lose so fair an Opportunity, and advanc'd, but went behind the Coaches; and when he came over-against the Door, through a great booted Velvet Coach, that stood between him and her, he shot; and she having the Train of her Gown and Petticoat on her Arm, in great Quantity, he missed her Body, and shot through her Clothes, between her Arm and her Body. She, frighten'd to find something hit her, and to see the Smoke, and hear the Report of the Pistol; running in, cried, *I am shot, I am dead.*

This Noise quickly alarm'd her Lover; and all the Coachmen and Footmen immediately ran, some one Way, and some another. One of 'em seeing a Man haste away in a Cloak; he being a lusty, bold *German*, stopped him; and drawing upon him, bad him stand, and deliver his Pistol, or he would run him through.

Tarquin being surprised at the Boldness of this Fellow to demand his Pistol, as if he positively knew him to be the Murderer (for so he thought himself, since he believed *Alcidiana* dead) had so much Presence of Mind as to consider, if he suffered himself to be taken, he should poorly die a publick Death; and therefore resolv'd upon one Mischief more, to secure himself from the first: And in the Moment that the *German* bad him deliver his Pistol, he cried, *Though I have no Pistol to deliver, I have a Sword to chastise thy Insolence.* And throwing off his Cloak, and flinging his Pistol from him, he drew, and wounded, and disarmed the Fellow.

This Noise of Swords brought every body to the Place; and immediately the Bruit ran, *The Murderer was taken, the Murderer was taken;* Tho' none knew which was he, nor as yet so much as the Cause of the Quarrel between the two fighting Men; for it was now darker than before. But at the Noise of the Murderer being taken, the Lover of *Alcidiana*, who by this Time found his Lady unhurt, all but the Trains of her Gown and Petticoat, came running to the Place, just as *Tarquin* had disarm'd the *German*, and was ready to kill him; when laying hold of his Arm, they arrested the Stroke, and redeemed the Footman.

They then demanded who this Stranger was, at whose Mercy the Fellow lay; but the Prince, who now found himself venturing for his last Stake, made no Reply; but with two Swords in his Hands went to fight his Way through the Rabble; And tho' there were above a hundred Persons, some with Swords, others with long Whips, (as Coachmen) so invincible was the Courage of this poor unfortunate Gentleman at that Time, that all these were not able to seize him; but he made his Way through the Ring that encompassed him, and ran away; but was, however, so closely pursued, the Company still gathering as they ran, that toiled with fighting, oppressed with Guilt, and Fear of being taken, he grew fainter and fainter, and suffered himself, at last, to yield to his Pursuers, who soon found him to be Prince *Tarquin* in Disguise: And they carry'd him directly to Prison, being *Sunday*, to wait the coming Day, to go before a Magistrate.

In an Hour's Time the whole fatal Adventure was carried all over the City, and every one knew that *Tarquin* was the intended Murderer of *Alcidiana*; and not one but had a real Sorrow and Compassion for him. They heard how bravely he had defended himself, how many he had wounded before he could be taken, and what numbers he had fought through : And even those that saw his Valour and Bravery, and who had assisted at his being seiz'd, now repented from the Bottom of their Hearts their having any Hand in the Ruin of so gallant a Man ; especially since they knew the Lady was not hurt. A thousand Addresses were made to her, not to prosecute him ; but her Lover, a hot-headed Fellow, more fierce than brave, would by no Means be pacified, but vowed to pursue him to the Scaffold.

The *Monday* came, and the Prince being examined, confessed the Matter of Fact, since there was no Harm done; believing a generous Confession the best of his Game : But he was sent back to closer Imprisonment, loaded with Irons, to expect the next Sessions. All his Household-Goods were seiz'd, and all they could find, for the Use of *Alcidiana*. And the Princess, all in Rage, tearing her Hair, was carried to the same Prison, to behold the cruel Effects of her hellish Designs.

One need not tell here how sad and horrid this Meeting appear'd between her Lord and her : Let it suffice, it was the most melancholy and mortifying Object that ever Eyes beheld. On *Miranda's* Part, 'twas sometimes all Rage and Fire, and sometimes all Tears and Groans ; but still 'twas sad Love, and mournful Tenderness on his. Nor could all his Sufferings, and the Prospect of Death itself, drive from his Soul one Spark of that Fire the obstinate God had fatally kindled there : And in the midst of all his Sighs, he would re-call himself, and cry,—*I have* Miranda *still*.

He was eternally visited by his Friends and Acquaintance ; and this last Action of Bravery had got him more than all his former Conduct had lost. The Fathers were perpetually with him ; and all join'd with one common Voice in this, That he ought to abandon a Woman so wicked as the Princess ; and that however Fate dealt with him, he could not shew himself a true Penitent, while he laid the Author of so much Evil in his Bosom : That Heaven would never bless him, till he had renounced her :

And on such Conditions he would find those that would employ their utmost Interest to save his Life, who else would not stir in this Affair. But he was so deaf to all, that he could not so much as dissemble a Repentance for having married her.

He lay a long Time in Prison, and all that Time the poor Father *Francisco* remained there also: And the good Fathers who daily visited these two amorous Prisoners, the Prince and Princess; and who found, by the Management of Matters, it would go very hard with *Tarquin*, entertained 'em often with holy Matters relating to the Life to to come; from which, before his Trial, he gathered what his Stars had appointed, and that he was destin'd to die.

This gave an unspeakable Torment to the now repenting Beauty, who had reduced him to it; and she began to appear with a more solid Grief: Which being perceived by the good Fathers, they resolved to attack her on the yielding Side; and after some Discourse upon the Judgment for Sin, they came to reflect on the Business of Father *Francisco;* and told her, she had never thriven since her accusing of that Father, and laid it very home to her Conscience; assuring her that they would do their utmost in her Service, if she would confess that secret Sin to all the World, so that she might atone for the Crime, by the saving that good Man. At first she seemed inclined to yield; but Shame of being her own Detector, in so vile a Matter, recalled her Goodness, and she faintly persisted in it.

At the End of six Months, Prince *Tarquin* was called to his Tryal; where I will pass over the Circumstances, which are only what is usual in such criminal Cases, and tell you, that he being found guilty of the Intent of killing *Alcidiana*, was condemned to lose his Head in the Market-Place, and the Princess to be banished her Country.

After Sentence pronounced, to the real Grief of all the Spectators, he was carry'd back to Prison, and now the

Fathers attack her anew; and she, whose Griefs daily encreased, with a Languishment that brought her very near her Grave, at last confess'd all her Life, all the Lewdness of her Practices with several Princes and great Men, besides her Lusts with People that served her, and others in mean Capacity: And lastly, the whole Truth of the young Friar; and how she had drawn the Page, and the Prince her Husband, to this design'd Murder of her Sister. This she signed with her Hand, in the Presence of the Prince, her Husband, and several Holy Men who were present. Which being signify'd to the Magistrates, the Friar was immediately deliver'd from his Irons (where he had languished more than two whole Years) in great Triumph, with much Honour, and lives a most exemplary pious Life, as he did before; for he is now living in *Antwerp*.

After the Condemnation of these two unfortunate Persons, who begot such different Sentiments in the Minds of the People (the Prince, all the Compassion and Pity imaginable; and the Princess, all the Contempt and Despite;) they languished almost six Months longer in Prison; so great an Interest there was made, in order to the saving his Life, by all the Men of the Robe. On the other side, the Princes, and great Men of all Nations, who were at the Court of *Brussels*, who bore a secret Revenge in their Hearts against a Man who had, as they pretended, set up a false Title, only to take Place of them; who indeed was but a Merchant's Son of *Holland*, as they said; so incens'd them against him, that they were too hard at Court for the Church-men. However, this Dispute gave the Prince his Life some Months longer than was expected; which gave him also some Hope, that a Reprieve for ninety Years would have been granted, as was desired. Nay, Father *Francisco* so interested himself in this Concern, that he writ to his Father, and several Princes of *Germany*, with whom the Marquis *Castel Roderigo* was well acquainted, to intercede with him for the saving of *Tarquin;* since 'twas more by his Persuasions, than those of all who attacked her, that made *Miranda* confess the Truth of her Affair with him. But at the End of six Months, when all Applications were found fruitless and vain, the Prince receiv'd News, that in two Days he was to die, as his Sentence had been before pronounced, and for which he prepared himself with all Chearfulness.

On the following *Friday*, as soon as it was light, all People of any Condition came to take their Leaves of him; and none departed with dry Eyes, or Hearts unconcern'd to the last Degree: For *Tarquin*, when he found his Fate inevitable bore it with a Fortitude that shewed no Signs of Regret; but address'd himself to all about him with the same chearful, modest, and great Air, he was wont to do in his most flourishing Fortune. His Valet was dressing him all the Morning, so many Interruptions they had by Visitors; and he was all in Mourning, and so were all his Followers; for even to the last he kept up his Grandeur, to the Amazement of all People. And indeed, he was so passionately belov'd by them, that those he had dismiss'd, serv'd him voluntarily, and would not be persuaded to abandon him while he liv'd.

The Princess was also dress'd in Mourning, and her two Women; and notwithstanding the unheard-of Lewdness and Villanies she had confess'd of her self, the Prince still ador'd her; for she had still those Charms that made him first do so; nor, to his last Moment, could he be brought to wish, that he had never seen her; but on the contrary, as a Man yet vainly proud of his Fetters, he said, 'All the Satisfaction this short Moment of Life could afford him, was, that he died in endeavouring to serve *Miranda*, his adorable Princess.'

After he had taken Leave of all, who thought it necessary to leave him to himself for some Time, he retir'd with his Confessor; where they were about an Hour in Prayer, all the Ceremonies of Devotion that were fit to

be done, being already past. At last the Bell toll'd, and
he was to take Leave of the Princess, as his last Work of
Life, and the most hard he had to accomplish. He threw
himself at her Feet, and gazing on her as she sat more
dead than alive, overwhelm'd with silent Grief, they both
remain'd some Moments speechless; and then, as if one
rising Tide of Tears had supply'd both their Eyes, it
burst out in Streams at the same Instant: and when his
Sighs gave Way, he utter'd a thousand Farewels, so soft,
so passionate, and moving, that all who were by were
extremely touch'd with it, and said, *That nothing could be
seen more deplorable and melancholy.* A thousand Times
they bad Farewel, and still some tender Look, or Word,
would prevent his going; then embrace, and bid Farewel
again. A thousand Times she ask'd his Pardon for being
the Occasion of that fatal Separation; a thousand Times
assuring him, she would follow him, for she could not live
without him. And Heaven knows when their soft and sad
Caresses would have ended, had not the Officers assur'd
him 'twas Time to mount the Scaffold. At which Words
the Princess fell fainting in the Arms of her Woman, and
they led *Tarquin* out of Prison.

When he came to the Market-Place, whither he walked
on Foot, follow'd by his own Domesticks, and some
bearing a black Velvet Coffin with Silver Hinges; the
Head's-man before him with his fatal Scimiter drawn, his
Confessor by his Side, and many Gentlemen and Church-
men, with Father *Francisco* attending him, the People
showring Millions of Blessings on him, and beholding him
with weeping Eyes, he mounted the Scaffold; which was
strewed with some Saw-dust, about the Place where he
was to kneel, to receive the Blood: For they behead
People kneeling, and with the Back-Stroak of a Scimiter;
and not lying on a Block, and with an Axe, as we in
England. The Scaffold had a low Rail about it, that every
body might more conveniently see. This was hung with

black, and all that State that such a Death could have, was here in most decent Order.

He did not say much upon the Scaffold: The Sum of what he said to his Friends was, to be kind, and take Care of the poor Penitent his Wife: To others, recommending his honest and generous Servants, whose Fidelity was so well known and commended, that they were soon promised Preferment. He was some time in Prayer, and a very short time in speaking to his Confessor; then he turned to the Head's-man, and desired him to do his Office well, and gave him twenty *Louis d'Ors;* and undressing himself with the Help of his Valet and Page, he pull'd off his Coat, and had underneath a white Sattin Waistcoat: He took off his Periwig, and put on a white Sattin Cap, with a Holland one done with Point under it, which he pulled over his Eyes; then took a chearful Leave of all, and kneel'd down, and said, 'When he lifted up his Hands the third Time, the Head's-man should do his Office.' Which accordingly was done, and the Head's-man gave him his last Stroke, and the Prince fell on the Scaffold. The People with one common Voice, as if it had been but one entire one, pray'd for his Soul; and Murmurs of Sighs were heard from the whole Multitude, who scrambled for some of the bloody Saw-dust, to keep for his Memory.

The Head's-man going to take up the Head, as the Manner is, to shew it to the People, he found he had not struck it off, and that the Body stirr'd; with that he stepped to an Engine, which they always carry with 'em, to force those who may be refractory; thinking, as he said, to have twisted the Head from the Shoulders, conceiving it to hang but by a small Matter of Flesh. Tho' 'twas an odd Shift of the Fellow's, yet 'twas done, and the best Shift he could suddenly propose. The Margrave, and another Officer, old Men, were on the Scaffold, with some of the Prince's Friends, and Servants; who seeing the Head's-man put the Engine about the Neck of the Prince, began to call out, and the People made a great Noise. The Prince, who found himself yet alive; or rather, who was past thinking but had some Sense of Feeling left, when the Head's-man took him up, and set his Back against the Rail, and clapp'd the Engine about his Neck, got his two Thumbs between the Rope and his Neck, feeling himself press'd there; and struggling between Life and Death, and bending himself over the Rail backward, while the Head's-man pulled forward, he threw himself quite over the Rail, by Chance, and not Design, and fell upon the Heads and Shoulders of the People, who were crying out with amazing Shouts of Joy. The Head's-man leap'd after him, but the Rabble had lik'd to have pull'd him to Pieces: All the City was in an Uproar, but none knew what the Matter was, but those who bore the Body of the Prince, whom they found yet living; but how, or by what strange Miracle preserv'd, they knew not, nor did examine; but with one Accord, as if the whole Crowd had been one Body, and had had but one Motion, they bore the Prince on their Heads about a hundred Yards from the Scaffold, where there is a Monastery of Jesuits; and there they secur'd him. All this was done, his be-heading, his falling, and his being secur'd, almost in a Moment's Time; the People rejoiceing, as at some extra-ordinary Victory won. One of the Officers being, as I said, an old timorous Man, was so frighten'd at the Accident, the Bustle, the Noise, and the Confusion, of which he was wholly ignorant, that he dy'd with Amazement and Fear; and the other was fain to be let blood.

The Officers of Justice went to demand the Prisoner, but they demanded in vain; the Jesuits had now a Right to protect him, and would do so. All his overjoy'd Friends went to see in what Condition he was, and all of Quality found Admittance: They saw him in Bed, going to be dress'd by the most skilful Surgeons, who yet could not assure him of Life. They desired no body should speak to him, or ask him any Questions. They found that the Head's-man had struck him too low, and had cut him into the Shoulder-bone. A very great Wound, you may be sure; for the Sword, in such Executions, carries an extreme Force: However, so great Care was taken on all Sides, and so greatly the Fathers were concern'd for him, that they found an Amendment, and Hopes of a good Effect of their incomparable Charity and Goodness.

At last, when he was permitted to speak, the first News he ask'd was after the Princess. And his Friends were very much afflicted to find, that all his Loss of Blood had not quenched that Flame, not let out that which made him still love that bad Woman. He was sollicited daily to think no more of her: And all her Crimes are laid so open to him, and so shamefully represented; and on the other Side, his Virtues so admir'd; and which, they said, would have been eternally celebrated, but for his Folly with this infamous Creature; that at last, by assuring him of all their Assistance if he abandon'd her; and to renounce him, and deliver him up, if he did not; they wrought so far upon him, as to promise, he would suffer her to go alone into Banishment, and would not follow her, or live with her any more. But alas! this was but his Gratitude that compell'd this Complaisance, for in his Heart he resolv'd never to abandon her; nor was he able to live, and think of doing it: However, his Reason assur'd him, he could not do a Deed more justifiable, and one that would regain his Fame sooner.

His Friends ask'd him some Questions concerning his Escape; and since he was not beheaded, but only wounded, why he did not immediately rise up? But he replied, he was so absolutely prepossessed, that at the third lifting up his Hands he should receive the Stroke of Death, that at the same Instant the Sword touch'd him, he had no Sense; nay, not even of Pain, so absolutely dead he was with Imagination; and knew not that he stirr'd, as the Head's-man found he did; nor did he remember any Thing, from the lifting up of his Hands, to his fall; and then awaken'd, as out of a Dream, or rather a Moment's Sleep without Dream, he found he liv'd, and wonder'd what was arriv'd to him, or how he came to live; having not, as yet, any Sense of his Wound, tho' so terrible an one.

After this, *Alcidiana*, who was extremely afflicted for having been the Prosecutor of this great Man ; who, bating this last Design against her, which she knew was at the Instigation of her Sister, had oblig'd her with all the Civility imaginable ; now sought all Means possible of getting his Pardon, and that of her Sister; tho' of an hundred thousand Crowns, which she should have paid her, she could get but ten thousand ; which was from the Sale of her rich Beds, and some other Furniture. So that the young Count, who before should have marry'd her, now went off for want of Fortune ; and a young Merchant (perhaps the best of the two) was the Man to whom she was destin'd.

At last, by great Intercession, both their Pardons were obtain'd ; and the Prince, who would be no more seen in a Place that had prov'd every way so fatal to him, left *Flanders*, promising never to live with the Fair Hypocrite more; but e'er he departed, he wrote her a Letter, wherein he order'd her, in a little Time, to follow him into *Holland ;* and left a Bill of Exchange with one of his trusty Servants, whom he had left to wait upon her, for Money for her Accommodation; so that she was now reduced to one Woman, one Page, and this Gentleman. The Prince, in this Time of his Imprisonment, had several Bills of great Sums from his Father, who was exceeding rich, and this all the Children he had in the World, and whom he tenderly loved.

As soon as *Miranda* was come into *Holland*, she was welcom'd with all imaginable Respect and Endearment by the old Father ; who was impos'd upon so, as that he knew not she was the fatal Occasion of all these Disasters to his Son; but rather look'd on her as a Woman, who had brought him an hundred and fifty thousand Crowns, which his Misfortunes had consum'd. But, above all, she was receiv'd by *Tarquin* with a Joy unspeakable; who, after some Time, to redeem his Credit, and gain himself a new Fame, put himself into the *French* Army, where he did Wonders; and after three Campaigns, his Father dying, he return'd home, and retir'd to a Country-House; where, with his Princess, he liv'd as a private Gentleman, in all the Tranquillity of a Man of good Fortune. They say *Miranda* has been very penitent for her Life past, and gives Heaven the Glory for having given her these Afflictions that have reclaim'd her, and brought her to as perfect a State of Happiness, as this troublesome World, can afford.

Since I began this Relation, I heard that Prince *Tarquin*, dy'd about three Quarters of a Year ago.

OROONOKO; OR
THE ROYAL SLAVE.

INTRODUCTION.

THE tale of *Oroonoko, the Royal Slave* is indisputedly Mrs. Behn's masterpiece in prose. Its originality and power have singled it out for a permanence and popularity none of her other works attained. It is vivid, realistic, pregnant with pathos, beauty, and truth, and not only has it so impressed itself upon the readers of more than two centuries, but further, it surely struck a new note in English literature and one which was re-echoed far and wide. It has been said that '*Oroonoko* is the first emancipation novel' and there is no little acumen in this remark. Certainly we may absolve Mrs. Behn from having directly written with a purpose such as animated Mrs. Harriet Beecher Stowe's *Uncle Tom's Cabin;* but none the less her sympathy with the oppressed blacks, her deep emotions of pity for outraged humanity, her anger at the cruelties of the slave-driver aye ready with knout or knife, are manifest in every line. Beyond the intense interest of the pure narrative we have passages of a rhythm that is lyric, exquisitely descriptive of the picturesque tropical scenery and exotic vegetations, fragrant and luxuriant; there are intimate accounts of adventuring and primitive life; there are personal touches which lend a colour only personal touches can, as Aphara tells her prose-epic of her Superman, Cæsar the slave, Oroonoko the prince.

It is not difficult to trace the influence of *Oroonoko*. We can see it in many an English author; in Bernardin de Saint-Pierre, in Chateaubriand. Her idyllic romance has inspired writers who perhaps but dimly remember even her name and her genius.

It was often reprinted separately from the rest. There is a little 12mo *Oroonoko*, 'the ninth edition corrected', published at Doncaster, 1759, 'for C. Plummer', which is rarely seen save in a torn and well-thumbed state.[1]

In 1777 the sentimental and highly proper Mrs. Elizabeth Griffith included *Oroonoko* in her three volume *Collection of Novels selected and revised*. *Oroonoko*, 'written originally by Mrs. Behn and revised by Mrs. Griffith'[2], was also issued separately, 'price sixpence',[3] in 1800, frontispieced by a very crude picture of a black-a-moor about to attack a tiger.

As early as 1709 we find *Lebens und Liebes-Geschichte des Königlichen Sclaven Oroonoko in West-Indien*, a German translation published at Hamburg, with a portrait of 'Die Sinnreiche Engelländerin Mrs. Afra Behn.'

In 1745 *Oroonoko* was 'traduit de l' Anglois de Madame Behn,' with the motto from Lucan 'Quo fata trahunt virtus secura sequetur.' There is a rhymed dedication 'A Madame La M. P. D'l . . .' (35 lines), signed D. L.****, i.e., Pierre-Antoine de la Place, a fecund but mediocre writer of the eighteenth century (1707–93), who also translated, *Venice Preserv'd*, *The Fatal Marriage*, *Tom Jones*, and other English masterpieces. There is

---

[1] There were also many chap-books on similar themes which enjoyed no small popularity. e.g., *The Royal African ; or, The Memoirs of the Young Prince of Annamaboe* (circa 1750), the romantic narrative of a negro prince, who became a slave in Barbadoes, from whence he was redeemed and brought to England.   [2] Mis-spelt 'Griffiths' in the 1800 edition.

[3] There was 'a superior edition on a fine wove paper, Hot-pressed, with Proof Impressions of the Plates. Price only Nine-pence.'

another edition of de la Place's version with fine plates engraved by C. Baron after Marillier, Londres, 1769.

In 1696 Southerne's great tragedy, founded upon Mrs. Behn's novel, was produced at Drury Lane. Oroonoko was created by Verbruggen, Powell acted Aboan, and the beautiful Mrs. Rogers Imoinda. The play has some magnificent passages, and long kept the stage. Southerne had further added an excellent comic underplot, full of humour and the truest *vis comica*. It is perhaps worth noting that the intrigues of Lucy and Charlotte and the Lackitt *ménage* were dished up as a short slap-bang farce by themselves with, curiously enough, two or three scenes *in extenso* from Fletcher's *Monsieur Thomas* (iii, iii, and v, ii). This hotch potch entitled *The Sexes Mis-match'd; or, A New Way to get a Husband* is printed in *The Strollers' Pacquet open'd*. (12mo, 1741.) On 1 December, 1759, there was brought out at Drury Lane a most insipid alteration of *Oroonoko* by Dr. Hawkesworth, who omitted all Southerne's lighter fare and inserted serious nonsense of his own. Garrick was the Oroonoko and Mrs. Cibber Imoinda. Although Hawkesworth's version was not tolerated, the underplot was none the less pruned in later productions to such an extent that it perforce lost nearly all its pristine wit and fun. There is another adaption of Southerne : ' *Oroonoko* altered from the original play . . . to which the editor has added near six hundred lines in place of the comic scenes, together with an addition of two new characters, intended for one of the theatres.' (8vo, 1760.) The two new characters are Maria, sister to the Lieutenant-Governor and contracted to Blandford, and one Heartwell; both thoroughly tiresome individuals. In the same year Frank Gentleman, a provincial actor, produced his idea of *Oroonoko* 'as it was acted at Edinburgh.' (12mo, 1760.) There is yet a fourth bastard : *The Prince of Angola*, by one J. Ferriar, 'a tragedy altered from the play of *Oroonoko* and adapted to the circumstances of the present times.'[1] (Manchester, 1788.) It must be confessed that all this tinkering with an original, which does not require from any point of view the slightest alteration or omission, is most uncalled for, crude, and unsuccessful.

In 1698 William Walker, a lad nineteen years old, the son of a wealthy Barbadoes planter, wrote in three weeks a tragedy entitled *Victorious Love* (4to, 1698), which is confessedly a close imitation of Southerne's theme. It was produced at Drury Lane in June, 1698, with the author himself as Dafila, a youth, and young Mrs. Cross as the heroine Zaraida, 'an European Shipwrack'd an Infant at Gualata'. Possibly Verbruggen acted Barnagasso, the captive king who corresponds to Oroonoko. The scene is laid in the Banze, or Palace of Tombut, whose Emperor, Jamoan, is Barnagasso's rival in Zaraida's love. There is a villain, Zanhaga, who after various more or less successful iniquities, poisons the Emperor ; whereon hero and heroine are happily united. *Victorious Love* is far from being entirely a bad play ; it is, however, very reminiscent of the heroic tragedies of two decades before.

Southerne's *Oroonoko* was (with some alterations) translated into German. This version is prose and probably either the work of W. H. von Dalberg or von Eisenthal. It has little merit, but proved popular and was printed in 1789 with a somewhat grotesque frontispiece of Oroonoko and Imoinda, both of whom are black ' as pitch or as the cole '.

---

[1] The Agitation for the Abolition of the Slave Trade.

THE HISTORY OF
THE *ROYAL SLAVE.*

I DO not pretend, in giving you the History of this *ROYAL SLAVE*, to entertain my Reader with the Adventures of a feign'd *Hero*, whose Life and Fortunes Fancy may manage at the Poet's Pleasure; nor in relating the Truth, design to adorn it with any Accidents, but such as arrived in earnest to him: And it shall come simply into the World, recommended by its own proper Merits, and natural Intrigues; there being enough of Reality to support it, and to render it diverting, without the Addition of Invention.

I was myself an Eye-witness to a great Part of what you will find here set down; and what I could not be Witness of, I receiv'd from the Mouth of the chief Actor in this History, the *Hero* himself, who gave us the whole Transactions of his Youth: And I shall omit, for Brevity's Sake, a thousand little Accidents of his Life, which, however pleasant to us, where History was scarce, and Adventures very rare, yet might prove tedious and heavy to my Reader, in a World where he finds Diversions for every Minute, new and strange. But we who were perfectly charm'd with the Character of this great Man, were curious to gather every Circumstance of his Life.

The Scene of the last Part of his Adventures lies in a Colony in *America*, called *Surinam*, in the *West-Indies.*

But before I give you the Story of this *Gallant Slave*, 'tis fit I tell you the Manner of bringing them to these new *Colonies*; those they make Use of there, not being *Natives* of the Place: for those we live with in perfect Amity, without daring to command 'em; but, on the contrary, caress 'em with all the brotherly and friendly Affection in the World; trading with them for their Fish, Venison, Buffaloes Skins, and little Rarities; as *Marmosets*, a sort of Monkey, as big as a Rat or Weasel, but of a marvellous and delicate Shape, having Face and Hands like a Human Creature; and *Cousheries*, a little Beast in the Form and Fashion of a Lion, as big as a Kitten, but so exactly made in all Parts like that Noble Beast, that it is it in *Miniature*: Then for little *Paraketoes*, great *Parrots*, *Muckaws*, and a thousand other Birds and Beasts of wonderful and surprizing Forms, Shapes, and Colours: For Skins of prodigious Snakes, of which there are some three-score Yards in Length; as is the Skin of one that may be seen at his Majesty's *Antiquary's;* where are also some rare Flies, of amazing Forms and Colours, presented to 'em by myself; some as big as my Fist, some less; and all of various Excellencies, such as Art cannot imitate. Then we trade for Feathers, which they order into all Shapes, make themselves little short Habits of 'em, and glorious Wreaths for their Heads, Necks, Arms and Legs, whose Tinctures are unconceivable. I had a Set of these presented to me, and I gave 'em to the *King's Theatre;* it was the Dress of the *Indian Queen*, infinitely admir'd by Persons of Quality; and was inimitable. Besides these, a thousand little Knacks, and Rarities in Nature; and some of Art, as their Baskets, Weapons, Aprons, &c. We dealt with 'em with Beads of all Colours, Knives, Axes, Pins and Needles, which they us'd only as Tools to drill Holes with in their Ears, Noses and Lips, where they hang a great many little Things; as long Beads, Bits of Tin, Brass or Silver beat thin, and any shining Trinket. The Beads they weave into Aprons about a Quarter of an Ell long, and of the same Breadth; working them very prettily in Flowers of several Colours; which Apron they wear just before 'em, as *Adam* and *Eve* did the Fig-leaves; the Men wearing

a long Stripe of Linen, which they deal with us for. They
thread these Beads also on long Cotton-threads, and make
Girdles to tie their Aprons to, which come twenty times,
or more, about the Waste, and then cross, like a Shoulder-
belt, both Ways, and round their Necks, Arms and Legs.
This Adornment, with their long black Hair, and the Face
painted in little Specks or Flowers here and there, makes
'em a wonderful Figure to behold. Some of the Beauties,
which indeed are finely shap'd, as almost all are, and who
have pretty Features, are charming and novel; for they
have all that is called Beauty, except the Colour, which
is a reddish Yellow; or after a new Oiling, which they
often use to themselves, they are of the Colour of a new
Brick, but smooth, soft and sleek. They are extreme
modest and bashful, very shy, and nice of being touch'd.
And tho' they are all thus naked, if one lives for ever
among 'em, there it not to be seen an indecent Action,
or Glance: and being continually us'd to see one another
so unadorn'd, so like our first Parents before the Fall, it
seems as if they had no Wishes, there being nothing to
heighten Curiosity: but all you can see, you see at once,
and every Moment see; and where there is no Novelty,
there can be no Curiosity. Not but I have seen a handsome young *Indian*, dying for Love of a very beautiful
young *Indian* Maid; but all his Courtship was, to fold his
Arms, pursue her with his Eyes, and Sighs were all his
Language: While she, as if no such Lover were present,
or rather as if she desired none such, carefully guarded
her Eyes from beholding him; and never approach'd him,
but she looked down with all the blushing Modesty I
have seen in the most Severe and Cautious of our World.
And these People represented to me an absolute *Idea* of the
first State of Innocence, before Man knew how to sin:
And 'tis most evident and plain, that simple Nature is the
most harmless, inoffensive and virtuous Mistress. 'Tis
she alone, if she were permitted, that better instructs the

World, than all the Inventions of Man: Religion would here but destroy that Tranquillity they possess by Ignorance; and Laws would but teach 'em to know Offences, of which now they have no Notion. They once made Mourning and Fasting for the Death of the *English* Governor, who had given his Hand to come on such a Day to 'em, and neither came nor sent; believing, when a Man's Word was past, nothing but Death could or should prevent his keeping it: And when they saw he was not dead, they ask'd him what Name they had for a Man who promis'd a Thing he did not do? The Governor told them, Such a Man was a *Lyar*, which was a Word of Infamy to a Gentleman. Then one of 'em reply'd, *Governor, you are a Lyar, and guilty of that Infamy.* They have a native Justice, which knows no Fraud; and they understand no Vice, or Cunning, but when they are taught by the *White* Men. They have Plurality of Wives; which, when they grow old, serve those that succeed 'em, who are young, but with a Servitude easy and respected; and unless they take Slaves in War, they have no other Attendants.

Those on that *Continent* where I was, had no King; but the oldest War-Captain was obey'd with great Resignation.

A War-Captain is a Man who has led them on to Battle with Conduct and Success; of whom I shall have Occasion to speak more hereafter, and of some other of their Customs and Manners, as they fall in my Way.

With these People, as I said, we live in perfect Tranquillity, and good Understanding, as it behoves us to do; they knowing all the Places where to seek the best Food of the Country, and the Means of getting it; and for very small and unvaluable Trifles, supplying us with what 'tis almost impossible for us to get; for they do not only in the Woods, and over the *Sevana's*, in Hunting, supply the Parts of Hounds, by swiftly scouring thro' those almost impassable Places, and by the mere Activity of their Feet, run down the nimblest Deer, and other eatable

Beasts; but in the Water, one would think they were Gods of the Rivers, or Fellow-Citizens of the Deep; so rare an Art they have in swimming, diving, and almost living in Water; by which they command the less swift Inhabitants of the Floods. And then for shooting, what they cannot take, or reach with their Hands, they do with Arrows; and have so admirable an Aim, that they will split almost an Hair, and at any Distance that an Arrow can reach: they will shoot down Oranges, and other Fruit, and only touch the Stalk with the Dart's Point, that they may not hurt the Fruit. So that they being on all Occasions very useful to us, we find it absolutely necessary to caress 'em as Friends, and not to treat 'em as Slaves; nor dare we do otherwise, their Numbers so far surpassing ours in that Continent.

Those then whom we make use of to work in our Plantations of Sugar, are *Negroes*, Black-Slaves altogether, who are transported thither in this Manner.

Those who want Slaves, make a Bargain with a Master, or a Captain of a Ship, and contract to pay him so much apiece, a Matter of twenty Pound a Head, for as many as he agrees for, and to pay for 'em when they shall be deliver'd on such a Plantation : So that when there arrives a Ship laden with Slaves, they who have so contracted, go aboard, and receive their Number by Lot; and perhaps in one Lot that may be for ten, there may happen to be three or four Men, the rest Women and Children. Or be there more or less of either Sex, you are obliged to be contented with your Lot.

Coramantien, a Country of *Blacks* so called, was one of those Places in which they found the most advantageous Trading for these Slaves, and thither most of our great Traders in that Merchandize traffick; for that Nation is very warlike and brave; and having a continual Campaign, being always in Hostility with one neighbouring Prince or other, they had the Fortune to take a great many Captives : for all they took in Battle were sold as Slaves;

at least those common Men who could not ransom themselves. Of these Slaves so taken, the General only has all
the Profit; and of these Generals our Captains and Masters
of Ships buy all their Freights.

The King of *Coramantien* was of himself a Man of an
hundred and odd Years old, and had no Son, tho' he had
many beautiful Black Wives: for most certainly there are
Beauties that can charm of that Colour. In his younger
Years he had had many gallant Men to his Sons, thirteen
of whom died in Battle, conquering when they fell; and
he had only left him for his Successor, one Grand-child,
Son to one of these dead Victors, who, as soon as he could
bear a Bow in his Hand, and a Quiver at his Back, was
sent into the Field, to be train'd up by one of the oldest
Generals to War; where, from his natural Inclination to
Arms, and the Occasions given him, with the good Conduct of the old General, he became, at the Age of seventeen, one of the most expert Captains, and bravest Soldiers
that ever saw the Field of *Mars*: so that he was ador'd
as the Wonder of all that World, and the Darling of the
Soldiers. Besides, he was adorn'd with a native Beauty,
so transcending all those of his gloomy Race, that he struck
an Awe and Reverence, even into those that knew not his
Quality; as he did into me, who beheld him with Surprize
and Wonder, when afterwards he arrived in our World.

He had scarce arrived at his seventeenth Year, when,
fighting by his Side, the General was kill'd with an Arrow
in his Eye, which the Prince *Oroonoko* (for so was this
gallant *Moor* call'd) very narrowly avoided; nor had he,
if the General who saw the Arrow shot, and perceiving
it aimed at the Prince, had not bow'd his Head between,
on Purpose to receive it in his own Body, rather than it
should touch that of the Prince, and so saved him.

'Twas then, afflicted as *Oroonoko* was, that he was proclaimed General in the old Man's Place: and then it was,
at the finishing of that War, which had continu'd for two

Years, that the Prince came to Court, where he had hardly been a Month together, from the Time of his fifth Year to that of seventeen : and 'twas amazing to imagine where it was he learn'd so much Humanity ; or to give his Accomplishments a juster Name, where 'twas he got that real Greatness of Soul, those refined Notions of true Honour, that absolute Generosity, and that Softness, that was capable of the highest Passions of Love and Gallantry, whose Objects were almost continually fighting Men, or those mangled or dead, who heard no Sounds but those of War and Groans. Some Part of it we may attribute to the Care of a *Frenchman* of Wit and Learning, who finding it turn to a very good Account to be a sort of Royal Tutor to this young Black, and perceiving him very ready, apt, and quick of Apprehension, took a great Pleasure to teach him Morals, Language and Science ; and was for it extremely belov'd and valu'd by him. Another Reason was, he lov'd when he came from War, to see all the *English* Gentlemen that traded thither ; and did not only learn their Language, but that of the *Spaniard* also, with whom he traded afterwards for Slaves.

I have often seen and conversed with this Great Man, and been a Witness to many of his mighty Actions ; and do assure my Reader, the most illustrious Courts could not have produced a braver Man, both for Greatness of Courage and Mind, a Judgment more solid, a Wit more quick, and a Conversation more sweet and diverting. He knew almost as much as if he had read much : He had heard of and admired the *Romans :* He had heard of the late Civil Wars in *England,* and the deplorable Death of our great Monarch ; and would discourse of it with all the Sense and Abhorrence of the Injustice imaginable. He had an extreme good and graceful Mien, and all the Civility of a well-bred Great Man. He had nothing of Barbarity in his Nature, but in all Points address'd himself as if his Education had been in some *European* Court.

This great and just Character of *Oroonoko* gave me an extreme Curiosity to see him, especially when I knew he spoke *French* and *English*, and that I could talk with him. But tho' I had heard so much of him, I was as greatly surprized when I saw him, as if I had heard nothing of him; so beyond all Report I found him. He came into the Room, and addressed himself to me, and some other Women, with the best Grace in the World. He was pretty tall, but of a Shape the most exact that can be fancy'd: The most famous Statuary could not form the Figure of a Man more admirably turn'd from Head to Foot. His Face was not of that brown rusty Black which most of that Nation are, but a perfect Ebony, or polished Jet. His Eyes were the most aweful that could be seen, and very piercing; the White of 'em being like Snow, as were his Teeth. His Nose was rising and *Roman*, instead of *African* and flat: His Mouth the finest shaped that could be seen; far from those great turn'd Lips, which are so natural to the rest of the Negroes. The whole Proportion and Air of his Face was so nobly and exactly form'd, that bating his Colour, there could be nothing in Nature more beautiful, agreeable and handsome. There was no one Grace wanting, that bears the Standard of true Beauty. His Hair came down to his Shoulders, by the Aids of Art, which was by pulling it out with a Quill, and keeping it comb'd; of which he took particular Care. Nor did the Perfections of his Mind come short of those of his Person; for his Discourse was admirable upon almost any Subject: and whoever had heard him speak, would have been convinced of their Errors, that all fine Wit is confined to the white Men, especially to those of Christendom; and would have confess'd that *Oroonoko* was as capable even of reigning well, and of governing as wisely, had as great a Soul, as politick Maxims, and was as sensible of Power, as any Prince civiliz'd in the most refined Schools of Humanity and Learning, or the most illustrious Courts.

This Prince, such as I have describ'd him, whose Soul and Body were so admirably adorned, was (while yet he was in the Court of his Grandfather, as I said) as capable of Love, as 'twas possible for a brave and gallant Man to be; and in saying that, I have named the highest Degree of Love: for sure great Souls are most capable of that Passion.

I have already said, the old General was kill'd by the Shot of an Arrow, by the Side of this Prince, in Battle; and that *Oroonoko* was made General. This old dead Hero had one only Daughter left of his Race, a Beauty, that to describe her truly, one need say only, she was Female to the noble Male; the beautiful Black *Venus* to our young *Mars*; as charming in her Person as he, and of delicate Virtues. I have seen a hundred White Men sighing after her, and making a thousand Vows at her Feet, all in vain and unsuccessful. And she was indeed too great for any but a Prince of her own Nation to adore.

Oroonoko coming from the Wars (which were now ended) after he had made his Court to his Grandfather, he thought in Honour he ought to make a Visit to *Imoinda*, the Daughter of his Foster-father, the dead General; and to make some Excuses to her, because his Preservation was the Occasion of her Father's Death; and to present her with those Slaves that had been taken in this last Battle, as the Trophies of her Father's Victories. When he came, attended by all the young Soldiers of any Merit, he was infinitely surpriz'd at the Beauty of this fair Queen of Night, whose Face and Person were so exceeding all he had ever beheld, that lovely Modesty with which she receiv'd him, that Softness in her Look and Sighs, upon the melancholy Occasion of this Honour that was done by so great a Man as *Oroonoko*, and a Prince of whom she had heard such admirable Things; the Awfulness wherewith she receiv'd him, and the Sweetness of her Words and Behaviour while he stay'd, gain'd a perfect Conquest over his fierce Heart, and made him feel, the Victor could be subdu'd. So that having made his first Compliments, and presented her an hundred and fifty Slaves in Fetters, he told her with his Eyes, that he was not insensible of her Charms; while *Imoinda*, who wish'd for nothing more than so glorious a Conquest, was pleas'd to believe, she understood that silent Language of new-born Love; and, from that Moment, put on all her Additions to Beauty.

The Prince return'd to Court with quite another Humour than before; and tho' he did not speak much of the fair *Imoinda*, he had the Pleasure to hear all his Followers speak of nothing but the Charms of that Maid, insomuch, that, even in the Presence of the old King, they were extolling her, and heightning, if possible, the Beauties they had found in her: so that nothing else was talk'd of, no other Sound was heard in every Corner where there were Whisperers, but *Imoinda! Imoinda!*

'Twill be imagin'd *Oroonoko* stay'd not long before he made his second Visit; nor, considering his Quality, not much longer before he told her, he ador'd her. I have often heard him say, that he admir'd by what strange Inspiration he came to talk Things so soft, and so passionate, who never knew Love, nor was us'd to the Conversation of Women; but (to use his own Words) he said, 'Most happily, some new, and, till then, unknown Power instructed his Heart and Tongue in the Language of Love; and at the same Time, in Favour of him, inspir'd *Imoinda* with a Sense of his Passion.' She was touch'd with what he said, and return'd it all in such Answers as went to his very Heart, with a Pleasure unknown before. Nor did he use those Obligations ill, that Love had done him, but turn'd all his happy Moments to the best Advantage; and as he knew no Vice, his Flame aim'd at nothing but Honour, if such a Distinction may be made in Love; and especially in that Country, where Men take to themselves as many as they can maintain; and where the only Crime and Sin against a Woman, is, to turn her off, to abandon her to Want, Shame and Misery: such ill Morals are only practis'd in *Christian* Countries, where they prefer the bare Name of Religion; and, without Virtue or Morality, think that sufficient. But *Oroonoko* was none of those Professors; but as he had right Notions of Honour, so he made her such Propositions as were not only and barely such; but, contrary to the Custom of his Country, he made her Vows, she should be the only Woman he would possess while he liv'd; that no Age or Wrinkles should incline him to change: for her Soul would be always fine, and always young; and he should have an eternal *Idea* in his Mind of the Charms she now bore; and should look into his Heart for that *Idea*, when he could find it no longer in her Face.

After a thousand Assurances of his lasting Flame, and her eternal Empire over him, she condescended to receive him for her Husband; or rather, receive him, as the greatest Honour the Gods could do her.

There is a certain Ceremony in these Cases to be observ'd, which I forgot to ask how 'twas perform'd; but 'twas concluded on both Sides, that in Obedience to him, the Grandfather was to be first made acquainted with the Design: For they pay a most absolute Resignation to the Monarch, especially when he is a Parent also.

On the other Side, the old King, who had many Wives, and many Concubines, wanted not Court-Flatterers to insinuate into his Heart a thousand tender Thoughts for this young Beauty; and who represented her to his Fancy, as the most charming he had ever possess'd in all the long Race of his numerous Years. At this Character, his old Heart, like an extinguish'd Brand, most apt to take Fire, felt new Sparks of Love, and began to kindle; and now grown to his second Childhood, long'd with Impatience to behold this gay Thing, with whom, alas! he could but innocently play. But how he should be confirm'd she was this *Wonder*, before he us'd his Power to call her to Court, (where Maidens never came, unless for the King's private Use) he was next to consider; and while he was so doing, he had Intelligence brought him, that *Imoinda* was most certainly Mistress to the Prince *Oroonoko*. This gave him some Chagrine: however, it gave him also an Opportunity, one Day, when the Prince was a hunting, to wait on a Man of Quality, as his Slave and Attendant, who should go and make a Present to *Imoinda*, as from the Prince; he should then, unknown, see this fair Maid, and have an Opportunity to hear what Message she would return the Prince for his Present, and from thence gather the State of her Heart, and Degree of her Inclination. This was put in Execution, and the old Monarch saw, and burn'd: He found her all he had heard, and would not delay his Happiness, but found he should have some Obstacle to overcome her Heart; for she express'd her Sense of the Present the Prince had sent her, in Terms so sweet, so soft and pretty, with an Air of Love and Joy that could not be dissembled, insomuch that 'twas past Doubt whether she lov'd *Oroonoko* entirely. This gave the old King some Affliction; but he salv'd it with this, that the Obedience the People pay their King, was not at all inferior to what they paid their Gods; and what Love would not oblige *Imoinda* to do, Duty would compel her to.

He was therefore no sooner got into his Apartment, but he sent the Royal Veil to *Imoinda*; that is the Ceremony of Invitation: He sends the Lady he has a Mind to honour with his Bed, a Veil, with which she is covered, and secur'd for the King's Use; and 'tis Death to disobey; besides, held a most impious Disobedience.

'Tis not to be imagin'd the Surprize and Grief that seiz'd the lovely Maid at this News and Sight. However, as Delays in these Cases are dangerous, and Pleading worse than Treason; trembling, and almost fainting, she was oblig'd to suffer herself to be cover'd, and led away.

They brought her thus to Court; and the King, who had caus'd a very rich Bath to be prepar'd, was led into it, where he sat under a Canopy, in State, to receive this long'd-for Virgin; whom he having commanded to be brought to him, they (after disrobing her) led her to the Bath, and making fast the Doors, left her to descend. The King, without more Courtship, bad her throw off her Mantle, and come to his Arms. But *Imoinda*, all in Tears, threw herself on the Marble, on the Brink of the Bath, and besought him to hear her. She told him, as she was a Maid, how proud of the Divine Glory she should have been, of having it in her Power to oblige her King: but as by the Laws he could not, and from his Royal Goodness would not take from any Man his wedded Wife; so she believ'd she should be the occasion of making him commit a great Sin, if she did not reveal her State and Condition; and tell him she was another's, and could not be so happy to be his.

The King, enrag'd at this Delay, hastily demanded the Name of the bold Man, that had married a Woman of her Degree, without his Consent. *Imoinda* seeing his Eyes fierce, and his Hands tremble, (whether with Age or Anger, I know not, but she fancy'd the last) almost repented she had said so much, for now she fear'd the Storm would fall on the Prince; she therefore said a thousand Things to appease the raging of his Flame, and to prepare him to hear who it was with Calmness: but before she spoke, he imagin'd who she meant, but would not seem to do so, but commanded her to lay aside her Mantle, and suffer herself to receive his Caresses, or, by his Gods he swore, that happy Man whom she was going to name should die, tho' it was even *Oroonoko* himself. *Therefore* (said he) *deny this Marriage, and swear thyself a Maid. That* (reply'd *Imoinda*) *by all our Powers I do; for I am not yet known to my Husband.* 'Tis enough (said the King) 'tis enough both to satisfy my Conscience and my Heart. And rising from his Seat, he went and led her into the Bath; it being in vain for her to resist.

In this Time, the Prince, who was return'd from Hunting, went to visit his *Imoinda*, but found her gone; and not only so, but heard she had receiv'd the Royal Veil. This rais'd him to a Storm; and in his Madness, they had much ado to save him from laying violent Hands on himself. Force first prevail'd, and then Reason: They urg'd all to him, that might oppose his Rage; but nothing weigh'd so greatly with him as the King's old Age, uncapable of injuring him with *Imoinda*. He would give Way to that Hope, because it pleas'd him most, and flatter'd best his Heart. Yet this serv'd not altogether to make him cease his different Passions, which sometimes rag'd within him, and soften'd into Showers. 'Twas not enough to appease him, to tell him, his Grandfather was old, and could not that Way injure him, while he retain'd that awful Duty which the young Men are us'd there to pay to their grave Relations. He could not be convinc'd he had no Cause to sigh and mourn for the Loss of a Mistress, he could not with all his Strength and Courage retrieve, and he would often cry, 'Oh, my Friends! were she in wall'd Cities, or confin'd from me in Fortifications of the greatest Strength; did Inchantments or Monsters detain her from me; I would venture thro' any Hazard to free her; But here, in the Arms of a feeble old Man, my Youth, my violent Love, my Trade in Arms, and all my vast Desire of Glory, avail me nothing. *Imoinda* is as irrecoverably lost to me, as if she were snatch'd by the cold Arms of Death: Oh! she is never to be retrieved. If I would wait tedious Years; till Fate should bow the old King to his Grave, even that would not leave me *Imoinda* free; but still that Custom that makes it so vile a Crime for a Son to marry his Father's Wives or Mistresses, would hinder my Happiness; unless I would either ignobly set an ill Precedent to my Successors, or abandon my Country, and fly with her to some unknown World who never heard our Story.'

But it was objected to him, That his Case was not the same : for *Imoinda* being his lawful Wife by solemn Contract, 'twas he was the injur'd Man, and might, if he so pleas'd, take *Imoinda* back, the Breach of the Law being on his Grandfather's Side ; and that if he could circumvent him, and redeem her from the *Otan*, which is the Palace of the King's Women, a sort of *Seraglio*, it was both just and lawful for him so to do.

This Reasoning had some Force upon him, and he should have been entirely comforted, but for the Thought that she was possess'd by his Grandfather. However, he lov'd her so well, that he was resolv'd to believe what most favour'd his Hope, and to endeavour to learn from *Imoinda's* own Mouth, what only she could satisfy him in, whether she was robb'd of that Blessing which was only due to his Faith and Love. But as it was very hard to get a Sight of the Women, (for no Men ever enter'd into the *Otan*, but when the King went to entertain himself with some one of his Wives or Mistresses ; and 'twas Death, at any other Time, for any other to go in) so he knew not how to contrive to get a Sight of her.

While *Oroonoko* felt all the Agonies of Love, and suffer'd under a Torment the most painful in the World, the old King was not exempted from his Share of Affliction. He was troubled, for having been forc'd, by an irresistible Passion, to rob his Son of a Treasure, he knew, could not but be extremely dear to him ; since she was the most beautiful that ever had been seen, and had besides, all the Sweetness and Innocence of Youth and Modesty, with a Charm of Wit surpassing all. He found, that however she was forc'd to expose her lovely Person to his wither'd Arms, she could only sigh and weep there, and think of *Oroonoko*; and oftentimes could not forbear speaking of him, tho' her Life were, by Custom, forfeited by owning her Passion.

But she spoke not of a Lover only, but of a Prince dear to him to whom she spoke; and of the Praises of a Man, who, 'till now, fill'd the old Man's Soul with Joy at every Recital of his Bravery, or even his Name. And 'twas this Dotage on our young Hero, that gave *Imoinda* a thousand Privileges to speak of him without offending; and this Condescension in the old King, that made her take the Satisfaction of speaking of him so very often.

Besides, he many times enquir'd how the Prince bore himself: And those of whom he ask'd, being entirely Slaves to the Merits and Virtues of the Prince, still answer'd what they they thought conduc'd best to his Service; which was, to make the old King fancy that the Prince had no more Interest in *Imoinda*, and had resign'd her willingly to the Pleasure of the King; that he diverted himself with his Mathematicians, his Fortifications, his Officers, and his Hunting.

This pleas'd the old Lover, who fail'd not to report these Things again to *Imoinda*, that she might, by the Example of her young Lover, withdraw her Heart, and rest better contented in his Arms. But, however she was forc'd to receive this unwelcome News, in all Appearance, with Unconcern and Content; her Heart was bursting within, and she was only happy when she could get alone, to vent her Griefs and Moans with Sighs and Tears.

What Reports of the Prince's Conduct were made to the King, he thought good to justify, as far as possibly he could, by his Actions; and when he appear'd in the Presence of the King, he shew'd a Face not at all betraying his Heart: so that in a little Time, the old Man, being entirely convinc'd that he was no longer a Lover of *Imoinda*, he carry'd him with him in his Train to the *Otan*, often to banquet with his Mistresses. But as soon as he enter'd, one Day, into the Apartment of *Imoinda*, with the King, at the first Glance from her Eyes, notwithstanding all his determined Resolution, he was ready to sink in the Place where he stood; and had certainly done so, but for the Support of *Aboan*, a young Man who was next to him; which, with his Change of Countenance, had betray'd him, had the King chanc'd to look that Way. And I have observ'd, 'tis a very great Error in those who laugh when one says, *A* Negro *can change Colour :* for I have seen 'em as frequently blush, and look pale, and that as visibly as ever I saw in the most beautiful *White*. And 'tis certain, that both these Changes were evident, this Day, in both these Lovers. And *Imoinda*, who saw with some Joy the Change in the Prince's Face, and found it in her own, strove to divert the King from beholding either, by a forc'd Caress, with which she met him; which was a new Wound in the Heart of the poor dying Prince. But as soon as the King was busy'd in looking on some fine Thing of *Imoinda's* making, she had Time to tell the Prince, with her angry, but Love-darting Eyes, that she resented his Coldness, and bemoan'd her own miserable Captivity. Nor were his Eyes silent, but answer'd her's again, as much as Eyes could do, instructed by the most tender and most passionate Heart that ever lov'd : And they spoke so well, and so effectually, as *Imoinda* no longer doubted but she was the only Delight and Darling of that Soul she found pleading in 'em its Right of Love, which none was more willing to resign than she. And 'twas this powerful Language alone that in an Instant convey'd all the Thoughts of their Souls to each other; that they both found there wanted but Opportunity to make them both entirely happy. But when he saw another Door open'd by *Onahal* (a former old Wife of the King's, who now had Charge of *Imoinda*) and saw the Prospect of a Bed of State made ready, with Sweets and Flowers for the Dalliance of the King, who immediately led the trembling Victim from his Sight, into that prepar'd Repose; what Rage! what wild Frenzies seiz'd his Heart! which forcing to keep within Bounds, and to suffer without Noise, it became the more insupportable, and rent his Soul with ten thousand Pains. He was forc'd to retire to vent his Groans, where he fell down on a Carpet, and lay struggling a long Time, and only breathing now and then—Oh *Imoinda!* When *Onahal* had finished her necessary Affair within, shutting the Door, she came forth, to wait till the King called ; and hearing some one sighing in the other Room, she pass'd on, and found the Prince in that deplorable Condition, which she thought needed her Aid. She gave him Cordials, but all in vain ; till finding the Nature of his Disease, by his Sighs, and naming *Imoinda*, she told him he had not so much Cause as he imagined to afflict himself : for if he knew the King so well as she did, he would not lose a Moment in Jealousy ; and that she was confident that *Imoinda* bore, at this Minute, Part in his Affliction. *Aboan* was of the same Opinion, and both together persuaded him to re-assume his Courage ; and all sitting down on the Carpet, the Prince said so many obliging Things to *Onahal*, that he half-persuaded her to be of his Party : and she promised him, she would thus far comply with his just Desires, that she would let *Imoinda* know how faithful he was, what he suffer'd, and what he said.

This Discourse lasted till the King called, which gave *Oroonoko* a certain Satisfaction ; and with the Hope *Onahal* had made him conceive, he assumed a Look as gay as 'twas possible a Man in his Circumstances could do : and presently after, he was call'd in with the rest who waited without. The King commanded Musick to be brought, and several of his young Wives and Mistresses came all together by his Command, to dance before him ; where *Imoinda* perform'd her Part with an Air and Grace so surpassing all the rest, as her Beauty was above 'em, and received the Present ordained as a Prize. The Prince was every Moment more charmed with the new Beauties and Graces he beheld in this Fair-One ; and while he gazed, and she danc'd, *Onahal* was retired to a Window with *Aboan*.

This *Onahal*, as I said, was one of the Cast-Mistresses of the old King; and 'twas these (now past their Beauty) that were made Guardians or Governantees to the new and the young ones, and whose Business it was to teach them all those wanton Arts of Love, with which they prevail'd and charm'd heretofore in their Turn ; and who now treated the triumphing Happy-ones with all the Severity, as to Liberty and Freedom, that was possible, in Revenge of the Honours they rob them of; envying them those Satisfactions, those Gallantries and Presents, that were once made to themselves, while Youth and Beauty lasted, and which they now saw pass, as it were regardless by, and paid only to the Bloomings. And certainly, nothing is more afflicting to a decay'd Beauty, than to behold in itself declining Charms, that were once ador'd ; and to find those Caresses paid to new Beauties, to which once she laid Claim; to hear them whisper, as she passes by, that once was a delicate Woman. Those abandon'd ladies therefore endeavour to revenge all the Despights and Decays of Time, on these flourishing Happy-ones. And 'twas this Severity that gave *Oroonoko* a thousand Fears he should never prevail with *Onahal* to see *Imoinda*. But, as I said, she was now retir'd to a Window with *Aboan*.

This young Man was not only one of the best Quality, but a Man extremely well made, and beautiful ; and coming often to attend the King to the *Otan*, he had subdu'd the Heart of the antiquated *Onahal*, which had not forgot how pleasant it was to be in love. And tho' she had some Decays in her Face, she had none in her Sense and Wit ; she was there agreeable still, even to *Aboan's* Youth : so that he took Pleasure in entertaining her with Discourses of Love. He knew also, that to make his Court to these She-favourites, was the Way to be great; these being the Persons that do all Affairs and Business at Court. He had also observed, that she had given him Glances more tender and inviting than she had done to others of his Quality. And now, when he saw that her Favour could so absolutely oblige the Prince, he fail'd not to sigh in her Ear, and look with Eyes all soft upon her, and gave her Hope that she had made some Impressions on his Heart. He found her pleas'd at this, and making a thousand Advances to him: but the Ceremony ending, and the King departing, broke up the Company for that Day, and his Conversation.

Aboan fail'd not that Night to tell the Prince of his Success, and how advantageous the Service of *Onahal* might be to his Amour with *Imoinda*. The Prince was over-joy'd with this good News, and besought him, if it were possible, to caress her so, as to engage her entirely, which he could not fail to do, if he comply'd with her Desires: *For then* (said the Prince) *her Life lying at your Mercy, she must grant you the Request you make in my Behalf. Aboan* understood him, and assur'd him he would make Love so effectually, that he would defy the most expert Mistress of the Art, to find out whether he dissembled it, or had it really. And 'twas with Impatience they waited the next Opportunity of going to the *Otan*.

The Wars came on, the Time of taking the Field approached; and 'twas impossible for the Prince to delay his going at the Head of his Army to encounter the Enemy; so that every Day seem'd a tedious Year, till he saw his *Imoinda*: for he believed he could not live, if he were forced away without being so happy. 'Twas with Impatience therefore that he expected the next Visit the King would make; and, according to his Wish, it was not long.

The Parley of the Eyes of these two Lovers had not pass'd so secretly, but an old jealous Lover could spy it; or rather, he wanted not Flatterers who told him they observ'd it: so that the Prince was hasten'd to the Camp, and this was the last Visit he found he should make to the *Otan*; he therefore urged *Aboan* to make the best of this last Effort, and to explain himself so to *Onahal*, that she deferring her Enjoyment of her young Lover no longer, might make Way for the Prince to speak to *Imoinda*.

The whole Affair being agreed on between the Prince and *Aboan*, they attended the King, as the Custom was, to the *Otan;* where, while the whole Company was taken up in beholding the Dancing, and Antick Postures the Women-Royal made to divert the King, *Onahal* singled out *Aboan*, whom she found most pliable to her Wish. When she had him where she believed she could not be heard, she sigh'd to him, and softly cry'd, 'Ah, *Aboan!* when will you be sensible of my Passion? I confess it with my Mouth, because I would not give my Eyes the Lye; and you have but too much already perceived they have confess'd my Flame: nor would I have you believe, that because I am the abandon'd Mistress of a King, I esteem myself altogether divested of Charms: No, *Aboan;* I have still a Rest of Beauty enough engaging, and have learn'd to please too well, not to be desirable. I can have Lovers still, but will have none but *Aboan*. Madam, *(reply'd the half-feigning Youth)* you have already, by my Eyes, found you can still conquer; and I believe 'tis in pity of me you condescend to this kind Confession. But, Madam, Words are used to be so small a Part of our Country-Courtship, that 'tis rare one can get so happy an Opportunity as to tell one's Heart; and those few Minutes we have, are forced to be snatch'd for more certain Proofs of Love than speaking and sighing: and such I languish for.'

He spoke this with such a Tone, that she hoped it true, and could not forbear believing it; and being wholly transported with Joy for having subdued the finest of all the King's Subjects to her Desires, she took from her Ears two large Pearls, and commanded him to wear 'em in his. He would have refused 'em, crying, *Madam these are not the Proofs of our Love that I expect; 'tis Opportunity, 'tis a Lone-Hour only, that can make me happy.* But forcing the Pearls into his Hand, she whisper'd softly to him; *Oh!*

do not fear a Woman's Invention, when Love sets her a thinking. And pressing his Hand, she cry'd, *This Night you shall be happy. Come to the Gate of the Orange-Grove, behind the* Otan, *and I will be ready about midnight to receive you.* 'Twas thus agreed, and she left him, that no Notice might be taken of their speaking together.

The Ladies were still dancing, and the King, laid on a Carpet, with a great deal of Pleasure was beholding them, especially *Imoinda*, who that Day appeared more lovely than ever, being enlivened with the good Tidings *Onahal* had brought her, of the constant Passion the Prince had for her. The Prince was laid on another Carpet at the other End of the Room, with his Eyes fixed on the Object of his Soul; and as she turned or moved, so did they; and she alone gave his Eyes and Soul their Motions. Nor did *Imoinda* employ her Eyes to any other use, than in beholding with infinite Pleasure the Joy she produced in those of the Prince. But while she was more regarding him than the Steps she took, she chanced to fall, and so near him, as that leaping with extreme Force from the Carpet, he caught her in his Arms as she fell; and 'twas visible to the whole Presence, the Joy wherewith he received her. He clasped her close to his Bosom, and quite forgot that Reverence that was due to the Mistress of a King, and that Punishment that is the Reward of a Boldness of this Nature. And had not the Presence of Mind of *Imoinda* (fonder of his Safety than her own) befriended him, in making her spring from his Arms, and fall into her Dance again, he had at that Instant met his Death; for the old King, jealous to the last Degree, rose up in Rage, broke all the Diversion, and led *Imoinda* to her Apartment, and sent out Word to the Prince, to go immediately to the Camp; and that if he were found another Night in Court, he should suffer the Death ordained for disobedient Offenders.

You may imagine how welcome this News was to

Oroonoko, whose unseasonable Transport and Caress of *Imoinda* was blamed by all Men that loved him : and now he perceived his Fault, yet cry'd, *That for such another Moment he would be content to die.*

All the *Otan* was in Disorder about this Accident ; and *Onahal* was particularly concern'd, because on the Prince's Stay depended her Happiness; for she could no longer expect that of *Aboan :* So that e'er they departed, they contrived it so, that the Prince and he should both come that Night to the Grove of the *Otan,* which was all of Oranges and Citrons, and that there they would wait her Orders.

They parted thus with Grief enough 'till Night, leaving the King in Possession of the lovely Maid. But nothing could appease the Jealousy of the old Lover ; he would not be imposed on, but would have it, that *Imoinda* made a false Step on Purpose to fall into *Oroonoko's* Bosom, and that all things looked like a Design on both Sides; and 'twas in vain she protested her Innocence : He was old and obstinate, and left her, more than half assur'd that his Fear was true.

The King going to his Apartment, sent to know where the Prince was, and if he intended to obey his Command. The Messenger return'd, and told him, he found the Prince pensive, and altogether unprepar'd for the Campaign ; that he lay negligently on the Ground, and answer'd very little. This confirmed the Jealousy of the King, and he commanded that they should very narrowly and privately watch his Motions; and that he should not stir from his Apartment, but one Spy or other should be employ'd to watch him : So that the Hour approaching, wherein he was to go to the Citron-Grove ; and taking only *Aboan* along with him, he leaves his Apartment, and was watched to the very Gate of the *Otan ;* where he was seen to enter, and where they left him, to carry back the Tidings to the King.

Oroonoko and *Aboan* were no sooner enter'd, but *Onahal* led the Prince to the Apartment of *Imoinda;* who, not knowing any thing of her Happiness, was laid in Bed. But *Onahal* only left him in her Chamber, to make the best of his Opportunity, and took her dear *Aboan* to her own ; where he shewed the Height of Complaisance for his Prince, when, to give him an Opportunity, he suffered himself to be caressed in Bed by *Onahal.*

The Prince softly waken'd *Imoinda,* who was not a little surpriz'd with Joy to find him there; and yet she trembled with a thousand Fears. I believe he omitted saying nothing to this young Maid, that might persuade her to suffer him to seize his own, and take the Rights of Love. And I believe she was not long resisting those Arms where she so longed to be ; and having Opportunity, Night, and Silence, Youth, Love, and Desire, he soon prevail'd, and ravished in a Moment what his old Grandfather had been endeavouring for so many Months.

'Tis not to be imagined the Satisfaction of these two young Lovers; nor the Vows she made him, that she remained a spotless Maid till that Night, and that what she did with his Grandfather had robb'd him of no Part of her Virgin-Honour; the Gods, in Mercy and Justice, having reserved that for her plighted Lord, to whom of Right it belonged. And 'tis impossible to express the Transports he suffer'd, while he listen'd to a Discourse so charming from her loved Lips; and clasped that Body in his Arms, for whom he had so long languished ; and nothing now afflicted him, but his sudden Departure from her ; for he told her the Necessity, and his Commands, but should depart satisfy'd in this, That since the old King had hitherto not been able to deprive him of those Enjoyments which only belonged to him, he believed for the future he would be less able to injure him ; so that, abating the Scandal of the Veil, which was no otherwise so, than that she was Wife to another, he believed her safe, even in the Arms of the King, and innocent; yet would he have ventur'd at the Conquest of the World, and have given it all to have had her avoided that Honour of receiving the *Royal Veil*. 'Twas thus, between a thousand Caresses, that both bemoan'd the hard Fate of Youth and Beauty, so liable to that cruel Promotion : 'Twas a Glory that could well have been spared here, tho' desired and aim'd at by all the young Females of that Kingdom.

But while they were thus fondly employ'd, forgetting how Time ran on, and that the Dawn must conduct him far away from his only Happiness, they heard a great Noise in the *Otan*, and unusual Voices of Men ; at which the Prince, starting from the Arms of the frighted *Imoinda*, ran to a little Battle-Ax he used to wear by his Side ; and having not so much Leisure as to put on his Habit, he opposed himself against some who were already opening the Door : which they did with so much Violence, that *Oroonoko* was not able to defend it ; but was forced to cry out with a commanding Voice, 'Whoever ye are that have the Boldness to attempt to approach this Apartment thus rudely ; know, that I, the Prince *Oroonoko*, will revenge it with the certain Death of him that first enters : Therefore stand back, and know, this Place is sacred to Love and Me this Night ; To-morrow 'tis the King's.'

This he spoke with a Voice so resolv'd and assur'd, that they soon retired from the Door ; but cry'd, ''Tis by the King's Command we are come ; and being satisfy'd by thy Voice, O Prince, as much as if we had enter'd, we can report to the King the Truth of all his Fears, and leave thee to provide for thy own Safety, as thou art advis'd by thy Friends.'

At these Words they departed, and left the Prince to take a short and sad Leave of his *Imoinda* ; who, trusting in the Strength of her Charms, believed she should appease the Fury of a jealous King, by saying, she was surprized, and that it was by Force of Arms he got into her Apartment.

All her Concern now was for his Life, and therefore she hasten'd him to the Camp, and with much ado prevail'd on him to go. Nor was it she alone that prevail'd; *Aboan* and *Onahal* both pleaded, and both assured him of a Lye that should be well enough contrived to secure *Imoinda*. So that at last, with a Heart sad as Death, dying Eyes, and sighing Soul, *Oroonoko* departed, and took his way to the Camp.

It was not long after, the King in Person came to the *Otan;* where beholding *Imoinda*, with Rage in his Eyes, he upbraided her Wickedness, and Perfidy; and threatning her Royal Lover, she fell on her Face at his Feet, bedewing the Floor with her Tears, and imploring his Pardon for a Fault which she had not with her Will committed; as *Onahal*, who was also prostrate with her, could testify: That, unknown to her, he had broke into her Apartment, and ravished her. She spoke this much against her Conscience; but to save her own Life, 'twas absolutely necessary she should feign this Falsity. She knew it could not injure the Prince, he being fled to an Army that would stand by him, against any Injuries that should assault him. However, this last Thought of *Imoinda's* being ravished, changed the Measures of his Revenge; and whereas before he designed to be himself her Executioner, he now resolved she should not die. But as it is the greatest Crime in Nature amongst them, to touch a Woman after having been possess'd by a Son, a Father, or a Brother, so now he looked on *Imoinda* as a polluted thing wholly unfit for his Embrace; nor would he resign her to his Grandson, because she had received the *Royal Veil:* He therefore removes her from the *Otan*, with *Onahal;* whom he put into safe Hands, with Order they should be both sold off as Slaves to another Country, either *Christian* or *Heathen*, 'twas no Matter where.

This cruel Sentence, worse than Death, they implor'd might be reversed; but their Prayers were vain, and it was put in Execution accordingly, and that with so much Secrecy, that none, either without or within the *Otan*, knew any thing of their Absence, or their Destiny.

The old King nevertheless executed this with a great deal of Reluctancy; but he believed he had made a very great Conquest over himself, when he had once resolved, and had perform'd what he resolved. He believed now, that his Love had been unjust; and that he could not expect the Gods, or *Captain of the Clouds* (as they call the unknown Power) would suffer a better Consequence from so ill a Cause. He now begins to hold *Oroonoko* excused; and to say, he had reason for what he did. And now every body could assure the King how passionately *Imoinda* was beloved by the Prince; even those confess'd it now, who said the contrary before his Flame was not abated. So that the King being old, and not able to defend himself in War, and having no Sons of all his Race remaining alive, but only this, to maintain him on his Throne; and looking on this as a man disobliged, first by the Rape of his Mistress, or rather Wife, and now by depriving him wholly of her, he fear'd, might make him desperate, and do some cruel thing, either to himself or his old Grandfather the Offender, he began to repent him extremely of the Contempt he had, in his Rage, put on *Imoinda*. Besides, he consider'd he ought in Honour to have killed her for this Offence, if it had been one. He ought to have had so much Value and Consideration for a Maid of her Quality, as to have nobly put her to Death, and not to have sold her like a common Slave; the greatest Revenge, and the most disgraceful of any, and to which they a thousand times prefer Death, and implore it; as *Imoinda* did, but could not obtain that Honour. Seeing therefore it was certain that *Oroonoko* would highly resent this Affront, he thought good to make some Excuse for his Rashness to him; and to that End, he sent a Messenger to the Camp, with Orders to treat with him about the Matter, to gain

his Pardon, and endeavour to mitigate his Grief: but that
by no Means he should tell him she was sold, but secretly
put to Death; for he knew he should never obtain his
Pardon for the other.

When the Messenger came, he found the Prince upon
the Point of engaging with the Enemy; but as soon as he
heard of the Arrival of the Messenger, he commanded him
to his Tent, where he embraced him, and received him
with Joy; which was soon abated by the down-cast Looks
of the Messenger, who was instantly demanded the Cause
by *Oroonoko*; who, impatient of Delay, ask'd a thousand
Questions in a Breath, and all concerning *Imoinda*. But
there needed little Return; for he could almost answer
himself of all he demanded, from his Sight and Eyes. At
last the Messenger casting himself at the Prince's Feet,
and kissing them with all the Submission of a Man that
had something to implore which he dreaded to utter, besought him to hear with Calmness what he had to deliver
to him, and to call up all his noble and heroick Courage,
to encounter with his Words, and defend himself against
the ungrateful Things he had to relate. *Oroonoko* reply'd,
with a deep Sigh, and a languishing Voice,—*I am armed
against their worst Efforts—For I know they will tell me,*
Imoinda *is no more—And after that, you may spare the rest.*
Then, commanding him to rise, he laid himself on a Carpet,
under a rich Pavilion, and remained a good while silent,
and was hardly heard to sigh. When he was come a little
to himself, the Messenger asked him Leave to deliver that
Part of his Embassy which the Prince had not yet divin'd:
And the Prince cry'd, *I permit thee*— Then he told him
the Affliction the old King was in, for the Rashness he
had committed in his Cruelty to *Imoinda*; and how he
deign'd to ask Pardon for his Offence, and to implore the
Prince would not suffer that Loss to touch his Heart too
sensibly, which now all the Gods could not restore him,
but might recompense him in Glory, which he begged he

would pursue; and that Death, that common Revenger of all Injuries, would soon even the Account between him and a feeble old Man.

Oroonoko bad him return his Duty to his Lord and Master; and to assure him, there was no Account of Revenge to be adjudged between them; If there was, he was the Aggressor, and that Death would be just, and, maugre his Age, would see him righted; and he was contented to leave his Share of Glory to Youths more fortunate and worthy of that Favour from the Gods: That henceforth he would never lift a Weapon, or draw a Bow, but abandon the small Remains of his Life to Sighs and Tears, and the continual Thoughts of what his Lord and Grandfather had thought good to send out of the World, with all that Youth, that Innocence and Beauty.

After having spoken this, whatever his greatest Officers and Men of the best Rank could do, they could not raise him from the Carpet, or persuade him to Action, and Resolutions of Life; but commanding all to retire, he shut himself into his Pavilion all that Day, while the Enemy was ready to engage: and wondring at the Delay, the whole Body of the chief of the Army then address'd themselves to him, and to whom they had much ado to get Admittance. They fell on their Faces at the Foot of his Carpet, where they lay, and besought him with earnest Prayers and Tears to lead them forth to Battle, and not let the Enemy take Advantages of them; and implored him to have Regard to his Glory, and to the World, that depended on his Courage and Conduct. But he made no other Reply to all their Supplications than this, That he had now no more Business for Glory; and for the World, it was a Trifle not worth his Care: *Go*, (continued he, sighing) *and divide it amongst you, and reap with Joy what you so vainly prize, and leave me to my more welcome Destiny.*

They then demanded what they should do, and whom he would constitute in his Room, that the Confusion of ambitious Youth and Power might not ruin their Order, and make them a Prey to the Enemy. He reply'd, he would not give himself that Trouble—but wished 'em to chuse the bravest Man amongst 'em, let his Quality or Birth be what it would: 'For, Oh my Friends! (says he) it is not Titles make Men Brave or Good; or Birth that bestows Courage and Generosity, or makes the Owner Happy. Believe this, when you behold *Oroonoko* the most wretched, and abandoned by Fortune, of all the Creation of the Gods.' So turning himself about, he would make no more Reply to all they could urge or implore.

The Army beholding their Officers return unsuccessful, with sad Faces and ominous Looks, that presaged no good Luck, suffer'd a thousand Fears to take Possession of their Hearts, and the Enemy to come even upon them before they could provide for their Safety by any Defence: and tho' they were assured by some who had a Mind to animate them, that they should be immediately headed by the Prince; and that in the mean time *Aboan* had Orders to command as General; yet they were so dismay'd for want of that great Example of Bravery, that they could make but a very feeble Resistance; and, at last, down-right fled before the Enemy, who pursued 'em to the very Tents, killing 'em: Nor could all *Aboan's* Courage, which that Day gained him immortal Glory, shame 'em into a manly Defence of themselves. The Guards that were left behind about the Prince's Tent, seeing the Soldiers flee before the Enemy, and scatter themselves all over the Plain, in great Disorder, made such Out-cries, as rouz'd the Prince from his amorous Slumber, in which he had remained buried for two Days, without permitting any Sustenance to approach him. But, in Spite of all his Resolutions, he had not the Constancy of Grief to that Degree, as to make him insensible of the Danger of his Army; and in that Instant he leaped from his Couch, and cry'd—'Come, if we must die, let us meet Death the noblest Way; and 'twill be more like *Oroonoko* to encounter him at an Army's Head, opposing the Torrent of a conquering Foe, than lazily on a Couch, to wait his lingering Pleasure, and die every Moment by a thousand racking Thoughts; or be tamely taken by an Enemy, and led a whining, love-sick Slave to adorn the Triumphs of *Jamoan*, that young Victor, who already is enter'd beyond the Limits I have prescrib'd him.'

While he was speaking, he suffer'd his People to dress him for the Field; and sallying out of his Pavilion, with more Life and Vigour in his Countenance than ever he shew'd, he appear'd like some Divine Power descended to save his Country from Destruction: And his People had purposely put him on all Things that might make him shine with most Splendor, to strike a reverend Awe into the Beholders. He flew into the thickest of those that were pursuing his Men; and being animated with Despair, he fought as if he came on Purpose to die, and did such Things as will not be believed that human Strength could perform; and such, as soon inspir'd all the rest with new Courage, and new Ardor. And now it was that they began to fight indeed; and so, as if they would not be out-done even by their ador'd Hero; who turning the Tide of the Victory, changing absolutely the Fate of the Day, gain'd an entire Conquest: And *Oroonoko* having the good Fortune to single out *Jamoan*, he took him Prisoner with his own Hand, having wounded him almost to Death.

This *Jamoan* afterwards became very dear to him, being a Man very Gallant, and of excellent Graces, and fine Parts; so that he never put him amongst the Rank of Captives as they used to do, without Distinction, for the common Sale, or Market, but kept him in his own Court, where he retain'd nothing of the Prisoner but the Name, and returned no more into his own Country; so great an Affection he took for *Oroonoko*, and by a thousand Tales and Adventures of Love and Gallantry, flatter'd his Disease of Melancholy and Languishment; which I have often heard him say, had certainly kill'd him, but for the Conversation of this Prince and *Aboan*, and the *French* Governor he had from his Childhood, of whom I have spoken before, and who was a Man of admirable Wit, great Ingenuity and Learning; all which he had infused into his young Pupil. This *Frenchman* was banished out of his own Country for some Heretical Notions he held ; and tho' he was a Man of very little Religion, yet he had admirable Morals, and a brave Soul.

After the total Defeat of *Jamoan's* Army, which all fled, or were left dead upon the Place, they spent some Time in the Camp ; *Oroonoko* chusing rather to remain a While there in his Tents, than to enter into a Palace, or live in a Court where he had so lately suffer'd so great a Loss, the Officers therefore, who saw and knew his Cause of Discontent, invented all sorts of Diversions and Sports to entertain their Prince : So that what with those Amusements abroad, and others at home, that is, within their Tents, with the Persuasions, Arguments, and Care of his Friends and Servants that he more peculiarly priz'd, he wore off in Time a great Part of that Chagrin, and Torture of Despair, which the first Efforts of *Imoinda's* Death had given him; insomuch, as having received a thousand kind Embassies from the King, and Invitation to return to Court, he obey'd, tho' with no little Reluctancy ; and when he did so, there was a visible Change in him, and for a long Time he was much more melancholy than before. But Time lessens all Extremes, and reduces 'em to Mediums, and Unconcern; but no Motives of Beauties, tho' all endeavour'd it, could engage him in any sort of Amour, tho' he had all the Invitations to it, both from his own Youth, and other Ambitions and Designs.

Oroonoko was no sooner return'd from this last Conquest, and receiv'd at Court with all the Joy and Magnificence that could be express'd to a young Victor, who was not only return'd Triumphant, but belov'd like a Deity, than there arriv'd in the Port an *English* Ship.

The Master of it had often before been in these Countries, and was very well known to *Oroonoko*, with whom he had traffick'd for Slaves, and had us'd to do the same with his Predecessors.

This Commander was a Man of a finer sort of Address and Conversation, better bred, and more engaging, than most of that sort of Men are; so that he seem'd rather never to have been bred out of a Court, than almost all his Life at Sea. This Captain therefore was always better receiv'd at Court, than most of the Traders to those Countries were; and especially by *Oroonoko*, who was more civiliz'd, according to the *European* Mode, than any other had been, and took more Delight in the *White* Nations; and, above all, Men of Parts and Wit. To this Captain he sold abundance of his Slaves; and for the Favour and Esteem he had for him, made him many Presents, and oblig'd him to stay at Court as long as possibly he could. Which the Captain seem'd to take as a very great Honour done him, entertaining the Prince every Day with Globes and Maps, and Mathematical Discourses and Instruments; eating, drinking, hunting, and living with him with so much Familiarity, that it was not to be doubted but he had gain'd very greatly upon the Heart of this gallant young Man. And the Captain, in Return of all these mighty Favours, besought the Prince to honour his Vessel with his Presence some Day or other at Dinner, before he should set sail; which he condescended to accept, and appointed his Day. The Captain, on his Part, fail'd not to have all Things in a Readiness, in the most magnificent Order he could possibly: And the Day being come, the Captain, in his Boat, richly adorn'd with Carpets and Velvet Cushions, rowed to the Shore, to receive the Prince; with another Long-boat, where was plac'd all his Musick and Trumpets, with which *Oroonoko* was extremely delighted; who met him on the Shore, attended by his *French* Governor, *Jamoan*, *Aboan*, and about an Hundred of the noblest of the Youths of the Court: And after they had first carried the Prince on Board, the Boats fetch'd the rest off; where they found a very splendid Treat, with all Sorts of fine Wines; and were as well entertain'd, as 'twas possible in such a Place to be.

The Prince having drank hard of Punch, and several Sorts of Wine, as did all the rest, (for great Care was taken they should want nothing of that Part of the Entertainment) was very merry, and in great Admiration of the Ship, for he had never been in one before; so that he was curious of beholding every Place where he decently might descend. The rest, no less curious, who were not quite overcome with drinking, rambled at their Pleasure *Fore* and *Aft*, as their Fancies guided 'em: So that the Captain, who had well laid his Design before, gave the Word, and seiz'd on all his Guests; they clapping great Irons suddenly on the Prince, when he was leap'd down into the Hold, to view that Part of the Vessel; and locking him fast down, secur'd him. The same Treachery was used to all the rest; and all in one Instant, in several Places of the Ship, were lash'd fast in Irons, and betray'd to Slavery. That great Design over, they set all Hands at Work to hoist Sail; and with as treacherous as fair a Wind they made from the Shore with this innocent and glorious Prize, who thought of nothing less than such an Entertainment.

Some have commended this Act, as brave in the Captain; but I will spare my Sense of it, and leave it to my Reader to judge as he pleases. It may be easily guess'd, in what Manner the Prince resented this Indignity, who may be best resembled to a Lion taken in a Toil; so he raged, so he struggled for Liberty, but all in vain: And they had so wisely managed his Fetters, that he could not use a Hand in his Defence, to quit himself of a Life that would by no Means endure Slavery; nor could he move from the Place where he was ty'd, to any solid Part of the Ship, against which he might have beat his Head, and have finish'd his Disgrace that Way. So that being deprived of all other Means, he resolv'd to perish for want of Food; and pleas'd at last with that Thought, and toil'd and tir'd by Rage and Indignation, he laid himself down, and sullenly resolv'd upon dying, and refused all Things that were brought him.

This did not a little vex the Captain, and the more so, because he found almost all of 'em of the same Humour; so that the Loss of so many brave Slaves, so tall and goodly to behold, would have been very considerable: He therefore order'd one to go from him (for he would not be seen himself) to *Oroonoko*, and to assure him, he was afflicted for having rashly done so unhospitable a Deed, and which could not be now remedied, since they were far from Shore; but since he resented it in so high a Nature, he assur'd him he would revoke his Resolution, and set both him and his Friends ashore on the next Land they should touch at; and of this the Messenger gave him his Oath, provided he would resolve to live. And *Oroonoko*, whose Honour was such, as he never had violated a Word in his Life himself, much less a solemn Asseveration, believ'd in an Instant what this Man said; but reply'd, He expected, for a Confirmation of this, to have his shameful Fetters dismis'd. This Demand was carried to the Captain; who return'd him Answer, That the Offence had been so great which he had put upon the Prince, that he durst not trust him with Liberty while he remain'd in the Ship, for fear, lest by a Valour natural to him, and a Revenge that would animate that Valour, he might commit some Outrage fatal to himself, and the King his Master, to whom the Vessel did belong. To this *Oroonoko* reply'd, He would engage his Honour to behave himself in all friendly Order and Manner, and obey the Command of the Captain, as he was Lord of the King's Vessel, and General of those Men under his Command.

This was deliver'd to the still doubting Captain, who could not resolve to trust a Heathen, he said, upon his

Parole, a Man that had no Sense or Notion of the God that he worshipp'd. *Oroonoko* then reply'd, He was very sorry to hear that the Captain pretended to the Knowledge and Worship of any Gods, who had taught him no better Principles, than not to credit as he would be credited. But they told him, the Difference of their Faith occasion'd that Distrust: for the Captain had protested to him upon the Word of a Christian, and sworn in the Name of a great GOD; which if he should violate, he must expect eternal Torments in the World to come. 'Is that all the Obligations he has to be just to his Oath? (reply'd *Oroonoko*) Let him know, I swear by my Honour; which to violate, would not only render me contemptible and despised by all brave and honest Men, and so give my self perpetual Pain, but it would be eternally offending and displeasing all Mankind; harming, betraying, circumventing, and outraging all Men. But Punishments hereafter are suffer'd by one's self; and the World takes no Cognizance whether this GOD has reveng'd 'em or not, 'tis done so secretly, and deferr'd so long; while the Man of no Honour suffers every Moment the Scorn and Contempt of the honester World, and dies every Day ignominiously in his Fame, which is more valuable than Life. I speak not this to move Belief, but to shew you how you mistake, when you imagine, that he who will violate his Honour, will keep his Word with his *Gods*.' So, turning from him with a disdainful Smile, he refused to answer him, when he urged him to know what Answer he should carry back to his Captain; so that he departed without saying any more.

The Captain pondering and consulting what to do, it was concluded, that nothing but *Oroonoko's* Liberty would encourage any of the rest to eat, except the *Frenchman*, whom the Captain could not pretend to keep Prisoner, but only told him, he was secur'd, because he might act something in Favour of the Prince; but that he should be freed as soon as they came to Land. So that they concluded it wholly necessary to free the Prince from his Irons, that he might shew himself to the rest; that they might have an Eye upon him, and that they could not fear a single Man.

This being resolved, to make the Obligation the greater, the Captain himself went to *Oroonoko*; where, after many Compliments, and Assurances of what he had already promis'd, he receiving from the Prince his Parole, and his Hand, for his good Behaviour, dismiss'd his Irons, and brought him to his own Cabin; where, after having treated and repos'd him a While, (for he had neither eat nor slept in four Days before) he besought him to visit those obstinate People in Chains, who refused all manner of Sustenance; and intreated him to oblige 'em to eat, and assure 'em of their Liberty the first Opportunity.

Oroonoko, who was too generous not to give Credit to his Words, shew'd himself to his People, who were transported with Excess of Joy at the Sight of their darling Prince; falling at his Feet, and kissing and embracing 'em; believing, as some divine Oracle, all he assur'd 'em. But he besought 'em to bear their Chains with that Bravery that became those whom he had seen act so nobly in Arms; and that they could not give him greater Proofs of their Love and Friendship, since 'twas all the Security the Captain (his Friend) could have against the Revenge, he said, they might possibly justly take for the Injuries sustained by him. And they all, with one Accord, assur'd him, that they could not suffer enough, when it was for his Repose and Safety.

After this, they no longer refus'd to eat, but took what was brought 'em, and were pleas'd with their Captivity, since by it they hoped to redeem the Prince, who, all the rest of the Voyage, was treated with all the Respect due to his Birth, tho' nothing could divert his Melancholy; and he would often sigh for *Imoinda*, and think this a Punishment due to his Misfortune, in having left that noble Maid behind him, that fatal Night, in the *Otan*, when he fled to the Camp.

Possess'd with a thousand Thoughts of past Joys with this fair young Person, and a thousand Griefs for her eternal Loss, he endur'd a tedious Voyage, and at last arriv'd at the Mouth of the River of *Surinam*, a Colony belonging to the King of *England*, and where they were to deliver some Part of their Slaves. There the Merchants and Gentlemen of the Country going on Board, to demand those Lots of Slaves they had already agreed on; and, amongst those, the Overseers of those Plantations where I then chanc'd to be : The Captain, who had given the Word, order'd his Men to bring up those noble Slaves in Fetters, whom I have spoken of; and having put 'em, some in one, and some in other Lots, with Women and Children, (which they call *Pickaninies*) they sold 'em off, as Slaves to several Merchants and Gentlemen ; not putting any two in one Lot, because they would separate 'em far from each other; nor daring to trust 'em together, lest Rage and Courage should put 'em upon contriving some great Action, to the Ruin of the Colony.

Oroonoko was first seiz'd on, and sold to our Overseer, who had the first Lot, with seventeen more of all Sorts and Sizes, but not one of Quality with him. When he saw this, he found what they meant; for, as I said, he understood *English* pretty well; and being wholly unarm'd and defenceless, so as it was in vain to make any Resistance, he only beheld the Captain with a Look all fierce and disdainful, upbraiding him with Eyes that forc'd Blushes on his guilty Cheeks, he only cry'd in passing over the Side of the Ship ; *Farewel, Sir, 'tis worth my Sufferings to gain so true a Knowledge, both of you, and of your Gods, by whom you swear*. And desiring those that held him to forbear their Pains, and telling 'em he would make no Resistance, he cry'd, *Come, my Fellow-Slaves, let us descend, and see if we can meet with more Honour and Honesty in the next*

World we shall touch upon. So he nimbly leapt into the Boat, and shewing no more Concern, suffer'd himself to be row'd up the River, with his seventeen Companions.

The Gentleman that bought him, was a young *Cornish* Gentleman, whose Name was *Trefry;* a Man of great Wit, and fine Learning, and was carried into those Parts by the Lord — Governor, to manage all his Affairs. He reflecting on the last Words of *Oroonoko* to the Captain, and beholding the Richness of his Vest, no sooner came into the Boat, but he fix'd his Eyes on him; and finding something so extraordinary in his Face, his Shape and Mein, a Greatness of Look, and Haughtiness in his Air, and finding he spoke *English,* had a great Mind to be enquiring into his Quality and Fortune; which, though *Oroonoko* endeavour'd to hide, by only confessing he was above the Rank of common Slaves, *Trefry* soon found he was yet something greater than he confess'd; and from that Moment began to conceive so vast an Esteem for him, that he ever after lov'd him as his dearest Brother, and shew'd him all the Civilities due to so great a Man.

Trefry was a very good Mathematician, and a Linguist; could speak *French* and *Spanish;* and in the three Days they remain'd in the Boat, (for so long were they going from the Ship to the Plantation) he entertain'd *Oroonoko* so agreeably with his Art and Discourse, that he was no less pleas'd with *Trefry,* than he was with the Prince; and he thought himself, at least, fortunate in this, that since he was a Slave, as long as he would suffer himself to remain so, he had a Man of so excellent Wit and Parts for a Master. So that before they had finish'd their Voyage up the River, he made no Scruple of declaring to *Trefry* all his Fortunes, and most Part of what I have here related, and put himself wholly into the Hands of his new Friend, who he found resented all the Injuries were done him, and was charm'd with all the Greatnesses of his Actions; which were recited with that Modesty, and delicate Sense, as wholly vanquish'd him, and subdu'd him to his Interest. And he promis'd him, on his Word and Honour, he would find the Means to re-conduct him to his own Country again; assuring him, he had a perfect Abhorrence of so dishonourable an Action; and that he would sooner have dy'd, than have been the Author of such a Perfidy. He found the Prince was very much concerned to know what became of his Friends, and how they took their Slavery; and *Trefry* promised to take Care about the enquiring after their Condition, and that he should have an Account of 'em.

Tho', as *Oroonoko* afterwards said, he had little Reason to credit the Words of a *Backearary*; yet he knew not why, but he saw a kind of Sincerity, and aweful Truth in the Face of *Trefry*; he saw Honesty in his Eyes, and he found him wise and witty enough to understand Honour: for it was one of his Maxims, *A Man of Wit could not be a Knave or Villain.*

In their Passage up the River, they put in at several Houses for Refreshment; and ever when they landed, Numbers of People would flock to behold this Man: not but their Eyes were daily entertain'd with the Sight of Slaves; but the Fame of *Oroonoko* was gone before him, and all People were in Admiration of his Beauty. Besides, he had a rich Habit on, in which he was taken, so different from the rest, and which the Captain could not strip him of, because he was forc'd to surprize his Person in the Minute he sold him. When he found his Habit made him liable, as he thought, to be gazed at the more, he begged *Trefry* to give him something more befitting a Slave, which he did, and took off his Robes: Nevertheless, he shone thro' all, and his *Osenbrigs* (a sort of brown *Holland* Suit he had on) could not conceal the Graces of his Looks and Mein; and he had no less Admirers than when he had his dazling Habit on: The Royal Youth appear'd in spite of the Slave, and People could not help treating him after a different Manner, without designing it. As soon as they approached him, they venerated and esteemed him; his Eyes insensibly commanded Respect, and his Behaviour insinuated it into every Soul. So that there was nothing talked of but this young and gallant Slave, even by those who yet knew not that he was a Prince.

I ought to tell you, that the Christians never buy any Slaves but they give 'em some Name of their own, their native ones being likely very barbarous, and hard to pronounce; so that Mr. *Trefry* gave *Oroonoko* that of *Cæsar*; which name will live in that Country as long as that (scarce more) glorious one of the great *Roman* : for 'tis most evident he wanted no Part of the personal Courage of that *Cæsar*, and acted Things as memorable, had they been done in some Part of the World replenished with People and Historians, that might have given him his Due. But his Misfortune was, to fall in an obscure World, that afforded only a Female Pen to celebrate his Fame; tho' I doubt not but it had lived from others Endeavours, if the *Dutch*, who immediately after his Time took that Country, had not killed, banished and dispersed all those that were capable of giving the World this great Man's Life, much better than I have done. And Mr. *Trefry*, who design'd it, died before he began it, and bemoan'd himself for not having undertook it in Time.

For the future therefore I must call *Oroonoko Cæsar*; since by that Name only he was known in our Western World, and by that Name he was received on Shore at *Parham-House*, where he was destin'd a Slave. But if the King himself (God bless him) had come ashore, there could not have been greater Expectation by all the whole Plantation, and those neighbouring ones, than was on ours at that Time; and he was received more like a Governor than a Slave : Notwithstanding, as the Custom was, they assigned him his Portion of Land, his House and his Business up in the Plantation. But as it was more for Form, than any Design to put him to his Task, he endured no

more of the Slave but the Name, and remain'd some Days
in the House, receiving all Visits that were made him,
without stirring towards that Part of the Plantation where
the *Negroes* were.

At last, he would needs go view his Land, his House,
and the Business assign'd him. But he no sooner came
to the Houses of the Slaves, which are like a little Town
by itself, the *Negroes* all having left Work, but they all
came forth to behold him, and found he was that Prince
who had, at several Times, sold most of 'em to these Parts;
and from a Veneration they pay to great Men, especially
if they know 'em, and from the Surprize and Awe they
had at the Sight of him, they all cast themselves at his
Feet, crying out, in their Language, *Live, O King! Long
live, O King!* and kissing his Feet, paid him even Divine
Homage.

Several *English* Gentlemen were with him, and what
Mr. *Trefry* had told 'em was here confirm'd; of which
he himself before had no other Witness than *Cæsar* himself: But he was infinitely glad to find his Grandeur
confirmed by the Adoration of all the Slaves.

Cæsar, troubled with their Over-Joy, and Over-Cere-
mony, besought 'em to rise, and to receive him as their
Fellow-Slave; assuring them he was no better. At which
they set up with one Accord a most terrible and hideous
Mourning and Condoling, which he and the *English* had
much ado to appease: but at last they prevailed with 'em,
and they prepared all their barbarous Musick, and every
one kill'd and dress'd something of his own Stock (for
every Family has their Land apart, on which, at their
Leisure-times, they breed all eatable Things) and clubbing
it together, made a most magnificent Supper, inviting
their *Grandee Captain*, their *Prince*, to honour it with his
Presence; which he did, and several *English* with him,
where they all waited on him, some playing, others dancing
before him all the Time, according to the Manners of

their several Nations, and with unwearied Industry endeavouring to please and delight him.

While they sat at Meat, Mr. *Trefry* told *Cæsar*, that most of these young Slaves were undone in Love with a fine She-Slave, whom they had had about six Months on their Land ; the Prince, who never heard the Name of *Love* without a Sigh, nor any Mention of it without the Curiosity of examining further into that Tale, which of all Discourses was most agreeable to him, asked, how they came to be so unhappy, as to be all undone for one fair Slave? *Trefry*, who was naturally amorous, and delighted to talk of Love as well as any Body, proceeded to tell him, they had the most charming Black that ever was beheld on their Plantation, about fifteen or sixteen Years old, as he guess'd ; that for his Part he had done nothing but sigh for her ever since she came; and that all the White Beauties he had seen, never charm'd him so absolutely as this fine Creature had done; and that no Man, of any Nation, ever beheld her, that did not fall in love with her; and that she had all the Slaves perpetually at her Feet; and the whole Country resounded with the Fame of *Clemene*, for so (said he) we have christen'd her : but she denies us all with such a noble Disdain, that 'tis a Miracle to see, that she who can give such eternal Desires, should herself be all Ice and all Unconcern. She is adorn'd with the most graceful Modesty that ever beautify'd Youth ; the softest Sigher—that, if she were capable of Love, one would swear she languished for some absent happy Man ; and so retired, as if she fear'd a Rape even from the God of Day, or that the Breezes would steal Kisses from her delicate Mouth. Her Task of Work, some sighing Lover every Day makes it his Petition to perform for her ; which she accepts blushing, and with Reluctancy, for Fear he will ask her a Look for a Recompence, which he dares not presume to hope ; so great an Awe she strikes into the Hearts of her Admirers. 'I do not wonder *(reply'd the*

Prince) that *Clemene* should refuse Slaves, being, as you say, so beautiful; but wonder how she escapes those that can entertain her as you can do: or why, being your Slave, you do not oblige her to yield?' 'I confess (*said* Trefry) when I have, against her Will, entertained her with Love so long, as to be transported with my Passion even above Decency, I have been ready to make Use of those Advantages of Strength and Force Nature has given me: But Oh! she disarms me with that Modesty and Weeping, so tender and so moving, that I retire, and thank my Stars she overcame me.' The Company laugh'd at his Civility to a Slave, and *Cæsar* only applauded the Nobleness of his Passion and Nature, since that Slave might be noble, or, what was better, have true Notions of Honour and Virtue in her. Thus passed they this Night, after having received from the Slaves all imaginable Respect and Obedience.

The next Day, *Trefry* ask'd *Cæsar* to walk when the Heat was allay'd, and designedly carried him by the Cottage of the fair Slave; and told him she whom he spoke of last Night lived there retir'd: *But* (says he) *I would not wish you to approach; for I am sure you will be in Love as soon as you behold her.* *Cæsar* assured him, he was Proof against all the Charms of that Sex; and that if he imagined his Heart could be so perfidious to love again after *Imoinda*, he believed he should tear it from his Bosom. They had no sooner spoke, but a little Shock-Dog, that *Clemene* had presented her, which she took great Delight in, ran out; and she, not knowing any Body was there, ran to get it in again, and bolted out on those who were just speaking of her: when seeing them, she would have run in again, but *Trefry* caught her by the Hand, and cry'd, Clemene, *however you fly a Lover, you ought to pay some Respect to this Stranger*, (pointing to *Cæsar*.) But she, as if she had resolved never to raise her Eyes to the Face of a Man again, bent 'em the more to the Earth, when he spoke, and gave the Prince the Leisure to look the more at her.

There needed no long gazing, or Consideration, to examine who this fair Creature was; he soon saw *Imoinda* all over her; in a Minute he saw her Face, her Shape, her Air, her Modesty, and all that call'd forth his Soul with Joy at his Eyes, and left his Body destitute of almost Life: it stood without Motion, and for a Minute knew not that it had a Being; and, I believe, he had never come to himself, so oppress'd he was with Over-joy, if he had not met with this Allay, that he perceived *Imoinda* fall dead in the Hands of *Trefry*. This awaken'd him, and he ran to her Aid, and caught her in his Arms, where by Degrees she came to her self; and 'tis needless to tell with what Transports, what Extasies of Joy, they both a While beheld each other, without speaking; then snatched each other to their Arms; then gaze again, as if they still doubted whether they possess'd the Blessing they grasped: but when they recover'd their Speech, 'tis not to be imagined what tender Things they express'd to each other; wondring what strange Fate had brought them again together. They soon inform'd each other of their Fortunes, and equally bewail'd their Fate; but at the same Time they mutually protested, that even Fetters and Slavery were soft and easy, and would be supported with Joy and Pleasure, while they could be so happy to possess each other, and to be able to make good their Vows. *Cæsar* swore he disdained the Empire of the World, while he could behold his *Imoinda*; and she despised Grandeur and Pomp, those Vanities of her Sex, when she could gaze on *Oroonoko*. He ador'd the very Cottage where she resided, and said, That little Inch of the World would give him more Happiness than all the Universe could do; and she vow'd it was a Palace, while adorned with the Presence of *Oroonoko*.

Trefry was infinitely pleased with this Novel, and found this *Clemene* was the fair Mistress of whom *Cæsar* had before spoke; and was not a little satisfy'd, that Heaven was so kind to the Prince as to sweeten his Misfortunes by so lucky an Accident; and leaving the Lovers to themselves, was impatient to come down to *Parham-House* (which was on the same Plantation) to give me an Account of what had happened. I was as impatient to make these Lovers a Visit, having already made a Friendship with *Cæsar*, and from his own Mouth learned what I have related; which was confirmed by his *Frenchman*, who was set on shore to seek his Fortune, and of whom they could not make a Slave, because a Christian; and he came daily to *Parham-Hill* to see and pay his Respects to his Pupil Prince. So that concerning and interesting myself in all that related to *Cæsar*, whom I had assured of Liberty as soon as the Governour arrived, I hasted presently to the Place where these Lovers were, and was infinitely glad to find this beautiful young Slave (who had already gain'd all our Esteems, for her Modesty and extraordinary Prettiness) to be the same I had heard *Cæsar* speak so much of. One may imagine then we paid her a treble Respect; and tho' from her being carved in fine Flowers and Birds all over her Body, we took her to be of Quality before, yet when we knew *Clemene* was *Imoinda*, we could not enough admire her.

I had forgot to tell you, that those who are nobly born of that Country, are so delicately cut and raised all over the Fore-part of the Trunk of their Bodies, that it looks as if it were japan'd, the Works being raised like high Point round the Edges of the Flowers. Some are only carved with a little Flower, or Bird, at the Sides of the Temples, as was *Cæsar*; and those who are so carved over the Body, resemble our antient *Picts* that are figur'd in the Chronicles, but these Carvings are more delicate.

From that happy Day *Cæsar* took *Clemene* for his Wife, to the general Joy of all People; and there was as much Magnificence as the Country could afford at the Celebration of this Wedding: And in a very short Time after she conceived with Child, which made *Cæsar* even adore her, knowing he was the last of his great Race. This new Accident made him more impatient of Liberty, and he was every Day treating with *Trefrey* for his and *Clemene's* Liberty, and offer'd either Gold, or a vast Quantity of Slaves, which should be paid before they let him go, provided he could have any Security that he should go when his Ransom was paid. They fed him from Day to Day with Promises, and delay'd him till the Lord-Governor should come; so that he began to suspect them of Falshood, and that they would delay him till the Time of his Wife's Delivery, and make a Slave of the Child too; for all the Breed is theirs to whom the Parents belong. This Thought made him very uneasy, and his Sullenness gave them some Jealousies of him; so that I was obliged, by some Persons who fear'd a Mutiny (which is very fatal sometimes in those Colonies that abound so with Slaves, that they exceed the Whites in vast Numbers) to discourse with *Cæsar*, and to give him all the Satisfaction I possibly could: They knew he and *Clemene* were scarce an Hour in a Day from my Lodgings; that they eat with me, and that I oblig'd them in all Things I was capable. I entertained them with the Lives of the *Romans*, and great Men, which charmed him to my Company; and her, with teaching her all the pretty Works that I was Mistress of, and telling her Stories of Nuns, and endeavouring to bring her to the Knowledge of the true God: But of all Discourses, *Cæsar* liked that the worst, and would never be reconciled to our Notions of the Trinity, of which he ever made a Jest; it was a Riddle he said would turn his Brain to conceive, and one could not make him understand what Faith was. However, these Conversations fail'd not altogether so well to divert him, that he liked the Company of us Women much above the Men, for he could not drink, and he is but an ill Companion in that Country that cannot. So that obliging him to love us very well, we had all the Liberty of Speech with him, especially my self, whom he call'd his *Great Mistress;* and indeed my Word would go a great Way with him. For these Reasons I had Opportunity to take Notice to him, that he was not well pleased of late, as he used to be ; was more retired and thoughtful ; and told him, I took it ill he should suspect we would break our Words with him, and not permit both him and *Clemene* to return to his own Kingdom, which was not so long a Way, but when he was once on his Voyage he would quickly arrive there. He made me some Answers that shew'd a Doubt in him, which made me ask, what Advantage it would be to doubt ? It would but give us a Fear of him, and possibly compel us to treat him so as I should be very loth to behold ; that is, it might occasion his Confinement. Perhaps this was not so luckily spoke of me, for I perceiv'd he resented that Word, which I strove to soften again in vain : However, he assur'd me, that whatsoever Resolutions he should take, he would act nothing upon the *White* People ; and as for myself, and those upon that *Plantation* where he was, he would sooner forfeit his eternal Liberty, and Life itself, than lift his Hand against his greatest Enemy on that Place. He besought me to suffer no Fears upon his Account, for he could do nothing that Honour should not dictate ; but he accused himself for having suffer'd Slavery so long ; yet he charg'd that Weakness on Love alone, who was capable of making him neglect even Glory itself ; and, for which, now he reproaches himself every Moment of the Day. Much more to this Effect he spoke, with an Air impatient enough to make me know he would not be long in Bondage; and tho' he suffer'd only the Name of a Slave, and had nothing of the Toil and Labour of one, yet that was sufficient to render him uneasy ; and he had been too long idle, who us'd to be always in Action, and in Arms. He had a Spirit all rough and fierce, and that could not be tam'd to lazy Rest : And tho' all Endeavours were us'd to exercise himself in such Actions and Sports as this

World afforded, as Running, Wrestling, Pitching the Bar, Hunting and Fishing, Chasing and Killing *Tygers* of a monstrous Size, which this Continent affords in abundance; and wonderful *Snakes*, such as *Alexander* is reported to have encounter'd at the River of *Amazons*, and which *Cæsar* took great Delight to overcome ; yet these were not Actions great enough for his large Soul, which was still panting after more renown'd Actions.

Before I parted that Day with him, I got, with much ado, a Promise from him to rest yet a little longer with Patience, and wait the Coming of the Lord Governour, who was every Day expected on our Shore : He assur'd me he would, and this Promise he desired me to know was given perfectly in Complaisance to me, in whom he had an entire Confidence.

After this, I neither thought it convenient to trust him much out of our View, nor did the Country, who fear'd him ; but with one Accord it was advis'd to treat him fairly, and oblige him to remain within such a Compass, and that he should be permitted, as seldom as could be, to go up to the Plantations of the *Negroes ;* or, if he did, to be accompany'd by some that should be rather, in Appearance, Attendants than Spies. This Care was for some time taken, and *Cæsar* look'd upon it as a Mark of extraordinary Respect, and was glad his Discontent had oblig'd 'em to be more observant to him ; he received new Assurance from the Overseer, which was confirmed to him by the Opinion of all the Gentlemen of the Country, who made their Court to him. During this Time that we had his Company more frequently than hitherto we had had, it may not be unpleasant to relate to you the Diversions we entertain'd him with, or rather he us.

My Stay was to be short in that Country ; because my Father dy'd at Sea, and never arriv'd to possess the Honour design'd him, (which was Lieutenant-General of six and thirty Islands, besides the Continent of *Surinam*) nor the

Advantages he hop'd to reap by them : So that though we were oblig'd to continue on our Voyage, we did not intend to stay upon the Place. Though, in a Word, I must say thus much of it; That certainly had his late Majesty, of sacred Memory, but seen and known what a vast and charming World he had been Master of in that Continent, he would never have parted so easily with it to the *Dutch*. 'Tis a Continent, whose vast Extent was never yet known, and may contain more noble Earth than all the Universe beside; for, they say, it reaches from East to West one Way as far as *China*, and another to *Peru:* It affords all Things, both for Beauty and Use; 'tis there eternal Spring, always the very Months of *April, May*, and *June;* the Shades are perpetual, the Trees bearing at once all Degrees of Leaves, and Fruit, from blooming Buds to ripe Autumn : Groves of Oranges, Lemons, Citrons, Figs, Nutmegs, and noble Aromaticks, continually bearing their Fragrancies : The Trees appearing all like Nosegays, adorn'd with Flowers of different Kinds; some are all White, some Purple, some Scarlet, some Blue, some Yellow; bearing at the same Time ripe Fruit, and blooming young, or producing every Day new. The very Wood of all these Trees has an intrinsic Value, above common Timber; for they are, when cut, of different Colours, glorious to behold, and bear a Price considerable, to inlay withal. Besides this, they yield rich Balm, and Gums; so that we make our Candles of such an aromatic Substance, as does not only give a sufficient Light, but as they burn, they cast their Perfumes all about. Cedar is the common Firing, and all the Houses are built with it. The very Meat we eat, when set on the Table, if it be native, I mean of the Country, perfumes the whole Room; especially a little Beast call'd an *Armadillo*, a Thing which I can liken to nothing so well as a *Rhinoceros;* 'tis all in white Armour, so jointed, that it moves as well in it, as if it had nothing on : This Beast is about the Bigness of a Pig of six Weeks old. But it were endless to give an Account of all the divers wonderful and strange Things that Country affords, and which we took a great Delight to go in Search of; tho' those Adventures are oftentimes fatal, and at least dangerous: But while we had *Cæsar* in our Company on these Designs, we fear'd no Harm, nor suffer'd any.

As soon as I came into the Country, the best House in it was presented me, call'd *St. John's Hill*: It stood on a vast Rock of white Marble, at the Foot of which, the River ran a vast Depth down, and not to be descended on that Side; the little Waves still dashing and washing the Foot of this Rock, made the softest Murmurs and Purlings in the World; and the opposite Bank was adorn'd with such vast Quantities of different Flowers eternally blowing, and every Day and Hour new, fenc'd behind 'em with lofty Trees of a thousand rare Forms and Colours, that the Prospect was the most ravishing that Sands can create. On the Edge of this white Rock, towards the River, was a Walk, or Grove, of Orange and Lemon-Trees, about half the Length of the *Mall* here, whose flowery and Fruit-bearing Branches met at the Top, and hinder'd the Sun, whose Rays are very fierce there, from entring a Beam into the Grove; and the cool Air that came from the River, made it not only fit to entertain People in, at all the hottest Hours of the Day, but refresh the sweet Blossoms, and made it always sweet and charming; and sure, the whole Globe of the World cannot shew so delightful a Place as this Grove was: Not all the Gardens of boasted *Italy* can produce a Shade to out-vie this, which Nature had join'd with Art to render so exceeding fine; and 'tis a Marvel to see how such vast Trees, as big as *English* Oaks, could take Footing on so solid a Rock, and in so little Earth as cover'd that Rock: But all Things by Nature there are rare, delightful, and wonderful. But to our Sports.

Sometimes we would go surprising, and in Search of young *Tygers* in their Dens, watching when the old ones went forth to forage for Prey; and oftentimes we have been in great Danger, and have fled apace for our Lives, when surpriz'd by the Dams. But once, above all other Times, we went on this Design, and *Cæsar* was with us; who had no sooner stoln a young *Tyger* from her Nest, but going off, we encounter'd the Dam, bearing a Buttock of a Cow, which she had torn off with her mighty Paw, and going with it towards her Den: We had only four Women, *Cæsar*, and an *English* Gentleman, Brother to *Harry Martin* the great *Oliverian;* we found there was no escaping this enraged and ravenous Beast. However, we Women fled as fast as we could from it; but our Heels had not saved our Lives, if *Cæsar* had not laid down her *Cub,* when he found the *Tyger* quit her Prey to make the more Speed towards him; and taking Mr. *Martin's* Sword, desired him to stand aside, or follow the Ladies. He obey'd him; and *Cæsar* met this monstrous Beast of mighty Size, and vast Limbs, who came with open Jaws upon him; and fixing his aweful stern Eyes full upon those of the Beast, and putting himself into a very steady and good aiming Posture of Defence, ran his Sword quite through his Breast, down to his very Heart, home to the Hilt of the Sword: The dying Beast stretch'd forth her Paw, and going to grasp his Thigh, surpriz'd with Death in that very Moment, did him no other Harm than fixing her long Nails in his Flesh very deep, feebly wounded him, but could not grasp the Flesh to tear off any. When he had done this, he hallow'd to us to return; which, after some Assurance of his Victory, we did, and found him lugging out the Sword from the Bosom of the *Tyger,* who was laid in her Blood on the Ground. He took up the *Cub,* and with an Unconcern that had nothing of the Joy or Gladness of Victory, he came and laid the Whelp at my Feet. We all extremely wonder'd at his daring, and at the Bigness of the Beast, which was about the Height of an Heifer, but of mighty great and strong Limbs.

Another time, being in the Woods, he kill'd a *Tyger*, that had long infested that Part, and borne away abundance of Sheep and Oxen, and other Things, that were for the Support of those to whom they belong'd. Abundance of People assail'd this Beast, some affirming they had shot her with several Bullets quite through the Body at several times; and some swearing they shot her through the very Heart; and they believed she was a Devil, rather than a mortal Thing. *Cæsar* had often said, he had a Mind to encounter this Monster, and spoke with several Gentlemen who had attempted her; one crying, I shot her with so many poison'd Arrows, another with his Gun in this Part of her, and another in that; so that he remarking all the Places where she was shot, fancy'd still he should overcome her, by giving her another Sort of a Wound than any had yet done; and one Day said (at the Table), 'What Trophies and Garlands, Ladies, will you make me, if I bring you home the Heart of this ravenous Beast, that eats up all your Lambs and Pigs?' We all promis'd he should be rewarded at our Hands. So taking a Bow, which he chose out of a great many, he went up into the Wood, with two Gentlemen, where he imagin'd this Devourer to be. They had not pass'd very far into it, but they heard her Voice, growling and grumbling, as if she were pleas'd with something she was doing. When they came in View, they found her muzzling in the Belly of a new ravish'd Sheep, which she had torn open; and seeing herself approach'd, she took fast hold of her Prey with her fore Paws, and set a very fierce raging Look on *Cæsar*, without offering to approach him, for Fear at the same Time of loosing what she had in Possession: So that *Cæsar* remain'd a good while, only taking Aim, and getting an Opportunity to shoot her where he design'd. 'Twas some Time before he could accomplish it; and to wound her, and not kill her, would but have enrag'd her the more, and endanger'd him. He had a Quiver of Arrows at his

Side, so that if one fail'd, he could be supply'd : At last, retiring a little, he gave her Opportunity to eat, for he found she was ravenous, and fell to as soon as she saw him retire, being more eager of her Prey, than of doing new Mischiefs; when he going softly to one Side of her, and hiding his Person behind certain Herbage, that grew high and thick, he took so good Aim, that, as he intended, he shot her just into the Eye, and the Arrow was sent with so good a Will, and so sure a Hand, that it stuck in her Brain, and made her caper, and become mad for a Moment or two ; but being seconded by another Arrow, she fell dead upon the Prey. *Cæsar* cut her open with a Knife, to see where those Wounds were that had been reported to him, and why she did not die of 'em. But I shall now relate a Thing that, possibly, will find no Credit among Men ; because 'tis a Notion commonly receiv'd with us, That nothing can receive a Wound in the Heart, and live: But when the Heart of this courageous Animal was taken out, there were seven Bullets of Lead in it, the Wound seam'd up with great Scars, and she liv'd with the Bullets a great While, for it was long since they were shot: This Heart the Conqueror brought up to us, and 'twas a very great Curiosity, which all the Country came to see ; and which gave *Cæsar* Occasion of many fine Discourses of Accidents in War, and strange Escapes.

At other times he would go a Fishing ; and discoursing on that Diversion, he found we had in that Country a very strange Fish, call'd a *Numb-Eel*, (an *Eel* of which I have eaten) that while it is alive, it has a Quality so cold, that those who are angling, tho' with a Line of ever so great a Length, with a Rod at the End of it, it shall in the same Minute the Bait is touch'd by this *Eel*, seize him or her that holds the Rod with a Numbness, that shall deprive 'em of Sense for a While ; and some have fallen into the Water, and others drop'd, as dead, on the Banks of the Rivers where they stood, as soon as this Fish touches the Bait. *Cæsar* us'd to laugh at this, and believ'd it impossible a Man could lose his Force at the Touch of a Fish; and could not understand that Philosophy, that a cold Quality should be of that Nature; however, he had a great Curiosity to try whether it would have the same Effect on him it had on others, and often try'd, but in vain. At last, the sought-for Fish came to the Bait, as he stood angling on the Bank; and instead of throwing away the Rod, or giving it a sudden Twitch out of the Water, whereby he might have caught both the *Eel*, and have dismiss'd the Rod, before it could have too much Power over him; for Experiment-sake, he grasp'd it but the harder, and fainting, fell into the River; and being still possess'd of the Rod, the Tide carry'd him, senseless as he was, a great Way, till an *Indian* Boat took him up; and perceiv'd, when they touch'd him, a Numbness seize them, and by that knew the Rod was in his Hand; which with a Paddle, (that is a short Oar) they struck away, and snatch'd it into the Boat, *Eel* and all. If *Cæsar* was almost dead, with the Effect of this Fish, he was more so with that of the Water, where he had remain'd the Space of going a League, and they found they had much ado to bring him back to Life; but at last they did, and brought him home, where he was in a few Hours well recover'd and refresh'd, and not a little asham'd to find he should be overcome by an *Eel*, and that all the People, who heard his Defiance, would laugh at him. But we chear'd him up; and he being convinc'd, we had the *Eel* at Supper, which was a quarter of an Ell about, and most delicate Meat; and was of the more Value, since it cost so dear as almost the Life of so gallant a Man.

About this Time we were in many mortal Fears, about some Disputes the *English* had with the *Indians;* so that we could scarce trust our selves, without great Numbers, to go to any *Indian* Towns, or Place where they abode, for fear they should fall upon us, as they did immediately

after my coming away; and the Place being in the Possession of the *Dutch*, they us'd them not so civilly as the
English; so that they cut in Pieces all they could take,
getting into Houses and hanging up the Mother, and all
her Children about her; and cut a Footman, I left behind
me, all in Joints, and nail'd him to Trees.

This Feud began while I was there; so that I lost half
the Satisfaction I propos'd, in not seeing and visiting the
Indian Towns. But one Day, bemoaning of our Misfortunes
upon this Account, *Cæsar* told us, we need not fear, for
if we had a Mind to go, he would undertake to be our
Guard. Some would, but most would not venture: About
eighteen of us resolv'd, and took Barge; and after eight
Days, arriv'd near an *Indian* Town: But approaching it,
the Hearts of some of our Company fail'd, and they would
not venture on Shore; so we poll'd, who would, and who
would not. For my Part, I said, if *Cæsar* would, I would
go. He resolv'd; so did my Brother, and my Woman, a
Maid of good Courage. Now none of us speaking the
Language of the People, and imagining we should have a
half Diversion in gazing only; and not knowing what
they said, we took a Fisherman that liv'd at the Mouth of
the River, who had been a long Inhabitant there, and
oblig'd him to go with us: But because he was known to
the *Indians*, as trading among 'em, and being, by long
living there, become a perfect *Indian* in Colour, we, who
had a Mind to surprize 'em, by making them see something they never had seen, (that is, *White* People) resolv'd
only my self, my Brother and Woman should go: So
Cæsar, the Fisherman, and the rest, hiding behind some
thick Reeds and Flowers that grew in the Banks, let us
pass on towards the Town, which was on the Bank of
the River all along. A little distant from the Houses, or
Huts, we saw some dancing, others busy'd in fetching and
carrying of Water from the River. They had no sooner
spy'd us, but they set up a loud Cry, that frighted us at

first; we thought it had been for those that should kill us, but it seems it was of Wonder and Amazement. They were all naked; and we were dress'd, so as is most commode for the hot Countries, very glittering and rich; so that we appear'd extremely fine; my own Hair was cut short, and I had a Taffety Cap, with black Feathers on my Head; my Brother was in a Stuff-Suit, with Silver Loops and Buttons, and abundance of green Ribbon. This was all infinitely surprising to them; and because we saw them stand still till we approach'd 'em, we took Heart and advanc'd, came up to 'em, and offer'd 'em our Hands; which they took, and look'd on us round about, calling still for more Company; who came swarming out, all wondering, and crying out *Tepeeme;* taking their Hair up in their Hands, and spreading it wide to those they call'd out to; as if they would say (as indeed it signify'd) *Numberless Wonders,* or not to be recounted, no more than to number the Hair of their Heads. By Degrees they grew more bold, and from gazing upon us round, they touch'd us, laying their Hands upon all the Features of our Faces, feeling our Breasts, and Arms, taking up one Petticoat, then wondering to see another; admiring our Shoes and Stockings, but more our Garters, which we gave 'em, and they ty'd about their Legs, being lac'd with Silver Lace at the Ends; for they much esteem any shining Things. In fine, we suffer'd 'em to survey us as they pleas'd, and we thought they would never have done admiring us. When *Cæsar,* and the rest, saw we were receiv'd with such Wonder, they came up to us; and finding the *Indian* Trader whom they knew, (for 'tis by these Fishermen, call'd *Indian* Traders, we hold a Commerce with 'em; for they love not to go far from home, and we never go to them) when they saw him therefore, they set up a new Joy, and cry'd in their Language, *Oh, here's our* Tiguamy, *and we shall know whether those Things can speak.* So advancing to him, some of 'em gave him their Hands, and cry'd, *Amora Tiguamy;* which is as much as, *How do you do?* or, *Welcome Friend;* and all, with one din, began to gabble to him, and ask'd, if we had Sense and Wit? If we could talk of Affairs of Life and War, as they could do? If we could hunt, swim, and do a thousand Things they use? He answer'd 'em, We could. Then they invited us into their Houses, and dress'd Venison and Buffalo for us; and going out, gather'd a Leaf of a Tree, called a *Sarumbo* Leaf, of six Yards long, and spread it on the Ground for a Table-Cloth; and cutting another in Pieces, instead of Plates, set us on little low *Indian* Stools, which they cut out of one entire Piece of Wood, and paint in a sort of Japan-Work. They serve every one their Mess on these Pieces of Leaves; and it was very good, but too high-season'd with Pepper. When we had eat, my Brother and I took out our Flutes, and play'd to 'em, which gave 'em new Wonder; and I soon perceiv'd, by an Admiration that is natural to these People, and by the extreme Ignorance and Simplicity of 'em, it were not difficult to establish any unknown or extravagant Religion among them, and to impose any Notions or Fictions upon 'em. For seeing a Kinsman of mine set some Paper on Fire with a Burning-Glass, a Trick they had never before seen, they were like to have ador'd him for a God, and begg'd he would give 'em the Characters or Figures of his Name, that they might oppose it against Winds and Storms: which he did, and they held it up in those Seasons, and fancy'd it had a Charm to conquer them, and kept it like a holy Relique. They are very superstitious, and call'd him the Great *Peeie*, that is, *Prophet*. They shewed us their *Indian Peeie*, a Youth of about sixteen Years old, as handsome as Nature could make a Man. They consecrate a beautiful Youth from his Infancy, and all Arts are used to compleat him in the finest Manner, both in Beauty and Shape: He is bred to all the little Arts and Cunning they are capable of; to all the legerdemain Tricks, and Slight of Hand, whereby he imposes on the Rabble; and is both a Doctor in Physick and Divinity: And by these Tricks makes the Sick believe he sometimes eases their Pains, by drawing from the afflicted Part little Serpents, or odd Flies, or Worms, or any strange Thing; and though they have besides undoubted good Remedies for almost all their Diseases, they cure the Patient more by Fancy than by Medicines, and make themselves feared, loved, and reverenced. This young *Peeie* had a very young Wife, who seeing my Brother kiss her, came running and kiss'd me. After this they kiss'd one another, and made it a very great Jest, it being so novel; and new Admiration and Laughing went round the Multitude, that they never will forget that Ceremony, never before us'd or known. *Cæsar* had a Mind to see and talk with their War-Captains, and we were conducted to one of their Houses, where we beheld several of the great Captains, who had been at Council: But so frightful a Vision it was to see 'em, no Fancy can create; no sad Dreams can represent so dreadful a Spectacle. For my Part, I took 'em for Hobgoblins, or Fiends, rather than Men; But however their Shapes appear'd, their Souls were very humane and noble; but some wanted their Noses, some their Lips, some both Noses and Lips, some their Ears, and others cut through each Cheek, with long Slashes, through which their Teeth appear'd: They had several other formidable Wounds and Scars, or rather Dismembrings. They had *Comitias*, or little Aprons before them; and Girdles of Cotton, with their Knives naked stuck in it; a Bow at their Back, and a Quiver of Arrows on their Thighs; and most had Feathers on their Heads of divers Colours. They cry'd *Amora Tiguamy* to us, at our Entrance, and were pleas'd we said as much to them: They seated us, and gave us Drink of the best Sort, and wonder'd as much as the others had done before to see us. *Cæsar* was marvelling

as much at their Faces, wondring how they should be all
so wounded in War; he was impatient to know how they
all came by those frightful Marks of Rage or Malice,
rather than Wounds got in noble Battle: They told us
by our Interpreter, That when any War was waging, two
Men, chosen out by some old Captain whose fighting was
past, and who could only teach the Theory of War, were
to stand in Competition for the Generalship, or great
War-Captain; and being brought before the old Judges,
now past Labour, they are ask'd, What they dare do, to
shew they are worthy to lead an Army? When he who
is first ask'd, making no Reply, cuts off his Nose, and
throws it contemptibly on the Ground; and the other
does something to himself that he thinks surpasses him,
and perhaps deprives himself of Lips and an Eye: So
they slash on 'till one gives out, and many have dy'd in
this Debate. And it's by a passive Valour they shew and
prove their Activity; a sort of Courage too brutal to be
applauded by our *Black* Hero; nevertheless, he express'd
his Esteem of 'em.

In this Voyage *Cæsar* begat so good an Understanding
between the *Indians* and the *English*, that there were no
more Fears or Heart-burnings during our Stay, but we
had a perfect, open, and free Trade with 'em. Many
Things remarkable, and worthy reciting, we met with in
this short Voyage; because *Cæsar* made it his Business
to search out and provide for our Entertainment, especially
to please his dearly ador'd *Imoinda*, who was a Sharer in
all our Adventures; we being resolv'd to make her Chains
as easy as we could, and to compliment the Prince in that
Manner that most oblig'd him.

As we were coming up again, we met with some
Indians of strange Aspects; that is, of a larger Size, and
other sort of Features, than those of our Country. Our
Indian Slaves, that row'd us, ask'd 'em some Questions;
but they could not understand us, but shew'd us a long

Cotton String, with several Knots on it, and told us, they had been coming from the Mountains so many Moons as there were Knots : they were habited in Skins of a strange Beast, and brought along with 'em Bags of Gold-Dust; which, as well as they could give as to understand, came streaming in little small Channels down the high Mountains, when the Rains fell; and offer'd to be the Convoy to any Body, or Persons, that would go to the Mountains. We carry'd these Men up to *Parham*, where they were kept till the Lord-Governor came : And because all the Country was mad to be going on this Golden Adventure, the Governor, by his Letters, commanded (for they sent some of the Gold to him) that a Guard should be set at the Mouth of the River of *Amazons* (a River so call'd, almost as broad as the River of *Thames*) and prohibited all People from going up that River, it conducting to those Mountains or Gold. But we going off for *England* before the Project was further prosecuted, and the Governor being drown'd in a Hurricane, either the Design died, or the *Dutch* have the Advantage of it : And 'tis to be bemoan'd what his Majesty lost, by losing that Part of *America*.

Though this Digression is a little from my Story, however, since it contains some Proofs of the Curiosity and Daring of this great Man, I was content to omit nothing of his Character.

It was thus for some Time we diverted him; but now *Imoinda* began to shew she was with Child, and did nothing but sigh and weep for the Captivity of her Lord, herself, and the Infant yet unborn; and believ'd, if it were so hard to gain the Liberty of two, 'twould be more difficult to get that for three. Her Griefs were so many Darts in the great Heart of *Cæsar*, and taking his Opportunity, one *Sunday*, when all the *Whites* were overtaken in Drink, as there were abundance of several Trades, and *Slaves* for four Years, that inhabited among the *Negro* Houses; and *Sunday* being their Day of Debauch, (otherwise they were a sort of

Spies upon *Cæsar*) he went, pretending out of Goodness to 'em, to feast among 'em, and sent all his Musick, and order'd a great Treat for the whole Gang, about three hundred *Negroes*, and about an hundred and fifty were able to bear Arms, such as they had, which were sufficient to do Execution, with Spirits accordingly: For the *English* had none but rusty Swords, that no Strength could draw from a Scabbard; except the People of particular Quality, who took Care to oil 'em, and keep 'em in good Order: The Guns also, unless here and there one, or those newly carried from *England*, would do no Good or Harm; for 'tis the Nature of that Country to rust and eat up Iron, or any Metals but Gold and Silver. And they are very expert at the Bow, which the *Negroes* and *Indians* are perfect Masters of.

Cæsar, having singled out these Men from the Women and Children, made an Harangue to 'em, of the Miseries and Ignominies of Slavery; counting up all their Toils and Sufferings, under such Loads, Burdens and Drudgeries, as were fitter for Beasts than Men; senseless Brutes, than human Souls. He told 'em, it was not for Days, Months or Years, but for Eternity; there was no End to be of their Misfortunes: They suffer'd not like Men, who might find a Glory and Fortitude in Oppression; but like Dogs, that lov'd the Whip and Bell, and fawn'd the more they were beaten: That they had lost the divine Quality of Men, and were become insensible Asses, fit only to bear: Nay, worse; an Ass, or Dog, or Horse, having done his Duty, could lie down in Retreat, and rise to work again, and while he did his Duty, endur'd no Stripes; but Men, villanous, senseless Men, such as they, toil'd on all the tedious Week 'till *Black Friday;* and then, whether they work'd or not, whether they were faulty or meriting, they, promiscuously, the Innocent with the Guilty, suffer'd the infamous Whip, the sordid Stripes, from their Fellow-Slaves, 'till their Blood trickled from all Parts of their Body;

Blood, whose every Drop ought to be revenged with a Life of some of those Tyrants that impose it. 'And why *(said he)* my dear Friends and Fellow-sufferers, should we be Slaves to an unknown People? Have they vanquished us nobly in Fight? Have they won us in Honourable Battle? And are we by the Chance of War become their Slaves? This would not anger a noble Heart; this would not animate a Soldier's Soul: No, but we are bought and sold like Apes or Monkeys, to be the Sport of Women, Fools and Cowards; and the Support of Rogues and Runagades, that have abandoned their own Countries for Rapine, Murders, Theft and Villanies. Do you not hear every Day how they upbraid each other with Infamy of Life, below the wildest Salvages? And shall we render Obedience to such a degenerate Race, who have no one human Virtue left, to distinguish them from the vilest Creatures? Will you, I say, suffer the Lash from such Hands?' *They all reply'd with one Accord,* 'No, No, No; *Cæsar* has spoke like a great Captain, like a great King.'

After this he would have proceeded, but was interrupted by a tall *Negro*, of some more Quality than the rest, his Name was *Tuscan;* who bowing at the Feet of *Cæsar*, cry'd, 'My Lord, we have listen'd with Joy and Attention to what you have said; and, were we only Men, would follow so great a Leader through the World: But O! consider we are Husbands and Parents too, and have Things more dear to us than Life; our Wives and Children, unfit for Travel in those unpassable Woods, Mountains and Bogs. We have not only difficult Lands to overcome, but Rivers to wade, and Mountains to encounter; ravenous Beasts of Prey,'—*To this* Cæsar *reply'd,* 'That Honour was the first Principle in Nature, that was to be obey'd; but as no Man would pretend to that, without all the Acts of Virtue, Compassion, Charity, Love, Justice and Reason, he found it not inconsistent with that, to take equal Care of their Wives and Children as they would of themselves; and that he did not design, when he led them to Freedom, and glorious Liberty, that they should leave that better Part of themselves to perish by the Hand of the Tyrant's Whip: But if there were a Woman among them so degenerate from Love and Virtue, to chuse Slavery before the Pursuit of her Husband, and with the Hazard of her Life, to share with him in his Fortunes; that such a one ought to be abandoned, and left as a Prey to the common Enemy.'

To which they all agreed—and bowed. After this, he spoke of the impassable Woods and Rivers; and convinced them, the more Danger the more Glory. He told them, that he had heard of one *Hannibal*, a great Captain, had cut his Way through Mountains of solid Rocks; and should a few Shrubs oppose them, which they could fire before 'em? No, 'twas a trifling Excuse to Men resolved to die, or overcome. As for Bogs, they are with a little Labour filled and harden'd; and the Rivers could be no Obstacle, since they swam by Nature, at least by Custom, from the first Hour of their Birth: That when the Children were weary, they must carry them by Turns, and the Woods and their own Industry would afford them Food. To this they all assented with Joy.

Tuscan then demanded, what he would do: He said he would travel towards the Sea, plant a new Colony, and defend it by their Valour; and when they could find a Ship, either driven by Stress of Weather, or guided by Providence that Way, they would seize it, and make it a Prize, till it had transported them to their own Countries: at least they should be made free in his Kingdom, and be esteem'd as his Fellow-Sufferers, and Men that had the Courage and the Bravery to attempt, at least, for Liberty; and if they died in the Attempt, it would be more brave, than to live in perpetual Slavery.

They bow'd and kiss'd his Feet at this Resolution, and with one Accord vow'd to follow him to Death; and that

Night was appointed to begin their March. They made it known to their Wives, and directed them to tie their Hamocks about their Shoulders, and under their Arms, like a Scarf and to lead their Children that could go, and carry those that could not. The Wives, who pay an entire Obedience to their Husbands, obey'd, and stay'd for 'em where they were appointed: The Men stay'd but to furnish themselves with what defensive Arms they could get; and all met at the Rendezvouz, where *Cæsar* made a new encouraging Speech to 'em and led 'em out.

But as they could not march far that Night, on *Monday* early, when the Overseers went to call 'em all together, to go to work, they were extremely surprized, to find not one upon the Place, but all fled with what Baggage they had. You may imagine this News was not only suddenly spread all over the Plantation, but soon reached the neighbouring ones; and we had by Noon about 600 Men, they call the Militia of the Country, that came to assist us in the Pursuit of the Fugitives: But never did one see so comical an Army march forth to War. The Men of any Fashion would not concern themselves, tho' it were almost the Common Cause; for such Revoltings are very ill Examples, and have very fatal Consequences oftentimes, in many Colonies: But they had a Respect for *Cæsar*, and all Hands were against the *Parhamites* (as they called those of *Parham-Plantation*) because they did not in the first Place love the Lord-Governor; and secondly, they would have it that *Cæsar* was ill used, and baffled with: and 'tis not impossible but some of the best in the Country was of his Council in this Flight, and depriving us of all the Slaves; so that they of the better sort would not meddle in the Matter. The Deputy-Governor, of whom I have had no great Occasion to speak, and who was the most fawning fair-tongu'd Fellow in the World, and one that pretended the most Friendship to *Cæsar*, was now the only violent Man against him; and though he had nothing, and so need fear nothing, yet talked and looked bigger than any Man. He was a Fellow, whose Character is not fit to be mentioned with the worst of the Slaves: This Fellow would lead his Army forth to meet *Cæsar*, or rather to pursue him. Most of their Arms were of those Sort of cruel Whips they call *Cat with nine Tails;* some had rusty useless Guns for Shew; others old Basket Hilts, whose Blades had never seen the Light in this Age; and others had long Staffs and Clubs. Mr. *Trefry* went along, rather to be a Mediator than a Conqueror in such a Battle; for he foresaw and knew, if by fighting they put the *Negroes* into Despair, they were a sort of sullen Fellows, that would drown or kill themselves before they would yield; and he advis'd that fair Means was best: But *Byam* was one that abounded in his own Wit, and would take his own Measures.

It was not hard to find these Fugitives; for as they fled, they were forced to fire and cut the Woods before 'em: So that Night or Day they pursu'd 'em by the Light they made, and by the Path they had cleared. But as soon as *Cæsar* found that he was pursu'd, he put himself in a Posture of Defence, placing all the Woman and Children in the Rear; and himself, with *Tuscan* by his Side, or next to him, all promising to die or conquer. Encouraged thus, they never stood to parley, but fell on pell-mell upon the *English*, and killed some, and wounded a great many; they having Recourse to their Whips, as the best of their Weapons. And as they observed no Order, they perplexed the Enemy so sorely, with lashing 'em in the Eyes; and the Women and Children seeing their Husbands so treated, being of fearful and cowardly Dispositions, and hearing the *English* cry out, *Yield and Live! Yield, and be Pardon'd!* they all ran in amongst their Husbands and Fathers, and hung about them, crying out, *Yield! Yield, and leave* Cæsar *to their Revenge;* that by Degrees the Slaves abandon'd *Cæsar*, and left him only

Tuscan and his Heroick *Imoinda*, who grown as big as she was, did nevertheless press near her Lord, having a Bow and a Quiver full of poisoned Arrows, which she managed with such Dexterity, that she wounded several, and shot the Governor into the Shoulder; of which Wound he had like to have died, but that an *Indian* Woman, his Mistress, sucked the Wound, and cleans'd it from the Venom: But however, he stir'd not from the Place till he had parly'd with *Cæsar*, who he found was resolved to die fighting, and would not be taken; no more would *Tuscan* or *Imoinda*. But he, more thirsting after Revenge of another Sort, than that of depriving him of Life, now made use of all his Art of Talking and Dissembling, and besought *Cæsar* to yield himself upon Terms which he himself should propose, and should be sacredly assented to, and kept by him. He told him, It was not that he any longer fear'd him, or could believe the Force of two Men, and a young Heroine, could overthrow all them, and with all the Slaves now on their Side also; but it was the vast Esteem he had for his Person, the Desire he had to serve so gallant a Man, and to hinder himself from the Reproach hereafter, of having been the Occasion of the Death of a Prince, whose Valour and Magnanimity deserved the Empire of the World. He protested to him, he looked upon his Action as gallant and brave, however tending to the Prejudice of his Lord and Master, who would by it have lost so considerable a Number of Slaves; that this Flight of his should be look'd on as a Heat of Youth, and a Rashness of a too forward Courage, and an unconsider'd Impatience of Liberty, and no more; and that he labour'd in vain to accomplish that which they would effectually perform as soon as any Ship arrived that would touch on his Coast: 'So that if you will be pleased *(continued he)* to surrender yourself, all imaginable Respect shall be paid you; and your Self, your Wife and Child, if it be born here, shall depart free out of our Land.' But *Cæsar* would hear of no Composition; though *Byam* urged, if he pursued and went on in his Design, he would inevitably perish, either by great Snakes, wild Beasts or Hunger; and he ought to have Regard to his Wife, whose Condition requir'd Ease, and not the Fatigues of tedious Travel, where she could not be secured from being devoured. But *Cæsar* told him, there was no Faith in the White men, or the Gods they ador'd; who instructed them in Principles so false, that honest Men could not live amongst them; though no People profess'd so much, none perform'd so little: That he knew what he had to do when he dealt with Men of Honour; but with them a Man ought to be eternally on his Guard, and never to eat and drink with Christians, without his Weapon of Defence in his Hand; and, for his own Security, never to credit one Word they spoke. As for the Rashness and Inconsiderateness of his Action, he would confess the Governor is in the right; and that he was ashamed of what he had done in endeavouring to make those free, who were by Nature Slaves, poor wretched Rogues, fit to be used as Christian Tools; Dogs, treacherous and cowardly, fit for such Masters; and they wanted only but to be whipped into the Knowledge of the Christian Gods, to be the vilest of all creeping Things; to learn to worship such Deities as had not Power to make them just, brave, or honest: In fine, after a thousand Things of this Nature, not fit here to be recited, he told *Byam*, He had rather die, than live upon the same Earth with such Dogs. But *Trefry* and *Byam* pleaded and protested together so much, that *Trefry* believing the Governor to mean what he said, and speaking very cordially himself, generously put himself into *Cæsar's* Hands, and took him aside, and persuaded him, even with Tears, to live, by surrendring himself, and to name his Conditions. *Cæsar* was overcome by his Wit and Reasons, and in Consideration of *Imoinda*; and demanding what he desired, and that it should be ratify'd by their Hands in

Writing, because he had perceived that was the common Way of Contract between Man and Man amongst the Whites; all this was performed, and *Tuscan's* Pardon was put in, and they surrender'd to the Governor, who walked peaceably down into the Plantation with them, after giving Order to bury their Dead. *Cæsar* was very much toil'd with the Bustle of the Day, for he had fought like a Fury; and what Mischief was done, he and *Tuscan* performed alone; and gave their Enemies a fatal Proof, that they durst do any Thing, and fear'd no mortal Force.

But they were no sooner arrived at the Place where all the Slaves receive their Punishments of Whipping, but they laid Hands on *Cæsar* and *Tuscan*, faint with Heat and Toil; and surprizing them, bound them to two several Stakes, and whipped them in a most deplorable and inhuman Manner, rending the very Flesh from their Bones, especially *Cæsar*, who was not perceived to make any Moan, or to alter his Face, only to roll his Eyes on the faithless Governor, and those he believed Guilty, with Fierceness and Indignation; and to complete his Rage, he saw every one of those Slaves who but a few Days before ador'd him as something more than Mortal, now had a Whip to give him some Lashes, while he strove not to break his Fetters; tho' if he had, it were impossible: but he pronounced a Woe and Revenge from his Eyes, that darted Fire, which was at once both aweful and terrible to behold.

When they thought they were sufficiently revenged on him, they unty'd him, almost fainting with Loss of Blood, from a thousand Wounds all over his Body; from which they had rent his Clothes, and led him bleeding and naked as he was, and loaded him all over with Irons; and then rubb'd his Wounds, to complete their Cruelty, with *Indian* Pepper, which had like to have made him raving mad; and, in this Condition made him so fast to the Ground, that he could not stir, if his Pains and Wounds would have given him Leave. They spared *Imoinda*, and did not let her see this Barbarity committed towards her Lord, but carried her down to *Parham*, and shut her up; which was not in Kindness to her, but for Fear she should die with the Sight, or miscarry, and then they should lose a young Slave, and perhaps the Mother.

You must know, that when the News was brought on *Monday* Morning, that *Cæsar* had betaken himself to the Woods, and carry'd with him all the *Negroes*, we were possess'd with extreme Fear, which no Persuasions could dissipate, that he would secure himself till Night, and then would come down and cut all our Throats. This Apprehension made all the Females of us fly down the River, to be secured; and while we were away, they acted this Cruelty; for I suppose I had Authority and Interest enough there, had I suspected any such Thing, to have prevented it: but we had not gone many Leagues, but the News overtook us, that *Cæsar* was taken and whipped liked a common Slave. We met on the River with Colonel *Martin*, a Man of great Gallantry, Wit, and Goodness, and whom I have celebrated in a Character of my new Comedy, by his own Name, in Memory of so brave a Man: He was wise and eloquent, and, from the Fineness of his Parts, bore a great Sway over the Hearts of all the Colony: He was a Friend to *Cæsar*, and resented this false Dealing with him very much. We carried him back to *Parham*, thinking to have made an Accommodation; when he came, the first News we heard, was, That the Governor was dead of a Wound *Imoinda* had given him; but it was not so well. But it seems, he would have the Pleasure of beholding the Revenge he took on *Cæsar;* and before the cruel Ceremony was finished, he dropt down; and then they perceived the Wound he had on his Shoulder was by a venom'd Arrow, which, as I said, his *Indian* Mistress healed by sucking the Wound.

We were no sooner arrived, but we went up to the Plantation to see *Cæsar;* whom we found in a very miserable and unexpressible Condition; and I have a thousand Times admired how he lived in so much tormenting Pain. We said all Things to him, that Trouble, Pity and Good-Nature could suggest, protesting our Innocency of the Fact, and our Abhorrence of such Cruelties; making a thousand Professions and Services to him, and begging as many Pardons for the Offenders, till we said so much, that he believed we had no Hand in his ill Treatment; but told us, He could never pardon *Byam*; as for *Trefry*, he confess'd he saw his Grief and Sorrow for his Suffering, which he could not hinder, but was like to have been beaten down by the very Slaves, for speaking in his Defence : But for *Byam*, who was their Leader, their Head —and should, by his Justice and Honour, have been an Example to 'em—for him, he wished to live to take a dire Revenge of him ; and said, *It had been well for him, if he had sacrificed me, instead of giving me the comtemptible Whip.* He refused to talk much ; but begging us to give him our Hands, he took them, and protested never to lift up his to do us any Harm. He had a great Respect for Colonel *Martin*, and always took his Counsel like that of a Parent ; and assured him, he would obey him in any Thing but his Revenge on *Byam*: 'Therefore *(said he)* for his own Safety, let him speedly dispatch me ; for if I could dispatch myself, I would not, till that Justice were done to my injured Person, and the Contempt of a Soldier : No, I would not kill myself, even after a Whipping, but will be content to live with that Infamy, and be pointed at by every grinning Slave, till I have completed my Revenge ; and then you shall see, that *Oroonoko* scorns to live with the Indignity that was put on *Cæsar*.' All we could do, could get no more Words from him ; and we took Care to have him put immediately into a healing Bath, to rid him of his Pepper, and ordered a Chirurgeon to anoint him with healing Balm, which he suffer'd, and in some Time he began to be able to walk and eat. We failed not to visit him every Day, and to that End had him brought to an Apartment at *Parham*.

The Governor had no sooner recover'd, and had heard of the Menaces of *Cæsar*, but he called his Council, who (not to disgrace them, or burlesque the Government there) consisted of such notorious Villains as *Newgate* never transported ; and, possibly, originally were such who understood neither the Laws of God or Man, and had no sort of Principles to make them worthy the Name of Men ; but at the very Council-Table would contradict and fight with one another, and swear so bloodily, that 'twas terrible to hear and see 'em. (Some of 'em were afterwards hanged, when the *Dutch* took Possession of the Place, others sent off in Chains.) But calling these special Rulers of the Nation together, and requiring their Counsel in this weighty Affair, they all concluded, that (damn 'em) it might be their own Cases; and that *Cæsar* ought to be made an Example to all the *Negroes*, to fright 'em from daring to threaten their Betters, their Lords and Masters; and at this Rate no Man was safe from his own Slaves; and concluded, *nemine contradicente,* That *Cæsar* should be hanged.

Trefry then thought it Time to use his Authority, and told *Byam,* his Command did not extend to his Lord's Plantation ; and that *Parham* was as much exempt from the Law as *White-Hall;* and that they ought no more to touch the Servants of the Lord—(who there represented the King's Person) than they could those about the King himself; and that *Parham* was a Sanctuary ; and tho' his Lord were absent in Person, his Power was still in being there, which he had entrusted with him, as far as the Dominions of his particular Plantations reached, and all that belonged to it ; the rest of the Country, as *Byam* was Lieutenant to his Lord, he might exercise his Tyranny upon. *Trefry* had others as powerful, or more, that interested themselves in *Cæsar's* Life, and absolutely said, he should be defended. So turning the Governor, and his wise Council, out of Doors, (for they sat at *Parham-House*) we set a Guard upon our Lodging-Place, and would admit none but those we called Friends to us and *Cæsar*.

The Governor having remain'd wounded at *Parham*, till his Recovery was completed, *Cæsar* did not know but he was still there, and indeed for the most Part, his Time was spent there: for he was one that loved to live at other Peoples Expence, and if he were a Day absent, he was ten present there; and us'd to play, and walk, and hunt, and fish with *Cæsar*: So that *Cæsar* did not at all doubt, if he once recover'd Strength, but he should find an Opportunity of being revenged on him; though, after such a Revenge, he could not hope to live: for if he escaped the Fury of the *English* Mobile, who perhaps would have been glad of the Occasion to have killed him, he was resolved not to survive his Whipping; yet he had some tender Hours, a repenting Softness, which he called his Fits of Cowardice, wherein he struggled with Love for the Victory of his Heart, which took Part with his charming *Imoinda* there; but for the most Part, his Time was pass'd in melancholy Thoughts, and black Designs. He consider'd, if he should do this Deed, and die either in the Attempt, or after it, he left his lovely *Imoinda* a Prey, or at best a Slave to the enraged Multitude; his great Heart could not endure that Thought: *Perhaps* (said he) *she may be first ravish'd by every Brute; expos'd first to their nasty Lusts, and then a shameful Death:* No, he could not live a Moment under that Apprehension, too insupportable to be borne. These were his Thoughts, and his silent Arguments with his Heart, as he told us afterwards: So that now resolving not only to kill *Byam*, but all those he thought had enraged him; pleasing his great Heart with the fancy'd Slaughter he should make over the whole Face of the Plantation; he first resolved on a Deed, (that however horrid it first appear'd to us all) when we had heard his Reasons, we thought it brave and just. Being able to walk, and, as he believed, fit for the Execution of his great Design, he begg'd *Trefry* to trust him into the Air, believing a Walk would do him good; which was granted him; and taking *Imoinda* with him, as he used to do in his more happy and calmer Days, he led her up into a Wood, where (after with a thousand Sighs, and long gazing silently on her Face, while Tears gush'd, in spite of him, from his Eyes) he told her his Design, first of killing her, and then his Enemies, and next himself, and the Impossibility of escaping, and therefore he told her the Necessity of dying. He found the heroick Wife faster pleading for Death, than he was to propose it, when she found his fix'd Resolution; and, on her Knees, besought him not to leave her a Prey to his Enemies. He (grieved to Death) yet pleased at her noble Resolution, took her up, and embracing of her with all the Passion and Languishment of a dying Lover, drew his Knife to kill this Treasure of his Soul, this Pleasure of his Eyes; while Tears trickled down his Cheeks, hers were smiling with Joy she should die by so noble a Hand, and be sent into her own Country (for that's their Notion of the next World) by him she so tenderly loved, and so truly ador'd in this: For Wives have a Respect for their Husbands equal to what any other People pay a Deity; and when a Man finds any Occasion to quit his Wife, if he love her, she dies by his Hand; if not, he sells her, or suffers some other to kill her. It being thus, you may believe the Deed was soon resolv'd on; and 'tis not to be doubted, but the parting, the eternal Leave-taking of two such Lovers, so greatly born, so sensible, so beautiful, so young, and so fond, must be very moving, as the Relation of it was to me afterwards.

All that Love could say in such Cases, being ended, and all the intermitting Irresolutions being adjusted, the lovely, young and ador'd Victim lays herself down before the Sacrificer; while he, with a Hand resolved, and a

Heart-breaking within, gave the fatal Stroke, first cutting
her Throat, and then severing her yet smiling Face from
that delicate Body, pregnant as it was with the Fruits of
tenderest Love. As soon as he had done, he laid the Body
decently on Leaves and Flowers, of which he made a Bed,
and conceal'd it under the same Cover-lid of Nature; only
her Face he left yet bare to look on: But when he found
she was dead, and past all Retrieve, never more to bless
him with her Eyes, and soft Language, his Grief swell'd
up to Rage; he tore, he rav'd, he roar'd like some Monster
of the Wood, calling on the lov'd Name of *Imoinda*. A
thousand Times he turned the fatal Knife that did the
Deed towards his own Heart, with a Resolution to go
immediately after her; but dire Revenge, which was now
a thousand Times more fierce in his Soul than before,
prevents him; and he would cry out, 'No, since I have
sacrific'd *Imoinda* to my Revenge, shall I lose that Glory
which I have purchased so dear, as at the Price of the
fairest, dearest, softest Creature that ever Nature made?
No, no!' Then at her Name Grief would get the Ascendant of Rage, and he would lie down by her Side, and
water her Face with Showers of Tears, which never were
wont to fall from those Eyes; and however bent he was
on his intended Slaughter, he had not Power to stir from
the Sight of this dear Object, now more beloved, and more
ador'd than ever.

He remained in this deplorable Condition for two Days,
and never rose from the Ground where he had made her
sad Sacrifice; at last rouzing from her Side, and accusing
himself with living too long, now *Imoinda* was dead, and
that the Deaths of those barbarous Enemies were deferred
too long, he resolved now to finish the great Work: but
offering to rise, he found his Strength so decay'd, that he
reeled to and fro, like Boughs assailed by contrary Winds;
so that he was forced to lie down again, and try to summon
all his Courage to his Aid. He found his Brains turned

round, and his Eyes were dizzy, and Objects appear'd not
the same to him they were wont to do; his Breath was
short, and all his Limbs surpriz'd with a Faintness he had
never felt before. He had not eat in two Days, which
was one Occasion of his Feebleness, but Excess of Grief
was the greatest; yet still he hoped he should recover
Vigour to act his Design, and lay expecting it yet six Days
longer; still mourning over the dead Idol of his Heart, and
striving every Day to rise, but could not.

In all this time you may believe we were in no little
Affliction for *Cæsar* and his Wife; some were of Opinion
he was escaped, never to return; others thought some
Accident had happened to him: But however, we fail'd
not to send out a hundred People several Ways, to search
for him. A Party of about forty went that Way he took,
among whom was *Tuscan*, who was perfectly reconciled
to *Byam*: They had not gone very far into the Wood, but
they smelt an unusual Smell, as of a dead Body; for Stinks
must be very noisom, that can be distinguish'd among such
a Quantity of natural Sweets, as every Inch of that Land
produces: so that they concluded they should find him
dead, or some body that was so; they pass'd on towards
it, as loathsom as it was, and made such rustling among
the Leaves that lie thick on the Ground, by continual
falling, that *Cæsar* heard he was approach'd; and though
he had, during the Space of these eight Days, endeavour'd
to rise, but found he wanted Strength, yet looking up, and
seeing his Pursuers, he rose, and reel'd to a neighbouring
Tree, against which he fix'd his Back; and being within
a dozen Yards of those that advanc'd and saw him, he
call'd out to them, and bid them approach no nearer, if
they would be safe. So that they stood still, and hardly
believing their Eyes, that would persuade them that it was
Cæsar that spoke to them, so much he was alter'd; they
ask'd him, what he had done with his Wife, for they smelt
a Stink that almost struck them dead? He pointing to the

dead Body, sighing, cry'd, *Behold her there.* They put off
the Flowers that cover'd her, with their Sticks, and found
she was kill'd, and cry'd out, *Oh, Monster! that hast
murder'd thy Wife.* Then asking him, why he did so cruel
a Deed? He reply'd, He had no Leisure to answer impertinent Questions: 'You may go back *(continued he)* and
tell the faithless Governor, he may thank Fortune that I
am breathing my last; and that my Arm is too feeble to
obey my Heart, in what it had design'd him': But his
Tongue faultering, and trembling, he could scarce end
what he was saying. The *English* taking Advantage by his
Weakness, cry'd, *Let us take him alive by all Means.* He
heard 'em; and, as if he had reviv'd from a Fainting, or a
Dream, he cried out, 'No, Gentlemen, you are deceived;
you will find no more *Cæsars* to be whipt; no more find a
Faith in me; Feeble as you think me, I have Strength yet
left to secure me from a second Indignity.' They swore
all anew; and he only shook his Head, and beheld them
with Scorn. Then they cry'd out, *Who will venture on this
single Man? Will nobody?* They stood all silent, while
Cæsar replied, *Fatal will be the Attempt of the first Adven-
turer, let him assure himself,* (and, at that Word, held up his
Knife in a menacing Posture:) *Look ye, ye faithless Crew,*
said he, *'tis not Life I seek, nor am I afraid of dying,* (and
at that Word, cut a Piece of Flesh from his own Throat,
and threw it at 'em) *yet still I would live if I could, till I
had perfected my Revenge: But, oh! it cannot be; I feel Life
gliding from my Eyes and Heart; and if I make not haste, I
shall fall a Victim to the shameful Whip.* At that, he rip'd
up his own Belly, and took his Bowels and pull'd 'em out,
with what Strength he could; while some, on their Knees
imploring, besought him to hold his Hand. But when they
saw him tottering, they cry'd out, *Will none venture on
him?* A bold *Englishman* cry'd, *Yes, if he were the Devil,*
(taking Courage when he saw him almost dead) and
swearing a horrid Oath for his farewel to the World, he

rush'd on him. *Cæsar* with his arm'd Hand, met him so
fairly, as stuck him to the Heart, and he Fell dead at his
feet. *Tuscan* seeing that, cry'd out, *I love thee, O* Cæsar!
and therefore will not let thee die, if possible; and running
to him, took him in his Arms; but, at the same time,
warding a Blow that *Cæsar* made at his Bosom, he receiv'd
it quite through his Arm; and *Cæsar* having not Strength
to pluck the Knife forth, tho' he attempted it, *Tuscan*
neither pull'd it out himself, nor suffer'd it to be pull'd
out, but came down with it sticking in his Arm; and the
Reason he gave for it, was, because the Air should not get
into the Wound. They put their Hands a-cross, and
carry'd *Cæsar* between six of 'em, fainting as he was, and
they thought dead, or just dying; and they brought him
to *Parham,* and laid him on a Couch, and had the
Chirurgeon immediately to him, who dressed his Wounds,
and sow'd up his Belly, and us'd Means to bring him to
Life, which they effected. We ran all to see him; and,
if before we thought him so beautiful a Sight, he was now
so alter'd, that his Face was like a Death's-Head black'd
over, nothing but Teeth and Eye-holes: For some Days
we suffer'd no Body to speak to him, but caused Cordials
to be poured down his Throat; which sustained his Life,
and in six or seven Days he recovered his Senses: For,
you must know, that Wounds are almost to a Miracle
cur'd in the *Indies;* unless Wounds in the Legs, which
they rarely ever cure.

When he was well enough to speak, we talk'd to him,
and ask'd him some Questions about his Wife, and the
Reasons why he kill'd her; and he then told us what I
have related of that Resolution, and of his Parting, and
he besought us we would let him die, and was extremely
afflicted to think it was possible he might live: He assur'd
us, if we did not dispatch him, he would prove very fatal
to a great many. We said all we could to make him live,
and gave him new Assurances; but he begg'd we would

not think so poorly of him, or of his Love to *Imoinda*, to imagine we could flatter him to Life again : But the Chirurgeon assur'd him he could not live, and therefore he need not fear. We were all (but *Cæsar*) afflicted at this News, and the Sight was ghastly : His Discourse was sad ; and the earthy Smell about him so strong, that I was persuaded to leave the Place for some time, (being my self but sickly, and very apt to fall into Fits of dangerous Illness upon any extraordinary Melancholy.) The Servants, and *Trefry*, and the Chirurgeons, promis'd all to take what possible Care they could of the Life of *Cæsar ;* and I, taking Boat, went with other Company to Colonel *Martin's*, about three Days Journey down the River. But I was no sooner gone, than the Governor taking *Trefry*, about some pretended earnest Business, a Day's Journey up the River, having communicated his Design to one *Banister*, a wild *Irish* Man, one of the Council, a Fellow of absolute Barbarity, and fit to execute any Villany, but rich ; he came up to *Parham*, and forcibly took *Cæsar*, and had him carried to the same Post where he was whipp'd ; and causing him to be ty'd to it, and a great Fire made before him, he told him he should die like a Dog, as he was. *Cæsar* replied, This was the first piece of Bravery that ever *Banister* did, and he never spoke Sense till he pronounc'd that Word ; and if he would keep it, he would declare, in the other World, that he was the only Man, of all the *Whites*, that ever he heard speak Truth. And turning to the Men that had bound him, he said, *My Friends, am I to die, or to be whipt?* And they cry'd, *Whipt! no, you shall not escape so well.* And then he reply'd, smiling, *A Blessing on thee ;* and assur'd them they need not tie him, for he would stand fix'd like a Rock, and endure Death so as should encourage them to die : *But if you whip me* (said he) *be sure you tie me fast.*

He had learn'd to take Tobacco ; and when he was assur'd he should die, he desir'd they would give him a

Pipe in his Mouth, ready lighted; which they did: And the Executioner came, and first cut off his Members, and threw them into the Fire; after that, with an ill-favour'd Knife, they cut off his Ears and his Nose, and burn'd them; he still smoak'd on, as if nothing had touch'd him; then they hack'd off one of his Arms, and still he bore up and held his Pipe; but at the cutting off the other Arm, his Head sunk, and his Pipe dropt, and he gave up the Ghost, without a Groan, or a Reproach. My Mother and Sister were by him all the While, but not suffer'd to save him; so rude and wild were the Rabble, and so inhuman were the Justices who stood by to see the Execution, who after paid dear enough for their Insolence. They cut *Cæsar* into Quarters, and sent them to several of the chief Plantations: One Quarter was sent to Colonel *Martin;* who refus'd it, and swore, he had rather see the Quarters of *Banister*, and the Governor himself, than those of *Cæsar*, on his Plantations; and that he could govern his *Negroes*, without terrifying and grieving them with frightful Spectacles of a mangled King.

Thus died this great Man, worthy of a better Fate, and a more sublime Wit than mine to write his Praise: Yet, I hope, the Reputation of my Pen is considerable enough to make his glorious Name to survive to all Ages, with that of the brave, the beautiful and the constant *Imoinda*.

AGNES DE CASTRO.

INTRODUCTION.

THE 'sweet sentimental tragedy' of Agnes de Castro was founded by Mrs. Behn upon a work by Mlle S. B. de Brillac, *Agnès de Castro, nouvelle portugaise* (1688), and various subsequent editions. In the same year (1688) as Mrs. Behn's *Agnes de Castro; or, The Force of Generous Blood* was published there appeared 'Two New Novels. i. *The Art of Making Love.*[1] ii. *The Fatal Beauty of Agnes de Castro:* Taken out of the History of Portugal. Translated from the French by P. B. G.[2] For R. Bentley' (12mo). Each has a separate title page. Bellon's version does not differ materially from Mrs. Behn, but she far exceeds him in spirit and niceness of style.

So much legend has surrounded the romantic history of the beautiful Ines de Castro that it is impossible fully to elucidate every detail of her life. Born in the early years of the fourteenth century, she was the daughter of Pedro Fernandez de Castro, major domo to Alphonso XI of Castille. She accompanied her relative, Dona Constança Manuel, daughter to the Duke of Peñafiel, to the court of Alphonso IV of Portugal when this lady was to wed the Infante Don Pedro. Here Ines excited the fondest love in Pedro's heart and the passion was reciprocated. She bore him several children, and there can be no doubt that Dona Constança was madly jealous of her husband's amour with her fair friend. 13 November, 1345, Constança died, and Pedro immediately married his mistress at Braganza in the presence of the Bishop of Guarda. Their nuptials were kept secret, and the old King kept pressing his son to take a wife. Before long his spies found out the reason of the Infante's constant refusals; and, beside himself with rage, he watched an opportunity whilst Pedro, on a great hunting expedition, was absent from Coimbra where they resided, and had Ines cruelly assassinated 7 January, 1355. The grief of Pedro was terrible, he plunged the country into civil war, and it was only by the tenderest solicitations of his mother and the authority of several holy monks and bishops that he was restrained from taking a terrible revenge upon his father. Alphonso died, his power curtailed, his end unhappy, May, 1357.

A very literature has grown up around the lovely Ines, and many more than a hundred items of interest could be enumerated. The best authority is J. de Araujo, whose monumental *Bibliographia Inesiana* was published in 1897. Mrs. Behn's novel was immensely popular and is included, with some

---

[1] Mr. Arundell Esdaile in his *Bibliography of Fiction (printed before 1740)* erroneously identifies this amusing little piece with Mrs. Behn's *The Lover's Watch*. It is, however, quite another thing, dealing with a pseudo-Turkish language of love.

[2] i.e., Peter Bellon, Gent. Bellon was an assiduous hackney writer and translator of the day. He has also left one comedy, *The Mock Duellist; or, The French Valet* (4to, 1675).

unnecessary moral observations as preface, in Mrs. Griffith's *A Collection of Novels* (1777), Vol. III, which has a plate illustrating the tale. It was turned into French by Marie-Geneviève-Charlotte Tiroux d' Arconville (1720–1805), wife of a councillor of the Parliament, an aimable blue-stocking who devoted her life wholly to literature, and translated freely from English. This work is to be found in *Romans (les deux premiers . . . tirés des Lettres Persanes . . . par M. Littleton et le dernier . . . d'un Recueil de Romans . . . de Madame Behn) traduits de l' Anglois.* (Amsterdam, 1761.) It occurs again in *Mélanges de Litterature* (12mo, 1775, etc.), Vol. VI.

A tragedy, *Agnes de Castro*, written by that philosophical lady, Catherine Trotter (afterwards Cockburn), at the early age of sixteen, and produced at the Theatre Royal, 1696, with Powell, Verbruggen, Mrs. Rogers in the principal parts, is directly founded upon Mrs. Behn. It is a mediocre play, and the same can even more truly be said of Mallet's cold *Elvira* (1763). This was acted, however, with fair success thirteen times. Garrick played Don Pedro, his last original part, and Mrs. Cibber Elvira. Such dull exercises as C. Symmons, *Inez, a tragedy* (1796), and *Ignez de Castro*, a tragedy in verse, intended for *Hoad's Magazine* call for no comment.

There is a French play by Lamotte on the subject of Ines de Castro, which was first produced 6 April, 1723. Voltaire found the first four acts execrable and laughed consumedly. The fifth was so tender and true that he melted into tears. In Italian we have, from the pen of Bertoletti, *Inez de Castro*, tragedia, Milano, 1826.

In Spanish and Portuguese there are, of course, innumerable poems, treaties, tragedies, studies, romances. Lope de Vega wrote *Dona Inez de Castro*, and the beautiful episode of Camoens is deservedly famous. Antonio Ferreira's splendid tragedy is well known. First published in *Comedias Famosas dos Doctores de Sa de Mirande* (4to, 1622), it can also be read in *Poemas lusitanos* (2 Vols., 8vo, Lisbon, 1771). Domingo dos Reis Quita wrote a drama, *Ignez de Castro*, a translation of which, by Benjamin Thompson, was published in 1800. There is also a play *Dona Ignez de Castro*, by Nicolas Luiz, which was Englished by John Adamson, whose version was printed at Newcastle, 1808.

THE HISTORY OF
AGNES de CASTRO.

Tho' Love, all soft and flattering, promises nothing but Pleasures; yet its Consequences are often sad and fatal. It is not enough to be in love, to be happy; since Fortune, who is capricious, and takes delight to trouble the Repose of the most elevated and virtuous, has very little respect for passionate and tender Hearts, when she designs to produce strange Adventures.

Many Examples of past Ages render this Maxim certain; but the Reign of *Don Alphonso* the IVth, King of *Portugal*, furnishes us with one, the most extraordinary that History can produce.

He was the Son of that *Don Denis*, who was so successful in all his Undertakings, that it was said of him, that he was capable of performing whatever he design'd, (and of *Isabella*, a Princess of eminent Virtue) who when he came to inherit a flourishing and tranquil State, endeavour'd to establish Peace and Plenty in abundance in his Kingdom.

And to advance this his Design, he agreed on a Marriage between his Son *Don Pedro* (then about eight Years of Age) and *Bianca*, Daughter of *Don Pedro*, King of *Castile*; and whom the young Prince married when he arriv'd to his sixteenth Year.

Bianca brought nothing to *Coimbra* but Infirmities and very few Charms. *Don Pedro*, who was full of Sweetness and Generosity, lived nevertheless very well with her; but those Distempers of the Princess degenerating into the Palsy, she made it her request to retire, and at her Intercession the Pope broke the Marriage, and the melancholy

Princess conceal'd her Languishment in a solitary Retreat: And *Don Pedro*, for whom they had provided another Match, married *Constantia Manuel*, Daughter of *Don John Manuel*, a Prince of the Blood of *Castile*, and famous for the Enmity he had to his King.

Constantia was promised to the King of *Castile;* but the King not keeping his word, they made no Difficulty of bestowing her on a young Prince, who was one Day to reign over a number of fine Provinces. He was but five and twenty years of Age, and the Man of all *Spain* that had the best Fashion and Grace : and with the most advantageous Qualities of the Body he possest those of the Soul, and shewed himself worthy in all things of the Crown that was destin'd for him.

The Princess *Constantia* had Beauty, Wit, and Generosity, in as great a measure as 'twas possible for a Woman to be possest with; her Merit alone ought to have attach'd *Don Pedro*, eternally to her; and certainly he had for her an Esteem, mix'd with so great a Respect, as might very well pass for Love with those that were not of a nice and curious Observation : but alas! his real Care was reserved for another Beauty.

Constantia brought into the World, the first Year after her Marriage, a Son, who was called *Don Louis:* but it scarce saw the Light, and dy'd almost as soon as born. The loss of this little Prince sensibly touched her, but the Coldness she observ'd in the Prince her Husband, went yet nearer her Heart; for she had given her self absolutely up to her Duty, and had made her Tenderness for him her only Concern : But puissant Glory, which ty'd her so entirely to the Interest of the Prince of *Portugal*, open'd her Eyes upon his Actions, where she observ'd nothing in his Caresses and Civilities that was natural, or could satisfy her delicate Heart.

At first she fancy'd her self deceiv'd, but time having confirmed her in what she fear'd, she sighed in secret;

yet had that Consideration for the Prince, as not to let him see her Disorder: and which nevertheless she could not conceal from *Agnes de Castro*, who lived with her, rather as a Companion, than a Maid of Honour, and whom her Friendship made her infinitely distinguish from the rest.

This Maid, so dear to the Princess, very well merited the Preference her Mistress gave her; she was beautiful to excess, wise, discreet, witty, and had more Tenderness for *Constantia* than she had for her self, having quitted her Family, which was illustrious, to give her self wholly to the Service of the Princess, and to follow her into *Portugal*. It was into the Bosom of this Maid, that the Princess unladed her first Moans; and the charming *Agnes* forgot nothing that might give ease to her afflicted Heart.

Nor was *Constantia* the only Person who complained of *Don Pedro*: Before his Divorce from *Bianca*, he had expressed some Care and Tenderness for *Elvira Gonzales*, Sister to Don *Alvaro Gonzales*, Favourite to the King of *Portugal*; and this Amusement in the young Years of the Prince, had made a deep Impression on *Elvira*, who flatter'd her Ambition with the Infirmities of *Bianca*. She saw, with a secret Rage, *Constantia* take her place, who was possest with such Charms, that quite divested her of all Hopes.

Her Jealousy left her not idle, she examined all the Actions of the Prince, and easily discover'd the little Regard he had for the Princess; but this brought him not back to her. And it was upon very good grounds that she suspected him to be in love with some other Person, and possessed with a new Passion; and which she promised herself, she would destroy as soon as she could find it out. She had a Spirit altogether proper for bold and hazardous Enterprizes; and the Credit of her Brother gave her so much Vanity, as all the Indifference of the Prince was not capable of humbling.

The Prince languished, and concealed the Cause with so much Care, that 'twas impossible for any to find it out.

No publick Pleasures were agreeable to him, and all Conversations were tedious ; and it was Solitude alone that was able to give him any ease.

This Change surprized all the World. The King, who loved his Son very tenderly, earnestly pressed him to know the Reason of his Melancholy ; but the Prince made no answer, but only this, That it was the effect of his Temper.

But Time ran on, and the Princess was brought to bed of a second Son, who liv'd, and was called *Fernando*. *Don Pedro* forc'd himself a little to take part in the publick Joy, so that they believ'd his Humour was changing ; but this Appearance of a Calm endur'd not long, and he fell back again into his black Melancholy.

The artful *Elvira* was incessantly agitated in searching out the Knowledge of this Secret. Chance wrought for her ; and, as she was walking, full of Indignation and Anger, in the Garden of the Palace of *Coimbra*, she found the Prince of *Portugal* sleeping in an obscure Grotto.

Her Fury could not contain it self at the sight of this loved Object, she roll'd her Eyes upon him, and perceived in spite of Sleep, that some Tears escaped his Eyes ; the Flame which burnt yet in her Heart, soon grew soft and tender there : But oh ! she heard him sigh, and after that utter these words, *Yes, Divine* Agnes, *I will sooner die than let you know it :* Constantia *shall have nothing to reproach me with*. *Elvira* was enraged at this Discourse, which represented to her immediately, the same moment, *Agnes de Castro* with all her Charms ; and not at all doubting, but it was she who possest the Heart of *Don Pedro*, she found in her Soul more Hatred for this fair Rival, than Tenderness for him.

The Grotto was not a fit Place to make Reflections in, or to form Designs. Perhaps her first Transports would have made her waken him, if see had not perceived a Paper lying under his Hand, which she softly seiz'd on ; and that she might not be surprized in the reading it, she went out of the Garden with as much haste as confusion.

When she was retired to her Apartment, she open'd the Paper, trembling, and found in it these Verses, writ by the Hand of *Don Pedro;* and which, in appearance, he had newly then compos'd.

> *In vain, Oh! Sacred Honour, you debate*
> *The mighty Business in my Heart:*
> *Love! Charming Love! rules all my Fate;*
> *Interest and Glory claim no part.*
> *The God, sure of his Victory, triumphs there,*
> *And will have nothing in his Empire share.*
>
> *In vain, Oh! Sacred Duty, you oppose;*
> *In vain, your Nuptial Tye you plead:*
> *Those forc'd Devoirs LOVE overthrows,*
> *And breaks the Vows he never made.*
> *Fixing his fatal Arrows every where,*
> *I burn and languish in a soft Despair.*
>
> *Fair Princess, you to whom my Faith is due;*
> *Pardon the Destiny that drags me on:*
> *'Tis not my fault my Heart's untrue,*
> *I am compell'd to be undone.*
> *My Life is yours, I gave it with my Hand,*
> *But my Fidelity I can't command.*

Elvira did not only know the Writing of *Don Pedro*, but she knew also that he could write Verses. And seeing the sad Part which *Constantia* had in these which were now fallen into her hands, she made no scruple of resolving to let the Princess see 'em: but that she might not be suspected, she took care not to appear in this Business her self; and since it was not enough for *Constantia* to know that the Prince did not love her, but that she must know also that he was a Slave to *Agnes de Castro*, *Elvira* caused these few Verses to be written in an unknown Hand, under those writ by the Prince.

Sleep betray'd th' unhappy Lover,
 While Tears were streaming from his Eyes;
His heedless Tongue without disguise,
 The Secret did discover:
The Language of his Heart declare,
That Agnes' *Image triumphs there.*

Elvira regarded neither Exactness nor Grace in these Lines: And if they had but the effect she design'd, she wished no more.

Her Impatience could not wait till the next day to expose them: she therefore went immediately to the Lodgings of the Princess, who was then walking in the Garden of the Palace; and passing without resistance, even to her Cabinet, she put the Paper into a Book, in which the Princess used to read, and went out again unseen, and satisfy'd with her good Fortune.

As soon as *Constantia* was return'd, she enter'd into her Cabinet, and saw the Book open, and the Verses lying in it, which were to cost her so dear: She soon knew the Hand of the Prince which was so familiar to her; and besides the Information of what she had always fear'd, she understood it was *Agnes de Castro* (whose Friendship alone was able to comfort her in her Misfortunes) who was the fatal Cause of it: she read over the Paper an hundred times, desiring to give her Eyes and Reason the Lye; but finding but too plainly she was not deceiv'd, she found her Soul possest with more Grief than Anger: when she consider'd, as much in love as the Prince was, he had kept his Torment secret. After having made her moan, without condemning him, the Tenderness she had for him, made her shed a Torrent of Tears, and inspir'd her with a Resolution of concealing her Resentment.

She would certainly have done it by a Virtue extraordinary, if the Prince, who missing his Verses when he waked, and fearing they might fall into indiscreet Hands, had not enter'd the Palace, all troubled with his Loss; and hastily going into *Constantia's* Apartment, saw her fair Eyes all wet with Tears, and at the same instant cast his own on the unhappy Verses that had escaped from his Soul, and now lay before the Princess.

He immediately turned pale at this sight, and appear'd so mov'd, that the generous Princess felt more Pain than he did : 'Madam, *said he*, (infinitely alarm'd) from whom had you that Paper? It cannot come but from the Hand of some Person, *answer'd* Constantia, who is an Enemy both to your Repose and mine. It is the Work, Sir, of your own Hand; and doubtless the Sentiment of your Heart. But be not surprized, and do not fear; for if my Tenderness should make it pass for a Crime in you, the same Tenderness which nothing is able to alter, shall hinder me from complaining.'

The Moderation and Calmness of *Constantia*, served only to render the Prince more asham'd and confus'd. *How generous are you, Madam*, (pursu'd he) *and how unfortunate am I!* Some Tears accompany'd his Words, and the Princess, who lov'd him with extreme Ardour, was so sensibly touch'd, that it was a good while before she could utter a word. *Constantia* then broke silence, and shewing him what *Elvira* had caus'd to be written: *You are betray'd, Sir*, (added she) *you have been heard speak, and your Secret is known.* It was at this very moment that all the Forces of the Prince abandon'd him; and his Condition was really worthy Compassion : He could not pardon himself the involuntary Crime he had committed, in exposing of the lovely and the innocent *Agnes*. And tho' he was convinced of the Virtue and Goodness of *Constantia*, the Apprehensions that he had, that this modest and prudent Maid might suffer by his Conduct, carry'd him beyond all Consideration.

The Princess, who heedfully survey'd him, saw so many Marks of Despair in his Face and Eyes, that she was afraid of the Consequences; and holding out her Hand, in a very

obliging manner to him, she said, 'I promise you, Sir, I will
never more complain of you, and that *Agnes* shall always
be very dear to me ; you shall never hear me make you
any Reproaches : And since I cannot possess your Heart,
I will content myself with endeavouring to render myself
worthy of it.' *Don Pedro*, more confus'd and dejected than
before he had been, bent one of his Knees at the feet of
Constantia, and with respect kiss'd that fair kind Hand she
had given him, and perhaps forgot *Agnes* for a moment.

But Love soon put a stop to all the little Advances of
Hymen ; the fatal Star that presided over the Destiny of
Don Pedro had not yet vented its Malignity ; and one
moment's sight of *Agnes* gave new Force to his Passion.

The Wishes and Desires of this charming Maid had no
part in this Victory ; her Eyes were just, tho' penetrating,
and they searched not in those of the Prince, what they
had a desire to discover to her.

As she was never far from *Constantia*, *Don Pedro* was
no sooner gone out of the Closet, but *Agnes* enter'd ; and
finding the Princess all pale and languishing in her Chair,
she doubted not but there was some sufficient Cause for
her Affliction : she put herself in the same Posture the
Prince had been in before, and expressing an Inquietude,
full of Concern ; 'Madam, *said she*, by all your Goodness,
conceal not from me the Cause of your Trouble. Alas,
Agnes, reply'd the Princess, what would you know ? And
what should I tell you ? The Prince, the Prince, my
dearest Maid, is in love ; the Hand that he gave me, was
not a Present of his Heart ; and for the Advantage of this
Alliance, I must become the Victim of it—What ! the
Prince in Love ! *(reply'd* Agnes, *with an Astonishment
mix'd with Indignation)* What Beauty can dispute the
Empire over a Heart so much your due ? Alas, Madam,
all the Respect I owe him, cannot hinder me from murmuring against him. Accuse him of nothing, *(interrupted*
Constantia) he does what he can ; and I am more oblig'd

to him for desiring to be faithful, than if I possess his real
Tenderness. It is not enough to fight, but to overcome;
and the Prince does more in the Condition wherein he is,
than I ought reasonably to hope for: In fine, he is my
Husband, and an agreeable one; to whom nothing is
wanting, but what I cannot inspire; that is, a Passion
which would have made me but too happy. Ah! Madam,
*(cry'd out Agnes, transported with her Tenderness for the
Princess)* he is a blind and stupid Prince, who knows not
the precious Advantages he possesses. He must surely
know something, *(reply'd the Princess modestly.)* But,
Madam, *(reply'd Agnes)* Is there any thing, not only in
Portugal, but in all *Spain,* that can compare with you?
And without considering the charming Qualites of your
Person, can we enough admire those of your Soul? My
dear *Agnes, (interrupted Constantia, sighing)* she who robs
me of my Husband's Heart, has but too many Charms to
plead his Excuse; since it is thou, Child, whom Fortune
makes use of, to give me the killing Blow. Yes, *Agnes,*
the Prince loves thee; and the Merit I know thou art
possest of, puts bounds to my Complaints, without suffering
me to have the least Resentment.'

The delicate *Agnes* little expected to hear what the
Princess told her: Thunder would have less surpriz'd, and
less oppres'd her. She remain'd a long time without speaking; but at last, fixing her Looks all frightful on *Constantia,*
' What say you, Madam? *(cry'd she)* And what Thoughts
have you of me? What, that I should betray you? And
coming hither only full of Ardor to be the Repose of your
Life, do I bring a fatal Poison to afflict it? What Detesta-
tion must I have for the Beauty they find in me, without
aspiring to make it appear? And how ought I to curse
the unfortunate Day, on which I first saw the Prince?—
But, Madam, it cannot be me whom Heaven has chosen
to torment you, and to destroy all your Tranquillity: No,
it cannot be so much my Enemy, to put me to so great

a Tryal. And if I were that odious Person, there is no Punishment, to which I would not condemn my self. It is *Elvira*, Madam, the Prince loves, and loved before his Marriage with you, and also before his Divorce from *Bianca;* and somebody has made an indiscreet Report to you of this Intrigue of his Youth : But, Madam, what was in the time of *Bianca*, is nothing to you. It is certain that *Don Pedro* loves you, *(answer'd the Princess)* and I have Vanity enough to believe, that, none besides your self could have disputed his Heart with me : But the Secret is discover'd, and *Don Pedro* has not disown'd it. What, *(interrupted* Agnes, *more surpriz'd than ever)* is it then from himself you have learned his Weakness ?' The Princess then shew'd her the Verses, and there was never any Despair like to hers.

While they were both thus sadly employ'd, both sighing, and both weeping, the impatient *Elvira*, who was willing to learn the Effect of her Malice, returned to the Apartment of the Princess, where she freely enter'd ; even to the Cabinet where these unhappy Persons were : who all afflicted and troubled as they were, blushed at her approach, whose Company they did not desire : She had the Pleasure to see *Constantia* hide from her the Paper which had been the Cause of all their Trouble, and which the Princess had never seen, but for her Spite and Revenge ; and to observe also in the Eyes of the Princess, and those of *Agnes*, an immoderate Grief : She staid in the Cabinet as long as it was necessary to be assur'd, that she had succeeded in her Design ; but the Princess, who did not desire such a Witness of the Disorder in which she then was, pray'd to be left alone. *Elvira* then went out of the Cabinet, and *Agnes de Castro* withdrew at the same time.

It was in her own Chamber, that *Agnes* examining more freely this Adventure, found it as cruel as Death. She loved *Constantia* sincerely, and had not till then any thing more than an Esteem, mixt with Admiration, for the

Prince of *Portugal;* which indeed, none could refuse to
so many fine Qualities. And looking on her self as the
most unfortunate of her Sex, as being the Cause of all the
Sufferings of the Princess, to whom she was obliged for
the greatest Bounties, she spent the whole Night in Tears
and Complaints, sufficient to have reveng'd *Constantia* for
all the Griefs she made her suffer.

The Prince, on his side, was in no great Tranquillity;
the Generosity of his Princess increas'd his Remorse,
without diminishing his Love: he fear'd, and with reason,
that those who were the occasion of *Constantia's* seeing
those Verses, should discover his Passion to the King, from
whom he hoped for no Indulgence: and he would most
willingly have given his Life, to have been free from this
Extremity.

In the mean time the afflicted Princess languished in a
most deplorable Sadness; she found nothing in those who
were the Cause of her Misfortunes, but things fitter to
move her Tenderness than her Anger: It was in vain that
Jealousy strove to combat the Inclination she had to love
her fair Rival; nor was there any occasion of making the
Prince less dear to her: and she felt neither Hatred, nor
so much as Indifference for innocent *Agnes.*

While these three disconsolate Persons abandon'd themselves to their Melancholy, *Elvira,* not to leave her
Vengeance imperfect, study'd in what manner she might
bring it to the height of its Effects. Her Brother, on whom
she depended, shew'd her a great deal of Friendship, and
judging rightly that the Love of *Don Pedro* to *Agnes de
Castro* would not be approved by the King, she acquainted
Don Alvaro her Brother with it, who was not ignorant of
the Passion the Prince had once protested to have for his
Sister. He found himself very much interested in this
News, from a second Passion he had for *Agnes;* which the
Business of his Fortune had hitherto hindred him from
discovering: and he expected a great many Favours from

the King, that might render the Effort of his Heart the
more considerable.

He hid not from his Sister this one thing, which he found
difficult to conceal; so that she was now possest with a
double Grief, to find *Agnes* Sovereign of all the Hearts to
which she had a pretension.

Don Alvaro was one of those ambitious Men, that are
fierce without Moderation, and proud without Generosity;
of a melancholy, cloudy Humour, of a cruel Inclination,
and to effect his Ends, found nothing difficult or unlawful.
Naturally he lov'd not the Prince, who, on all accounts,
ought to have held the first Rank in the Heart of the
King, which should have set bounds to the Favour of
Don Alvaro; who when he knew the Prince was his
Rival, his Jealousy increas'd his Hate of him: and he
conjured *Elvira* to employ all her Care, to oppose an
Engagement that could not but be destructive to them
both; she promised him, and he not very well satisfy'd,
rely'd on her Address.

Don Alvaro, who had too lively a Representation within
himself, of the Beauties and Grace of the Prince of
Portugal, thought of nothing, but how to combat his
Merits, he himself not being handsome, or well made:
His Fashion was as disagreeable as his Humour, and *Don
Pedro* had all the Advantages that one Man may possibly
have over another. In fine, all that *Don Alvaro* wanted,
adorn'd the Prince: but as he was the Husband of *Constantia*, and depended upon an absolute Father, and that
Don Alvaro was free, and Master of a good Fortune, he
thought himself more assur'd of *Agnes*, and fixed his Hopes
on that Thought.

He knew very well, that the Passion of *Don Pedro* could
not but inspire a violent Anger in the Soul of the King.
Industrious in doing ill, his first Business was to carry this
unwelcome News to him. After he had given time to his
Grief, and had compos'd himself to his Desire, he then

besought the King to interest himself in his amorous Affair, and to be the Protector of his Person.

Tho' *Don Alvaro* had no other Merit to recommend him to the King, than a continual and blind Obedience to all his Commands; yet he had favour'd him with several Testimonies of his vast Bounty: and considering the Height to which the King's Liberality had rais'd him, there were few Ladies that would have refused his Alliance. The King assured him of the Continuation of his Friendship and Favour, and promised him, if he had any Authority, he would give him the charming *Agnes*.

Don Alvaro, perfectly skilful in managing his Master, answer'd the King's last Bounties with a profound Submission. He had yet never told *Agnes* what he felt for her; but he thought now he might make a publick Declaration of it, and sought all means to do it.

The Gallantry which *Coimbra* seem'd to have forgotten, began now to be awakened. The King to please *Don Alvaro*, under pretence of diverting *Constantia*, order'd some publick Sports, and commanded that every thing should be magnificent.

Since the Adventure of the Verses, *Don Pedro* endeavour'd to lay a constraint on himself, and to appear less troubled; but in his heart he suffer'd always alike: and it was not but with great uneasiness he prepar'd himself for the Tournament. And since he could not appear with the Colours of *Agnes*, he took those of his Wife, without Device, or any great Magnificence.

Don Pedro adorn'd himself with the Liveries of *Agnes de Castro*; and this fair Maid, who had yet found no Consolation from what the Princess had told her, had this new cause of being displeas'd.

Don Pedro. appear'd in the List with an admirable Grace; and *Don Alvaro*, who looked on this Day as his own, appear'd there all shining with Gold, mix'd with Stones of Blue, which were the Colours of *Agnes*; and

there were embroider'd all over his Equipage, flaming
Hearts of Gold on blue Velvet, and Nets for the Snares of
Love, with abundance of double *A's;* his Device was a
Love coming out of a Cloud, with these Verses written
underneath :

> *Love from a Cloud breaks like the God of Day,*
> *And to the World his Glories does display;*
> *To gaze on charming Eyes, and make 'em know,*
> *What to soft Hearts, and to his Power they owe.*

The Pride of *Don Alvaro* was soon humbled at the feet
of the Prince of *Portugal,* who threw him against the
Ground, with twenty others, and carry'd alone the Glory
of the Day. There was in the Evening a noble Assembly
at *Constantia's,* where *Agnes* would not have been, unless
expresly commanded by the Princess. She appear'd there
all negligent and careless in her Dress, but yet she
appear'd all beautiful and charming. She saw, with disdain, her Name, and her Colours, worn by *Don Alvaro,*
at a publick Triumph; and if her Heart was capable of
any tender Motions, it was not for such a Man as he for
whom her Delicacy destin'd them : She look'd on him
with a Contempt, which did not hinder him from pressing
so near, that there was a necessity for her to hear what he
had to declare to her.

She treated him not uncivilly, but her Coldness would
have rebated the Courage of any but *Alvaro.* 'Madam,
said he, (when he could be heard of none but herself) I
have hitherto concealed the Passion you have inspired me
with, fearing it should displease you; but it has committed
a Violence on my Respect; and I could no longer conceal
it from you. I never reflected on your Actions (answer'd
Agnes with all the Indifference of which she was capable)
and if you think you offend me, you are in the wrong to
make me perceive it. This Coldness is but an ill Omen

for me (reply'd *Don Alvaro*) and if you have not found me
out to be your Lover to-day, I fear you will never approve
my Passion.

'Oh! what a time have you chosen to make it appear
to me? (pursued *Agnes*.) Is it so great an Honour for me,
that you must take such care to shew it to the World?
And do you think that I am so desirous of Glory, that I
must aspire to it by your Actions? If I must, you have
very ill maintain'd it in the Tournament; and if it be that
Vanity that you depend upon, you will make no great
progress on a Soul that is not fond of Shame. If you were
possest of all the Advantages, which the Prince has this
day carried away, you yet ought to consider what you are
going about; and it is not a Maid like me, who is touched
with Enterprizes, without respect or permission.'

The Favourite of the King was too proud to hear *Agnes*,
without Indignation : but as he was willing to conceal it,
and not offend her, he made not his Resentment appear;
and considering the Observation she made on the Triumphs
of *Don Pedro*, (which increased his Jealousies) 'If I have
not overcome at the Tournament, reply'd he, I am not
the less in love for being vanquish'd, nor less capable of
Success on occasion.'

They were interrupted here, but from that day, *Don
Alvaro*, who had open'd the first Difficulties, kept no more
his wonted Distance, but perpetually persecuted *Agnes;*
yet, tho' he were protected by the King, that inspir'd in
her never the more Consideration for him. *Don Pedro* was
always ignorant by what means the Verses he had lost in
the Garden, fell into the hands of *Constantia*. As the
Princess appeared to him indulgent, he was only concerned
for *Agnes;* and the love of *Don Alvaro*, which was then
so well known, increas'd the Pain : and had he been
possess'd of the Authority, he would not have suffer'd her
to have been expos'd to the Persecutions of so unworthy
a Rival. He was also afraid of the King's being advertised

of his Passion, but he thought not at all of *Elvira*, nor apprehended any Malice from her Resentment.

While she burnt with a Desire of destroying *Agnes*, against whom she vented all her Venom, she was never weary of making new Reports to her Brother, assuring him, that tho' they could not prove that *Agnes* made any returns to the Tenderness of the Prince, yet that was the Cause of *Constantia's* Grief : And, that if this Princess should die of it, *Don Pedro* might marry *Agnes*. In fine, she so incens'd the jealous *Don Alvaro's* Jealousy, that he could not hinder himself from running immediately to the King, with the discovery of all he knew, and all he guest, and who, he had the pleasure to find, was infinitely inrag'd at the News. 'My dear *Alvaro*, said the King, you shall instantly marry this dangerous Beauty : And let Possession assure your Repose and mine. If I have protected you on other Occasions, judge what a Service of so great an Importance for me, would make me undertake ; and without any reserve, the Forces of this State are in your power, and almost any thing that I can give shall be assured you, so you render your self Master of the Destiny of *Agnes*.'

Don Alvaro pleas'd, and vain with his Master's Bounty, made use of all the Authority he gave him : He passionately lov'd *Agnes*, and would not, on the sudden, make use of Violence; but resolv'd with himself to employ all possible Means to win her fairly ; yet if that fail'd, to have recourse to force, if she continued always insensible.

While *Agnes de Castro* (importun'd by his Assiduities, despairing at the Grief of *Constantia*, and perhaps made tender by those she had caus'd in the Prince of *Portugal*) took a Resolution worthy of her Virtue ; yet, amiable as *Don Pedro* was, she found nothing in him, but his being Husband to *Constantia*, that was dear to her : And, far from encouraging the Power she had got over his Heart, she thought of nothing but of removing from *Coimbra*. The Passion of *Don Alvaro*, which she had no inclination to favour, served her as a Pretext; and press'd with the fear of causing, in the end, a cruel Divorce between the Prince and his Princess, she went to find *Constantia*, with a trouble, which all her Care was not able to hide from her.

The Princess easily found it out; and their common Misfortunes having not chang'd their Friendship—'What ails you, *Agnes*? (said the Princess to her, in a soft Tone, and with her ordinary Sweetness) And what new Misfortune causes that sadness in thy Looks? Madam (reply'd *Agnes*, shedding a Rivulet of Tears) the Obligations and Ties I have to you, put me upon a cruel Tryal; I had bounded the Felicity of my Life in hope of passing it near your Highness, yet I must carry to some other part of the World this unlucky Face of mine, which renders me nothing but ill Offices: And it is to obtain that Liberty, that I am come to throw my self at your feet; looking upon you as my Sovereign.'

Constantia was so surpriz'd and touch'd with the Proposition of *Agnes*, that she lost her Speech for some moments; Tears, which were sincere, express'd her first Sentiments: And after having shed abundance, to give a new mark of her Tenderness to the fair afflicted *Agnes*, she with a sad and melancholy Look, fix'd her Eyes upon her, and holding out her Hand to her, in a most obliging manner, sighing, cry'd—'You will then, my dear *Agnes*, leave me; and expose me to the Griefs of seeing you no more? Alas, Madam, (interrupted this lovely Maid) hide from the unhappy *Agnes* a Bounty which does but increase her Misfortunes: It is not I, Madam, that would leave you; it is my Duty, and my Reason that orders my Fate. And those Days which I shall pass far from you, promise me nothing to oblige me to this Design, if I did not see my self absolutely forc'd to it. I am not ignorant of what passes at *Coimbra*; and I shall be an Accomplice of the Injustice there committed, if I should stay there any longer.—Ah, I know your Virtue, (cry'd *Constantia*) and you may remain here in all safety, while I am your Protectress; and let what will happen, I will accuse you of nothing. There's no answering for what's to come, (reply'd *Agnes*, sadly) and I shall be sufficiently guilty, if my Presence cause Sentiments, which cannot be innocent. Besides, Madam, the Importunities of *Don Alvaro* are insupportable to me; and tho' I find nothing but Aversion to him, since the King protects his Insolence, and he's in a condition of undertaking any thing, my Flight is absolutely necessary. But, Madam, tho' he has nothing but what seems odious to me; I call Heaven to witness, that if I could cure the Prince by marrying *Don Alvaro*, I would not consider of it a moment; and finding in my Punishment the Consolation of sacrificing my self to my Princess, I would support it without murmuring. But if I were the Wife of *Don Alvaro*, *Don Pedro* would always look upon me with the same Eyes: So that I find nothing more reasonable for me, than to hide my self in some Corner of the World; where, tho' I shall most certainly live without Pleasure, yet I shall preserve the Repose of my dearest Mistress. All the Reason you find in this Design, (answered the Princess) cannot oblige me to approve of your Absence: Will it restore me the Heart of *Don Pedro?* And will he not fly away with you? His Grief is mine, and my Life is ty'd to his; do not make him despair then, if you love me. I know you, I tell you so once more; and let your Power be ever so great over the Heart of the Prince, I will not suffer you to abandon us.'

Tho' *Agnes* thought she had perfectly known *Constantia*, yet she did not expect to find so intire a Virtue in her, which made her think her self more happy, and the Prince more criminal. 'Oh, Wisdom! Oh, Bounty without Example! (cry'd she) Why is it, that the cruel Destinies do not give you all you deserve? You are the disposer of my Actions, (continued she in kissing the Hand of *Constantia*) I'll do nothing but what you'll have me: But consider, and weigh well the Reasons that ought to counsel you in the Measures you oblige me to take.'

Don Pedro, who had not seen the Princess all that day, came in then, and finding 'em both extremely troubled, with a fierce Impatience, demanded the Cause: 'Sir, answered Constantia, Agnes too wise, and too scrupulous, fears the Effects of her Beauty, and will live no longer at Coimbra; and it was on this Subject, (which cannot be agreeable to me) that she ask'd my Advice.' The Prince grew pale at this Discourse, and snatching the Words from her Mouth (with more concern than possest either of them) cry'd with a Voice very feeble, 'Agnes cannot fail if she follow your Counsel, Madam: and I leave you full liberty to give it her.' He then immediately went out, and the Princess, whose Heart he perfectly possest, not being able to hide her Displeasure, said, 'My dear Agnes, if my Satisfaction did not only depend on your Conversation, I should desire it of you, for Don Pedro's sake; it is the only Advantage that his unfortunate Love can hope: And would not the World have reason to call me barbarous, if I contribute to deprive him of that? But the sight of me will prove a Poison to him—(reply'd Agnes) And what should I do, my Princess, if after the Reserve he has hitherto kept, his Mouth should add anything to the Torments I have already felt, by speaking to me of his Flame? You would hear him sure, without causing him to despair, (reply'd Constantia) and I should put this Obligation to the account of the rest you have done. Would you then have me expect those Events which I fear, Madam? (reply'd Agnes) Well—I will obey, but just Heaven (pursued she) if they prove fatal, do not punish an innocent Heart for it.' Thus this Coversation ended. Agnes withdrew into her Chamber, but it was not to be more at ease.

What Don Pedro had learn'd of the Design of Agnes, caus'd a cruel Agitation in his Soul; he wished he had never loved her, and desir'd a thousand times to die: But

it was not for him to make Vows against a thing which
Fate had design'd him; and whatever Resolutions he
made, to bear the Absence of *Agnes*, his Tenderness had
not force enough to consent to it.

After having, for a long time, combated with himself,
he determined to do what was impossible for him to let
Agnes do. His Courage reproach'd him with the Idleness,
in which he past the most youthful and vigorous part of
his Days: and making it appear to the King, that his
Allies, and even the Prince *Don John Emanuel,* his Father-
in-law, had concerns in the World which demanded his
Presence on the Frontiers, he easily obtain'd Liberty to
make this Journey, to which the Princess would put no
Obstacle.

Agnes saw him part without any Concern, but it was
not upon the account of any Aversion she had to him.
Don Alvaro began then to make his Importunity an open
Persecution; he forgot nothing that might touch the
insensible *Agnes,* and made use, a long time, only of the
Arms of Love: But seeing that this Submission and Respect
was to no purpose, he form'd strange Designs.

As the King had a deference for all his Counsels, it was
not difficult to inspire him with what he had a mind to:
He complain'd of the ungrateful *Agnes,* and forgot nothing
that might make him perceive that she was not cruel to
him on his account, but from the too much Sensibility she
had for the Prince. The King, who was extreme angry
at this, reiterated all the Promises he had made him.

The King had not yet spoken to *Agnes* in favour of *Don
Alvaro;* and not doubting but his Approbation would
surmount all Obstacles, he took an occasion to entertain
her with it: And removing some distance from those who
might hear him, 'I thought *Don Alvaro* had Merit enough
(said he to her) to have obtained a little share in your
Esteem; and I could not imagine there would have been
any necessity of my solliciting it for him: I know you are

very charming, but he has nothing that renders him un-
worthy of you ; and when you shall reflect on the Choice
my Friendship has made of him from among all the great
Men of my Court, you will do him at the same time Justice.
His Fortune is none of the meanest, since he has me for
his Protector : He is nobly born, a Man of Honour and
Courage : he adores you, and it seems to me that all these
Reasons are sufficient to vanquish your Pride.'

The Heart of *Agnes* was so little disposed to give it self
to *Don Alvaro*, that all the King of *Portugal* had said had
no effect on her in his favour. 'If *Don Alvaro*, Sir,
(answered she) were without Merit, he possesses Advantages enough in the Bounty your Majesty is pleased to
honour him with, to make him Master of all things, it is
not that I find any Defect in him that I answer not his
Desires : But, Sir, by what obstinate Power would you
that I should love, if Heaven has not given me a Soul that
is tender? And why should you pretend that I should
submit to him, when nothing is dearer to me than my
liberty ? You are not so free, nor so insensible, as you say,
(answer'd the King, blushing with Anger ;) and if your
Heart were exempt from all sorts of Affection, he might
expect a more reasonable Return than what he finds. But
imprudent Maid, conducted by an ill Fate, (added he in
fury) what Pretensions have you to *Don Pedro*? Hitherto
I have hid the Chagrin, which his Weakness, and yours
give me ; but it was not the less violent for being hid.
And since you oblige me to break out, I must tell you,
that if my Son were not already married to *Constantia*, he
should never be your Husband ; renounce then those vain
Ideas, which will cure him, and justify you.'

The courageous *Agnes* was scarce Mistress of the first
Transports, at a Discourse so full of Contempt ; but calling
her Virtue to the aid of her Anger, she recover'd herself
by the assistance of Reason : And considering the Outrage
she receiv'd, not as coming from a great King, but a Man

blinded and possest by *Don Alvaro*, she thought him not
worthy of her Resentment; her fair Eyes animated themselves with so shining a vivacity, they answer'd for the
purity of her Sentiments; and fixing them steadfastly on
the King, 'If the Prince *Don Pedro* have Weaknesses,
(reply'd she, with an Air disdainful) he never communicated 'em to me; and I am certain, I never contributed
wilfully to 'em: But to let you see how little I regard
your Defiance, and to put my Glory in safety, I will live
far from you, and all that belongs to you: Yes, Sir, I will
quit *Coimbra* with pleasure; and for this Man, who is so
dear to you, (answer'd she with a noble Pride and Fierceness, of which the King felt all the force) for this Favourite,
so worthy to possess the most tender Affections of a great
Prince, I assure you, that into whatever part of the World
Fortune conducts me, I will not carry away the least
Remembrance of him.' At these words she made a profound Reverence, and made such haste from his Presence,
that he could not oppose her going if he would.

The King was now more strongly convinc'd than ever,
that she favour'd the Passion of *Don Pedro*, and immediately
went to *Constantia*, to inspire her with the same Thought;
but she was not capable of receiving such Impressions, and
following her own natural Inclinations, she generously
defended the Virtue of his Actions. The King, angry to
see her so well intentioned to her Rival, whom he would
have had her hated, reproached her with the sweetness of
her Temper, and went thence to mix his Anger with *Don
Alvaro's* Rage, who was totally confounded when he saw
the Negotiation of his Master had taken no effect. The
haughty Maid braves me then, Sir, said he to the King,
and despises the Honour which your Bounty offered her!
Why cannot I resist so fatal a Passion? But I must love
her, in spite of my self; and if this Flame consume me,
I can find no way to extinguish it. What can I further
do for you, replied the King? Alas, Sir, answered *Don*

Alvaro, I must do by force, what I cannot otherwise hope from the proud and cruel *Agnes*. Well then, added the King, since it is not fit for me to authorize publickly a Violence in the midst of my Kingdom, chuse those of my Subjects whom you think most capable of serving you, and take away by force the Beauty that charms you; and if she do not yield to your Love, put that Power you are Master of in execution, to oblige her to marry you.

Don Alvaro, ravish'd with this Proposition, which at the same time flatter'd both his Love and his Anger, cast himself at the Feet of the King, and renewed his Acknowledgments by fresh Protestations, and thought of nothing but employing his unjust Authority against *Agnes*.

Don Pedro had been about three Months absent, when *Alvaro* undertook what the King counselled him to; tho' the Moderation was known to him, yet he feared his Presence, and would not attend the return of a Rival, with whom he would avoid all Disputes.

One Night, when the said *Agnes*, full of her ordinary Inquietudes, in vain expected the God of Sleep, she heard a Noise, and after saw some Men unknown enter her Chamber, whose Measures being well consulted, they carried her out of the Palace, and putting her in a close Coach, forced her out of *Coimbra*, without being hinder'd by any Obstacle. She knew not of whom to complain, nor whom to suspect: *Don Alvaro* seem'd too puissant to seek his Satisfaction this way; and she accus'd not the Prince of this attempt, of whom she had so favourable an Opinion: whatever she could think or say, she could not hinder her ill Fortune: They hurried her on with diligence, and before it was Day, were a considerable way off from the Town.

As soon as Day began to break, she surveyed those that encompassed her, without so much as knowing one of them; and seeing that her Cries and Prayers were all in vain with these deaf Ravishers, she satisfied her self with imploring the Protection of Heaven, and abandon'd herself to its Conduct.

While she sat thus overwhelmed with Grief, uncertain of her Destiny, she saw a Body of Horse advance towards the Troop which conducted her : the Ravishers did not shun them, thinking it to be *Don Alvaro :* but when he approached more near, they found it was the Prince of *Portugal* who was at the head of 'em, and who, without foreseeing the occasion that would offer it self of serving *Agnes*, was returning to *Coimbra* full of her Idea, after having performed what he ought in this Expedition.

Agnes, who did not expect him, changed now her Opinion, and thought that it was the Prince that had caused her to be stolen away. 'Oh, Sir ! (said she to him, having still the same Thought) is it you that have torn me from the Princess ? And could so cruel a Blow come from a Hand that is so dear to her ? What will you do with an unfortunate Creature, who desires nothing but Death ? And why will you obscure the Glory of your Life, by an Artifice unworthy of you ?' This Language astonish'd the Prince no less than the sight of *Agnes* had done; he found by what she had said, that she was taken away by force ; and immediately passing to the height of Rage, he made her understand by one only Look, that he was not the base Author of her trouble. 'I tear you from *Constantia*, whose only Pleasure you are ! replied he : What Opinion have you of *Don Pedro ?* No, Madam, tho' you see me here, I am altogether innocent of the Violence that has been done you ; and there is nothing I will refuse to hinder it.' He then turned himself to behold the Ravishers, but his Presence had already scatter'd 'em, he order'd some of his Men to pursue 'em, and to seize some of 'em, that he might know what Authority it was that set 'em at work.

During this, *Agnes* was no less confus'd than before ; she admir'd the Conduct of her Destiny, that brought the

Prince at a time when he was so necessary to her. Her
Inclinations to do him justice, soon repair'd the Offence
her Suspicions had caus'd ; she was glad to have escap'd
a Misfortune, which appear'd certain to her : but this was
not a sincere Joy, when she consider'd that her Lover was
her Deliverer, and a Lover worthy of all her Acknowledgments, but who owed his Heart to the most amiable
Princess in the World.

While the Prince's Men were pursuing the Ravishers
of *Agnes*, he was left almost alone with her ; and tho' he
had always resolv'd to shun being so, yet his Constancy was
not proof against so fair an Occasion : 'Madam, said he
to her, is it possible that Men born amongst those that
obey us, should be capable of offending you ? I never
thought my self destin'd to revenge such an Offence ; but
since Heaven has permitted you to receive it, I will either
perish or make them repent it.' 'Sir, replied *Agnes*, more
concern'd at this Discourse than at the Enterprize of
Don Alvaro, those who are wanting in their respect to the
Princess and you, are not obliged to have any for me. I
do not in the least doubt that *Don Alvaro* was the under-
taker of this Enterprize ; and I judged what I ought to
fear from him, by what his Importunities have already
made me suffer. He is sure of the King's Protection, and
he will make him an Accomplice in his Crime : but, Sir,
Heaven conducted you hither happily for me, and I am
indebted to you for the liberty I have of serving the
Princess yet longer.' You will do for *Constantia*, replied
the Prince, what 'tis impossible not to do for you ; your
Goodness attaches you to her, and my Destiny engages me
to you for ever.'

The modest *Agnes*, who fear'd this Discourse as much as
the Misfortune she had newly shunned, answer'd nothing
but by down-cast Eyes ; and the Prince, who knew the
trouble she was in, left her to go to speak to his Men, who
brought back one of those that belong'd to *Don Alvaro*,

by whose Confession he found the truth : He pardon'd him, thinking not fit to punish him, who obey'd a Man whom the Weakness of his Father had render'd powerful.

Afterwards they conducted *Agnes* back to *Coimbra*, where her Adventure began to make a great Noise : the Princess was ready to die with Despair, and at first thought it was only a continuation of the design this fair Maid had of retiring ; but some Women that served her having told the Princess, that she was carried away by Violence, *Constantia* made her Complaint to the King, who regarded her not at all.

'Madam, said he to her, let this fatal Plague remove it self, who takes from you the Heart of your Husband ; and without afflicting your self for her absence, bless Heaven and me for it.'

The generous Princess took *Agnes's* part with a great deal of Courage, and was then disputing her defence with the King, when *Don Pedro* arrived at *Coimbra*.

The first Object that met the Prince's Eyes was *Don Alvaro*, who was passing thro' one of the Courts of the Palace, amidst a Croud of Courtiers, whom his Favour with the King drew after him. This sight made *Don Pedro* rage ; but that of the Princess and *Agnes* caus'd in *Alvaro* another sort of Emotion : He easily divin'd, that it was *Don Pedro*, who had taken her from his Men, and, if his Fury had acted what it would, it might have produc'd very sad effects.

'*Don Alvaro*, said the Prince to him, is it thus you make use of the Authority which the King my Father hath given you? Have you receiv'd Employments and Power from him, for no other end but to do these base Actions, and to commit Rapes on Ladies? Are you ignorant how the Princess interests her self in all that concerns this Maid? And do you not know the tender and affectionate Esteem she has for her.' No, replied *Don Alvaro*, (with an Insolence that had like to have put the Prince past all patience)

'I am not ignorant of it, nor of the Interest your Heart takes in her.' 'Base and treacherous as thou art, replied the Prince, neither the Favour which thou hast so much abused, nor the Insolence which makes thee speak this, should hinder me from punishing thee, wert thou worthy of my Sword; but there are other ways to humble thy Pride, and 'tis not fit for such an Arm as mine to seek so base an Employment to punish such a Slave as thou art.'

Don Pedro went away at these Words, and left *Alvaro* in a Rage, which is not to be express'd; despairing to see himself defeated in an Enterprize he thought so sure; and at the Contempt the Prince shewed him, he promis'd himself to sacrifice all to his Revenge.

Tho' the King lov'd his Son, he was so prepossessed against his Passion, that he could not pardon him what he had done, and condemn'd him as much for this last act of Justice, in delivering *Agnes*, as if it had been the greatest of Crimes.

Elvira, whom the sweetness of Hope flatter'd some moments, saw the return of *Agnes* with a sensible Displeasure, which suffer'd her to think of nothing but irritating her Brother.

In fine, the Prince saw the King, but instead of being receiv'd by him with a Joy due to the success of his Journey, he appear'd all sullen and out of humour. After having paid him his first Respects, and given him an exact account of what he had done, he spoke to him about the Violence committed against the Person of *Agnes de Castro*, and complain'd to him of it in the Name of the Princess, and of his own: 'You ought to be silent in this Affair, replied the King; and the Motive which makes you speak is so shameful for you, that I sigh and blush at it. What is it to you, if this Maid, whose Presence is troublesome to me, be removed hence, since 'tis I that desire it?' 'But, Sir, interrupted the Prince, what necessity is there of employing Force, Artifice, and the Night, when the least of your Orders had been sufficient? *Agnes* would willingly have obey'd you; and if she continue at *Coimbra*, it is perhaps against her Will: but be it as it will, Sir, *Constantia* is offended, and if were not for fear of displeasing you, (the only thing that retains me) the Ravisher should not have gone unpunished.' 'How happy are you, replied the King, smiling with disdain, in making use of the Name of *Constantia* to uphold the Interest of your Heart! You think I am ignorant of it, and that this unhappy Princess looks on the Injury you do her with Indifference. Never speak to me more of *Agnes*, (with a Tone very severe.) Content your self, that I pardon what's past, and think maturely of the Considerations I have for *Don Alvaro*, when you would design any thing against him.' 'Yes, Sir, replied the Prince with fierceness, I will speak to you no more of *Agnes*; but *Constantia* and I will never suffer, that she should be any more expos'd to the Insolence of your Favourite.' The King had like to have broke out into a Rage at this Discourse: but he had yet a rest of Prudence left that hinder'd him. 'Retire (said he to *Don Pedro*) and go make Reflections on what my Power can do, and what you owe me.'

During this Conversation, *Agnes* was receiving from the Princess, and from all the Ladies of the Court, great Expressions of Joy and Friendship: *Constantia* saw again her Husband, with a great deal of satisfaction: and far from being sorry at what he had lately done for *Agnes*, she privately return'd him thanks for it, and still was the same towards him, notwithstanding all the Jealousy which was endeavour'd to be inspir'd in her.

Don Alvaro, who found in his Sister a Maliciousness worthy of his trust, did not conceal his Fury from her. After she had made vain attempts to moderate it, in blotting *Agnes* out of his Heart, seeing that his Disease was incurable, she made him understand, that so long as *Constantia* should not be jealous, there were no hopes:

That if *Agnes* should once be suspected by her, she would not fail of abandoning her, and that then it would be easy to get Satisfaction, the Prince being now so proud of *Constantia's* Indulgency. In giving this Advice to her Brother, she promis'd to serve him effectually; and having no need of any body but her self to perform ill things, she recommended *Don Alvaro* to manage well the King.

Four Years were pass'd in that melancholy Station, and the Princess, besides her first dead Child, and *Ferdinando*, who was still living, had brought two Daughters into the World.

Some days after *Don Pedro's* return, *Elvira*, who was most dextrous in the Art of well-governing any wicked Design, did gain one of the Servants who belong'd to *Constantia's* Chamber. She first spoke her fair, then overwhelm'd her with Presents and Gifts; and finding in her as ill a Disposition as in her self, she readily resolv'd to employ her.

After she was sure of her, she compos'd a Letter, which was after writ over again in an unknown Hand, which she deposited in that Maid's Hands, that she might deliver to *Constantia* with the first Opportunity, telling her, that *Agnes* had drop'd it. This was the Substance of it:

I Employ not my own Hand to write to you, for Reasons that I shall acquaint you with. How happy am I to have overcome all your Scruples! And what Happiness shall I find in the Progress of our Intrigue! The whole Course of my Life shall continually represent to you the Sincerity of my Affections; pray think on the secret Conversation that I require of you: I dare not speak to you in publick, therefore let me conjure you here, by all that I have suffer'd, to come to-night to the Place appointed, and speak to me no more of Constantia; *for she must be content with my Esteem, since my Heart can be only yours.*

The unfaithful *Portuguese* serv'd *Elvira* exactly to her Desires; and the very next day seeing *Agnes* go out from the

Princess, she carry'd *Constantia* the Letter; which she
took, and found there what she was far from imagining:
Tenderness never produc'd an Effect more full of grief,
than what it made her suffer. 'Alas! they are both culpable, (said she, sighing) and in spite of the Defence my
Heart would make for 'em, my Reason condemns 'em.
Unhappy Princess, the sad subject of the Capriciousness
of Fortune! Why dost not thou die, since thou hast not
a Heart of Honour to revenge it self? O *Don Pedro!*
why did you give me your Hand, without your Heart?
And thou, fair, and ungrateful! wert thou born to be the
Misfortune of my Life, and perhaps the only cause of
my Death?' After having given some Moments to the
Violence of her Grief, she called the Maid, who brought
her the Letter, commanding her to speak of it to no body,
and to suffer no one to enter into her Chamber.

She consider'd then of that Prince with more liberty,
whose Soul she was not able to touch with the least
Tenderness; and of the cruel Fair One that had betray'd
her: Yet, even while her Soul was upon the Rack, she
was willing to excuse 'em, and ready to do all she could
for *Don Pedro;* at least, she made a firm Resolution, not
to complain of him.

Elvira was not long without being inform'd of what
had pass'd, nor of the Melancholy of the Princess, from
whom she hop'd all she desir'd.

Agnes, far from foreseeing this Tempest, return'd to
Constantia; and hearing of her Indisposition, pass'd the
rest of the Day at her Chamber-door, that she might
from time to time learn news of her Health: for she was
not suffer'd to come in, at which *Agnes* was both surpriz'd
and troubled. The Prince had the same Destiny, and was
astonish'd at an Order which ought to have excepted him.

The next day *Constantia* appear'd, but so alter'd, that
'twas not difficult to imagine what she had suffer'd. *Agnes*
was the most impatient to approach her, and the Princess

could not forbear weeping, They were both silent for some time, and *Constantia* attributed this silence of *Agnes* to some Remorse which she felt : and this unhappy Maid being able to hold no longer; 'Is it possible, Madam, (said she) that two Days should have taken from me all the Goodness you had for me? What have I done? And for what do you punish me?' The Princess regarded her with a languishing Look, and return'd her no Answer but Sighs. *Agnes*, offended with this reserve, went out with very great Dissatisfaction and Anger ; which contributed to her being thought criminal. The Prince came in immediately after, and found *Constantia* more disorder'd than usual, and conjur'd her in a most obliging manner to take care of her Health : *The greatest good for me* (said she) *is not the Continuation of my Life ; I should have more care of it if I loved you less : but*— She could not proceed; and the Prince, excessively afflicted at her trouble, sigh'd sadly, without making her any answer, which redoubled her Grief. Spite then began to mix it self; and all things persuading the Princess that they made a Sacrifice of her, she would enter into no Explanation with her Husband, but suffered him to go away without saying any thing to him.

Nothing is more capable of troubling our Reason, and consuming our Health, than secret Notions of Jealousy in Solitude.

Constantia, who us'd to open her Heart freely to *Agnes*, now believing she had deceiv'd her, abandon'd her self so absolutely to Grief, that she was ready to sink under it ; she immediately fell sick with the violence of it, and all the Court was concern'd at this Misfortune : *Don Pedro* was truly afflicted at it, but *Agnes* more than all the World beside. *Constantia's* Coldness towards her, made her continually sigh ; and her Distemper created merely by fancy, caus'd her to reflect on every thing that offer'd it self to her Memory : so that at last she began even to fear her self, and to reproach her self for what the Princess suffer'd.

But the Distemper began to be such, that they fear'd *Constantia's* Death, and she her self began to feel the Approaches of it. This Thought did not at all disquiet her : she look'd on Death as the only relief from all her Torments ; and regarded the Despair of all that approach'd her without the least concern.

The King, who lov'd her tenderly, and who knew her Virtue, was infinitely mov'd at the Extremity she was in. And *Don Alvaro*, who lost not the least Occasion of making him understand that it was Jealousy which was the cause of *Constantia's* Distemper, did but too much incense him against Criminals, worthy of Compassion. The King was not of a Temper to conceal his Anger long : 'You give fine Examples, (said he to the Prince) and such as will render yonr Memory illustrious ! The Death of *Constantia* (of which you are only to be accus'd) is the unhappy Fruit of your guilty Passion. Fear Heaven after this : and behold your self as a Monster that does not deserve to see the Light. If the Interest you have in my Blood did not plead for you, what ought you not to fear from my just Resentment ? But what must not imprudent *Agnes*, to whom nothing ties me, expect from my hands ? If *Constantia* dies, she, who has the Boldness, in my Court, to cherish a foolish Flame by vain Hopes, and make us lose the most amiable Princess, whom thou art not worthy to possess, shall feel the Effects of her Indiscretion.'

Don Pedro knew very well, that *Constantia* was not ignorant of his Sentiments for *Agnes ;* but he knew also with what Moderation she receiv'd it : He was very sensible of the King's Reproaches ; but as his Fault was not voluntary, and that a commanding Power, a fatal Star, had forc'd him to love in spite of himself, he appear'd afflicted and confus'd : 'You condemn me, Sir, (answer'd he) without having well examin'd me ; and if my Intentions were known to you ; perhaps you would not find me so criminal : I would take the Princess for my Judge, whom you say I sacrifice, if she were in a condition to be consulted. If I am guilty of any Weakness, her Justice never reproach'd me for it; and my Tongue never inform'd *Agnes* of it. But suppose I have committed any Fault, why would you punish an innocent Lady, who perhaps condemns me for it as much as you? Ah, Villain! (interrupted the King) she has but too much favour'd you: You would not have lov'd thus long, had she not made you some Returns. Sir, (reply'd the Prince, pierced with Grief for the Outrage that was committed against *Agnes*) you offend a Virtue, than which nothing can be purer; and those Expressions which break from your Choler, are not worthy of you. *Agnes* never granted me any Favours; I never asked any of her; and I protest to Heaven, I never thought of any thing contrary to the Duty I owe *Constantia*.'

As they thus argued, one of the Princess's Women came all in Tears to acquaint *Don Pedro*, that the Princess was in the last Extremities of Life: 'Go see thy fatal Work, (said the King) and expect from a too-long patient Father the Usage thou deservest.'

The Prince ran to *Constantia*, whom he found dying, and *Agnes* in a swoon, in the Arms of some of the Ladies. What caus'd this double Calamity, was, that *Agnes*, who could suffer no longer the Indifferency of the Princess, had conjur'd her to tell her what was her Crime, and either to take her Life from her, or restore her to her Friendship.

Constantia, who found she must die, could no longer keep her secret Affliction from *Agnes*; and after some Words, which were a Preparation to the sad Explanation, she shewed her that fatal Billet, which *Elvira* had caus'd to be written: 'Ah, Madam! (cry'd out the fair *Agnes*, after having read it) Ah, Madam! how many cruel Inquietudes had you spared me had you open'd your Heart to me with your wonted Bounty! 'Tis easy to see that this Letter is counterfeit, and that I have Enemies without

Compassion. Could you believe the Prince so imprudent, to make use of any other Hand but his own, on an occasion like this? And do you believe me so simple to keep about me this Testimony of my Shame, with so little Precaution? You are neither betray'd by your Husband nor me; I attest Heaven, and those Efforts I have made to leave *Coimbra*. Alas, my dear Princess, how little have you known her, whom you have so much honoured? Do not believe that when I have justify'd my self, I will have any more Communication with the World: No, no; there will be no Retreat far enough from hence for me. I will take care to hide this unlucky Face, where it shall be sure to do no more harm.'

The Princess touched at this Discourse, and the Tears of *Agnes*, press'd her hand, which she held in hers; and fixing Looks upon her capable of moving Pity in the most insensible Souls, 'If I have committed any Offence, my dear *Agnes*, (answer'd she) Death, which I expect in a moment, shall revenge it. I ought also to protest to you, That I have not ceas'd loving you, and that I believe every thing you have said, giving you back my most tender Affections.'

'Twas at this time that the Grief, which equally oppress'd 'em, put the Princess into such an Extremity, that they sent for the Prince. He came, and found himself almost without Life or Motion at this sight. And what secret Motive soever might call him to the aid of *Agnes*, 'twas to *Constantia* he ran. The Princess, who finding her last Moments drawing on, by a cold Sweat that cover'd her all over; and finding she had no more business with Life, and causing those Persons she most suspected to retire, 'Sir, (said she to *Don Pedro*) if I abandon Life without regret, it is not without Trouble that I part with you. But, Prince, we must vanquish when we come to die; and I will forget my self wholly, to think of nothing but of you. I have no Reproaches to make against you, knowing that 'tis Inclination that disposes Hearts, and not Reason. *Agnes* is beautiful enough to inspire the most ardent Passion, and virtuous enough to deserve the first Fortunes in the World. I ask her, once more, pardon for the Injustice I have done her, and recommend her to you, as a Person most dear to me. Promise me, my dear Prince, before I expire, to give her my Place in your Throne: it cannot be better fill'd: you cannot chuse a Princess more perfect for your People, nor a better Mother for our little Children. And you my dear and faithful *Agnes* (pursu'd she) listen not to a Virtue too scrupulous, that may make any opposition to the Prince of *Portugal:* Refuse him not a Heart of which he is worthy; and give him that Friendship which you had for me, with that which is due to his Merit. Take care of my little *Fernando,* and the two young Princesses: let them find me in you, and speak to them sometimes of me. Adieu, live both of you happy, and receive my last Embraces.'

The afflicted *Agnes,* who had recover'd a little her Forces, lost them again a second time; Her Weakness was follow'd with Convulsions so vehement, that they were afraid of her Life; but *Don Pedro* never removed from *Constantia:* 'What, Madam (said he) you will leave me then; and you think 'tis for my Good. Alas, *Constantia!* if my Heart has committed an Outrage against you, your Virtue has sufficiently revenged you on me in spite of you. Can you think me so barbarous?'—As he was going on, he saw Death shut the Eyes of the most generous Princess for ever; and he was within a very little of following her.

But what Loads of Grief did this bring upon *Agnes,* when she found in that Interval, wherein Life and Death were struggling in her Soul, that *Constantia* was newly expir'd! She would then have taken away her own Life, and have let her Despair fully appear.

At the noise of the Death of the Princess, the Town and the Palace were all in Tears. *Elvira,* who saw then

Don Pedro free to engage himself, repented of having contributed to the Death of *Constantia*; and thinking her self the Cause of it, promis'd in her Griefs never to pardon herself.

She had need of being guarded several days together; during which time she fail'd not incessantly to weep. And the Prince gave all those days to deepest Mourning. But when the first Emotions were past, those of his Love made him feel that he was still the same.

He was a long time without seeing *Agnes*; but this Absence of his served only to make her appear the more charming when he did see her.

Don Alvaro, who was afraid of the Liberty of the Prince, made new Efforts to move *Agnes de Castro*, who was now become insensible to every thing but Grief. *Elvira*, who was willing to make the best of the Design she had begun, consulted all her Womens Arts, and the Delicacy of her Wit, to revive the Flames with which the Prince once burnt for her: But his Constancy was bounded, and it was *Agnes* alone that was to reign over his Heart. She had taken a firm Resolution, since the Death of *Constantia*, to pass the rest of her Days in a solitary Retreat. In spite of the precaution she took to hide this Design, the Prince was informed of it, and did all he was able to dispose his Constancy and Fortitude to it. He thought himself stronger than he really was; but after he had well consulted his Heart, he found but too well how necessary the Presence of *Agnes* was to him. 'Madam (said he to her one day, with a Heart big, and his Eyes in Tears) which Action of my Life has made you determine my Death? Tho' I never told you how much I loved you, yet I am persuaded you are not ignorant of it. I was constrained to be silent during some Years for your sake, for *Constantia's*, and my own; but 'tis not possible for me to put this force upon my Heart for ever: I must once at least tell you how it languishes. Receive then the Assurances of a Passion, full of Respect

and Ardour, with an offer of my Fortune, which I wish
not better, but for your advantage.'

Agnes answer'd not immediately to these words, but with
abundance of Tears; which having wiped away, and
beholding *Don Pedro* with an air which made him easily
comprehend she did not agree with his Desires; 'If I were
capable of the Weakness with which you'd inspire me,
you'd be obliged to punish me for it: What! (said she)
Constantia is scarce bury'd, and you would have me offend
her! No, my Prince (added she with more Softness) no,
no, she whom you have heap'd so many Favours on, will
not call down the Anger of Heaven, and the Contempt of
Men upon her, by an Action so perfidious. Be not obstinate then in a Design in which I will never shew you
Favour. You owe to *Constantia*, after her Death, a
Fidelity that may justify you: and I, to repair the Ills I
have made her suffer ought to shun all converse with you.'
Go, Madam (reply'd the Prince, growing pale) go, and
expect the News of my Death; in that part of the World,
whither your Cruelty shall lead you, the News shall follow
close after; you shall quickly hear of it: and I will go
seek it in those Wars which reign among my Neighbours.'

These Words made the fair *Agnes de Castro* perceive that
her Innocency was not so great as she imagined, and that
her Heart interested it self in the Preservation of *Don Pedro:*
You ought, Sir, to preserve your Life (reply'd *Agnes*) for
the sake of the little Prince and Princesses, which *Constantia* has left you. Would you abandon their Youth
continued she, with a tender Tone) to the Cruelty of
Don Alvaro? Live! Sir, live! and let the unhappy *Agnes*
be the only Sacrifice.' 'Alas, cruel Maid! (interrupted
Don Pedro) Why do you command me to live, if I cannot
live with you? Is it an effect of your Hatred?' 'No, Sir,
reply'd *Agnes*) I do not hate you; and I wish to God that
I could be able to defend my self against the Weakness
with which I find my self possess'd. Oblige me to say no

more, Sir : you see my Blushes, interpret them as you
please : but consider yet, that the less Aversion I find I
have to you, the more culpable I am; and that I ought
no more to see, or speak to you. In fine, Sir, if you oppose
my Retreat, I declare to you, that *Don Alvaro*, as odious
as he is to me, shall serve for a Defence against you ; and
that I will sooner consent to marry a Man I abhor, than
to favour a Passion that cost *Constantia* her Life.' 'Well
then, *Agnes* (reply'd the Prince, with Looks all languishing and dying) follow the Motions which barbarous Virtue
inspires you with ; take these Measures you judge necessary
against an unfortunate Lover, and enjoy the Glory of
having cruelly refused me.'

At these Words he went away; and troubled as *Agnes* was,
she would not stay him : Her Courage combated with her
Grief, and she thought now, more than ever, of departing.

'Twas difficult for her to go out of *Coimbra ;* and not
to defer what appear'd to her so necessary, she went immediately to the Apartment of the King, notwithstanding the
Interest of *Don Alvaro.* The King received her with a
Countenance severe, not being able to consent to what she
demanded : *You shall not go hence,* (said he) *and if you are
wise, you shall enjoy here with* Don Alvaro *both my Friendship and my Favour. I have taken another Resolution*
(answer'd *Agnes*) *and the World has no part in it. You will
accept* Don Pedro (reply'd the King) *his Fortune is sufficient
to satisfy an ambitious Maid : but you will not succeed*
Constantia, *who lov'd you so tenderly ; and* Spain *has
Princesses enough to fill up part of the Throne which I shall
leave him. Sir,* (reply'd *Agnes,* piqu'd at this Discourse) *if
I had a Disposition to love, and a Design to marry, perhaps
the Prince might be the only Person on whom I would fix it :
And you know, if my Ancestors did not possess Crowns, yet
they were worthy to wear 'em. But let it be how it will, I
am resolved to depart, and to remain no longer a Slave in a
Place to which I came free.*

This bold Answer, which shew'd the Character of *Agnes*, anger'd and astonished the King. *You shall go when we think fit* (reply'd he) *and without being a Slave at* Coimbra, *you shall attend our order.*

Agnes saw she must stay, and was so griev'd at it, that she kept her Chamber several days, without daring to inform herself of the Prince; and this Retirement spared her the Affliction of being visited by *Don Alvaro.*

During this, *Don Pedro* fell sick, and was in so great danger, that there was a general apprehension of his Death. *Agnes* did not in the least doubt, but it was an effect of his Discontent: she thought at first she had Strength and Resolution enough to see him die, rather than to favour him; but had she reflected a little, she had soon been convinc'd to the contrary. She found not in her Heart that cruel Constancy she thought there so well established: She felt Pains and Inquietude, shed Tears, made Wishes; and, in fine, discover'd that she lov'd.

'Twas impossible to see the Heir of the Crown, a Prince that deserved so well, even at the point of Death, without a general Affliction. The People who loved him, pass'd whole days at the Palace-gate to hear News of him: The Court was all over-whelm'd with Grief.

Don Alvaro knew very well how to conceal a malicious Joy, under an Appearance of Sadness. *Elvira*, full of Tenderness, and perhaps of Remorse, suffer'd also on her side. The King, altho' he condemned the Love of his Son, yet still had a Tenderness for him, and could not resolve to lose him. *Agnes de Castro*, who knew the Cause of his Distemper, expected the End of it with strange Anxieties: In fine, after a Month had pass'd away in Fears, they began to have a little hopes of his Recovery. The Prince and *Don Alvaro* were the only Persons that were not glad of it: But *Agnes* rejoic'd enough for all the rest.

Don Pedro, seeing that he must live whether he wou'd or no, thought of nothing but passing his days in melancholy and discontent : As soon as he was in a condition to walk, he sought out the most solitary Places, and gain'd so much upon his own Weakness, to go every where, where *Agnes* was not; but her Idea followed him always, and his Memory, faithful to represent her to him with all her Charms, render'd her always dangerous.

One day, when they had carry'd him into the Garden, he sought out a Labyrinth which was at the farthest part of it, to hide his Melancholy, during some hours ; there he found the sad *Agnes*, whom Grief, little different from his, had brought thither ; the sight of her whom he expected not, made him tremble : She saw by his pale and meagre Face the remains of his Distemper ; his Eyes full of Languishment troubled her, and tho' her Desire was so great to have fled from him, an unknown Power stopt her, and 'twas impossible for her to go.

After some Moments of Silence, which many Sighs interrupted, *Don Pedro* rais'd himself from the Place where his Weakness had forced him to sit; he made *Agnes* see, as he approach'd her, the sad Marks of his Sufferings : and not content with the Pity he saw in her Eyes, *You have resolved my Death then, cruel* Agnes, (said he) *my desire was the same with yours; but Heaven has thought fit to reserve me for other Misfortunes, and I see you again, as unhappy, but more in love than ever.*

There was no need of these Words to move *Agnes* to compassion, the Languishment of the Prince spoke enough; and the Heart of this fair Maid was but too much disposed to yield it self : She thought then that *Constantia* ought to be satisfy'd; Love, which combated for *Don Pedro*, triumphed over Friendship, and found that happy Moment, for which the Prince of *Portugal*, had so long sighed.

Do not reproach me, for that which has cost me more than you, Sir, (replied she) *and do not accuse a Heart, which is neither ingrateful nor barbarous : and I must tell you, that I love you. But now I have made you that Confession, what*

is it farther that you require of me? Don *Pedro*, who
expected not a Change so favourable, felt a double Satisfaction; and falling at the Feet of *Agnes*, he express'd
more by the Silence his Passion created, than he could
have done by the most eloquent Words.

After having known all his good Fortune, he then
consulted with the amiable *Agnes*, what was to be feared
from the King; they concluded that the cruel Billet,
which so troubled the last days of *Constantia*, could come
from none but *Elvira* and Don *Alvaro*. The Prince, who
knew that his Father had searched already an Alliance for
him, and was resolv'd on his Favourite's marrying *Agnes*,
conjur'd her so tenderly to prevent these Persecutions, by
consenting to a secret Marriage, that, after having a long
time consider'd, she at last consented. *I will do what you
will have me* (said she) *tho' I presage nothing but fatal
Events from it; all my Blood turns to Ice, when I think of
this Marriage, and the Image of* Constantia *seems to hinder
me from doing it.*

The amorous Prince surmounted all her Scruples, and
separated himself from *Agnes*, with a Satisfaction which
soon redoubled his Forces; he saw her afterward with the
Pleasure of a Mystery: And the Day of their Union being
arrived, Don *Gill*, Bishop of *Guarda*, performed the Ceremony of the Marriage, in the Presence of several Witnesses,
faithful to Don *Pedro*, who saw him Possessor of all the
Charms of the fair *Agnes*.

She lived not the more peaceable for belonging to the
Prince of *Portugal;* her Enemies, who continually persecuted her, left her not without Troubles: and the King,
whom her Refusal inrag'd, laid his absolute Commands on
her to marry Don *Alvaro*, with Threats to force her to it,
if she continu'd rebellious.

The Prince took loudly her part; and this, join'd to the
Refusal he made of marrying the Princess of *Arragon*,
caus'd Suspicions of the Truth in the King his Father.

He was seconded by those that were too much interested, not to unriddle this Secret. *Don Alvaro* and his Sister acted with so much care, gave so many Gifts, and made so many Promises, that they discover'd the secret Engagements of *Don Pedro* and *Agnes*.

The King wanted but little of breaking out into all the Rage and Fury so great a Disappointment could inspire him with, against the Princess. *Don Alvaro*, whose Love was changed into the most violent Hatred, appeased the first Transports of the King, by making him comprehend, that if they could break the Marriage of 'em, that would not be a sufficient Revenge; and so poison'd the Soul of the King, to consent to the Death of *Agnes*.

The barbarous *Don Alvaro* offered his Arm for this terrible Execution, and his Rage was Security for the Sacrifice.

The King, who thought the Glory of his Family disgraced by this Alliance, and his own in particular in the Procedure of his Son, gave full Power to this Murderer, to make the innocent *Agnes* a Victim to his Rage.

It was not easy to execute this horrid Design: Tho' the Prince saw *Agnes* but in secret, yet all his Cares were still awake for her, and he was marry'd to her above a Year, before *Don Alvaro* could find out an opportunity so long sought for.

The Prince diverted himself but little, and very rarely went far from *Coimbra*; but on a Day, an unfortunate Day, and marked out by Heaven for an unheard-of and horrid Assassination, he made a Party to hunt at a fine House, which the King of *Portugal* had near the City.

Agnes lov'd every thing that gave the Prince satisfaction; but a secret Trouble made her apprehend some Misfortune in this unhappy Journey. *Sir*, (said she to him, alarm'd, without knowing the Reason why) *I tremble, seeing you to-day as it were designed the last of my Life: Preserve your self, my dear Prince; and tho' the Exercise you take be not*

*very dangerous, beware of the least Hazards, and bring me
back all that I trust with you.* Don Pedro, who had never
found her so handsome and so charming before, embraced
her several times, and went out of the Palace with his
Followers, with a Design not to return till the next Day.

He was no sooner gone, but the cruel *Don Alvaro* prepared himself for the Execution he had resolv'd on ; he
thought it of that importance, that it required more Hands
than his own, and so chose for his Companions *Don Lopez
Pacheo*, and *Pedro Cuello*, two Monsters like himself, whose
Cruelty he was assur'd of by the Presents he had made 'em.

They waited the coming of the Night, and the lovely
Agnes was in her first Sleep, which was the last of her Life,
when these Assassins approach'd her Bed. Nothing made
resistance to *Don Alvaro*, who could do every thing, and
whom the blackest Furies introduced to *Agnes;* she
waken'd, and opening her Curtains, saw, by the Candle
burning in her Chamber, the Ponyard with which *Don
Alvaro* was armed ; he having his Face not cover'd, she
easily knew him, and forgetting her self, to think of nothing
but the Prince : *Just Heaven* (said she, lifting up her fine
Eyes) *if you will revenge* Constantia, *satisfy your self with
my Blood only, and spare that of* Don Pedro. The barbarous
Man that heard her, gave her not time to say more ; and
finding he could never (by all he could do by Love) touch
the Heart of the fair *Agnes*, he pierc'd it with his Ponyard :
his Accomplices gave her several Wounds, tho' there was
no necessity of so many to put an end to an innocent Life.

What a sad Spectacle was this for those who approach'd
her Bed the next day ! And what dismal News was this
to the unfortunate Prince of *Portugal!* He returned to
Coimbra at the first report of this Adventure, and saw what
had certainly cost him his Life, if Men could die of Grief.
After having a thousand times embraced the bloody Body
of *Agnes*, and said all that a just Despair could inspire him
with, he ran like a Mad-man into the Palace, demanding

the Murderers of his Wife, of things that could not hear
him. In fine, he saw the King, and without observing any
respect, he gave a loose to his Resentment : after having
rail'd a long time, overwhelm'd with Grief, he fell into a
Swoon, which continu'd all that day. They carry'd him
into his Apartment : and the King, believing that his
Misfortune would prove his Cure, repented not of what
he had permitted.

Don Alvaro, and the two other Assassins, quitted
Coimbra. This Absence of theirs made 'em appear guilty
of the Crime ; for which the afflicted Prince vow'd a speedy
Vengeance to the Ghost of his lovely *Agnes*, resolving to
pursue them to the uttermost part of the Universe ; He
got a considerable number of Men together, sufficient to
have made resistance, even to the King of *Portugal* himself, if he should yet take the part of the Murderers : with
these he ravaged the whole Country, as far as the *Duero*
Waters, and carry'd on a War, even till the Death of the
King, continually mixing Tears with Blood, which he
gave to the revenge of his dearest *Agnes*.

Such was the deplorable End of the unfortunate Love
of *Don Pedro* of *Portugal*, and of the fair *Agnes de Castro*,
whose Remembrance he faithfully preserv'd in his Heart,
even upon the Throne, to which he mounted by the Right
of his Birth, after the Death of the King.

THE HISTORY OF THE NUN;
OR, THE FAIR VOW-BREAKER.

（ 259 ）

INTRODUCTION.

In the Epistle Dedicatory to Antony Hammond, Esq., of Somersham-Place, prefacing that pathetic tragedy, *The Fatal Marriage; or, The Innocent Adultery*[1] (4to, 1694), Southerne writes : 'I took the Hint of the Tragical part of this Play from a Novel of Mrs. *Behn's*, call'd *The Fair Vow-Breaker;* you will forgive me for calling it a Hint, when you find I have little more than borrow'd the Question, how far such a Distress was to be carry'd, upon the Misfortune of a Woman's having innocently two Husbands, at the same time'.

In the many collected editions of Mrs. Behn's popular novels and histories, from the first, published under the auspices of Gildon in 1696, to the ninth (2 vols, 12mo, London, 1751), there appears, however, no such novel as *The Fair Vow-Breaker*, but on the other hand all contain *The Nun ; or, the Perjur'd Beauty.* For over two hundred years then, critics, theatrical historians, bibliographers alike have laid down that *The Fair Vow-Breaker* is merely another title for *The Nun ; or, The Perjur'd Beauty*, and that it is to this romance we must look for the source of Southerne's tragedy. The slight dissimilarity of name was truly of no great account. On the title-page of another novel we have *The Fair Jilt; or, The History of Prince Tarquin and Miranda ;* on the half-title of the same *The Fair Hypocrite; or, The Amours of Prince Tarquin and Miranda* (12mo, 1688). And so Thomas Evans in the preface to his edition of Southerne (3 vols, 1774), writing the dramatist's life, says : 'the plot by the author's confession is taken from a novel of Mrs. Behn's called *The Nun ; or, The Fair Vow-Breaker'.* All the modern writers have duly, but wrongly, accepted this; and Miss Charlotte E. Morgan in her monograph, *The English Novel till 1749*, informs us in more than one place that *The Fair Vow-Breaker* (12mo, 1689) was the name of the editio princeps of *The Nun ; or, The Perjur'd Beauty.*

A crux, however, was soon apparent. Upon investigation it is obvious that the plot of *The Fatal Marriage; or, The Innocent Adultery* has simply nothing in common with *The Nun ; or, The Perjur'd Beauty.* Mrs. Behn's Ardelia is a mere coquette who through her trifling with three different men is responsible for five deaths : her lovers', Elvira's, and her own. Isabella, Southerne's heroine, on the other hand, falls a sad victim to the machinations of Carlos, her wicked brother-in-law. She is virtuous and constant; Ardelia is a jade capable of heartless treachery. Both novel and play end tragically it is true, but from entirely different motives and in a dissimilar manner. There is no likeness between them.

---

[1] This has nothing to do with Scarron's novel, *L' Innocent Adultère* which translated was so popular in the 17th and 18th centuries. Bellmour carried it in his pocket when he went a-courting Laetitia, to the horror of old Fondlewife who discovered the tome, (*The Old Batchelor*, 1693), and Lydia Languish was partial to its perusal in 1775.

Whence then did Southerne derive his plot, and what exactly did he mean by the statement that he owed 'the Hint of the Tragical part' of his drama to a novel of Mrs. Behn's?

Professor Paul Hamelius of Liège set out to solve the difficulty, and in a scholarly article (*Modern Language Review*, July, 1909), he marshals the facts and seeks a solution. 'Among her [Mrs. Behn's] collected novels'[1] he writes 'there is one entitled *The Nun; or, The Perjur'd Beauty* and Mr. Gosse has kindly informed me that the story is identical with *The Nun; or, The Fair Vow-Breaker* which appears in the editio princeps of 1689 (inaccessible to me).' Unfortunately he can find no analogy and is obliged to draw attention to other sources. He points to *The Virgin Captive*, the fifth story in Roger L'Estrange's *The Spanish Decameron* (1687). Again: there is the famous legend of the lovers of Teruel as dramatized in 1638 by Juan Perez de Montalvan, *Los Amantes de Teruel*. An earlier comedia exists on the same subject written by A. Rey de Artieda, 1581, and yet another play by Tirso de Molina, 1635, based on Artieda. Hamelius was obviously not satisfied with his researches, and with a half-suggestion that Southerne may have merely intended to pay a compliment to his 'literary friend Mrs. Behn,' his conclusion is that 'the question is naturally still open whether Southerne was not drawing from some more immediate source—possibly even from some lost version of the story by Mrs. Behn herself.'

In the course of my preparing the present edition of Mrs. Behn's complete works, Mr. Gosse, adding yet another to innumerable kindnesses and encouragements, entrusted me with a little volume[2] from his private library: *The History of the Nun; or, The Fair Vow-Breaker* (12mo, 1689, Licensed 22 October, 1688), and I soon found this to be the immediate source of Southerne's tragedy, a totally different novel from *The Nun; or, The Perjur'd Beauty*, and one, moreover, which has never till now been included in any edition of Mrs. Behn's works or, indeed, reprinted in any form. It were superfluous to compare novel and tragedy detail by detail. Many striking, many minor points are the same in each. In several instances the nomenclature has been preserved. The chief divergence is, of course, the main catastrophe. Mrs. Behn's execution could ill have been represented on the boards, and Southerne's heroine, the victim of villainies and intrigue, is, it must be confessed, an infinitely more pathetic figure than guilty Isabella in the romance.

The story of a man returning after long absence and finding his spouse (or betrothed) wedded to another, familiarized to the generality of modern readers by Tennyson's *Enoch Arden*, occurs in every shape and tongue. No. 69 of *Les Cent Nouvelles Nouvelles* is *L'Honneste femme à Deux Maris*.[3] A more famous exemplar we have in the *Decameron*, Day IV, Novella 8, whose rubric runs: 'Girolamo ama la Salvestra: va, costretto da' prieghi

---

[1] Hamelius used the collected edition of 1705.

[2] It is interesting to note that the book originally belonged to Scott's friend and critic, Charles Kirkpatrick Sharpe.

[3] Reproduced by Celio Malespini *Ducento Novelle*, No. 9 (Venice, 4to, 1609, but probably written about thirty years before).

della madre, a Parigi : torna, e truovala maritata : entrale di nascoso in casa, e muorle allato ; e portato in una chiesa, muore la Salvestra allata a lui.'

Scenes of the amusing underplot of *The Fatal Marriage*, which contain some excellent comedy, Southerne took directly from *The Night Walker ; or, The Little Thief* (printed as Fletcher's in 1640 and 'corrected by Shirley' in 1633 according to Herbert's license). The purgatorial farce may be traced to the *Decameron*, Day III, 8. 'Ferondo, mangiata certa polvere, è sotterrato per morto : e dall' abate, chi la moglie di lui si gode, tratto dalla sepoltura, è messo in prigione e fattogli credere, che egli è in purgatoro ; e poi risuscitato . . .' It is the *Feronde ; ou, le Purgatoire* of La Fontaine.

The Fatal Marriage ; or, The Innocent Adultery long kept the stage.[1] On 2 December, 1757, Garrick's version, which omitting the comic relief weakens and considerably shortens the play, was produced at Drury Lane with himself as Biron and Mrs. Cibber as Isabella. The actual name of the tragedy, however, was not changed to *Isabella* till some years after. Mrs. Barry, the original Isabella, was acknowledged supreme in this tragedy, and our greatest actresses, Mrs. Porter, Mrs. Crawford, Miss Young, Mrs. Siddons, Miss O' Neill, have all triumphed in the rôle.

---

[1] A French prose translation of Southerne is to be found in Vol. VIII of *Le Théâtre Anglois*, Londres, 1746. It is entitled *L'Adultère Innocent ;* but the comic underplot is very sketchily analyzed, scene by scene, and the whole is very mediocre withal.

To the Most Illustrious Princess,
The Dutchess of Mazarine.

Madam,

There are none of an Illustrious Quality, who have not been made, by some Poet or other, the Patronesses of his Distress'd Hero, or Unfortunate Damsel; and such Addresses are Tributes, due only to the most Elevated, where they have always been very well receiv'd, since they are the greatest Testimonies we can give, of our Esteem and Veneration.

Madam, when I survey'd the whole Toor of Ladies at Court, which was adorn'd by you, who appear'd there with a Grace and Majesty, peculiar to Your Great Self only, mix'd with an irresistible Air of Sweetness, Generosity, and Wit, I was impatient for an Opportunity, to tell Your Grace, how infinitely one of Your own Sex ador'd You, and that, among all the numerous Conquest, Your Grace has made over the Hearts of Men, Your Grace had not subdu'd a more entire Slave; I assure you, Madam, there is neither Compliment nor Poetry, in this humble Declaration, but a Truth, which has cost me a great deal of Inquietude, for that Fortune has not set me in such a Station, as might justifie my Pretence to the honour and satisfaction of being ever near Your Grace, to view eternally that lovely Person, and hear that surprizing Wit; what can be more grateful to a Heart, than so great, and so agreeable, an Entertainment? And how few Objects are there, that can render it so entire a Pleasure, as at once to hear you speak, and to look upon your Beauty? A Beauty that is heighten'd, if possible, with an air of Negligence, in Dress, wholly Charming, as if your Beauty disdain'd those little Arts of your Sex, whose Nicety alone is their greatest Charm, while yours, Madam, even without the Assistance of your exalted Birth, begets an Awe and Reverence in all that do approach you, and every one is proud, and pleas'd, in paying you Homage their several ways, according to their Capacities and Talents; mine, Madam, can only be exprest by my Pen, which would be infinitely honour'd, in being permitted to celebrate your great Name for ever, and perpetually to serve, where it has so great an inclination.

In the mean time, Madam, I presume to lay this little Trifle at your Feet; the Story is true, as it is on the Records of the Town, where it was transacted; and if my fair unfortunate VOW-BREAKER do not deserve the honour of your Graces Protection, at least, she will be found worthy of your Pity; which will be a sufficient Glory, both for her, and,

Madam,

Your Graces most humble,

and most obedient Servant,

A. BEHN.

THE HISTORY OF THE NUN;
or, The Fair Vow-Breaker.

OF all the sins, incident to Human Nature, there is none, of which Heaven has took so particular, visible, and frequent Notice, and Revenge, as on that of *Violated Vows*, which never go unpunished; and the *Cupids* may boast what they will, for the encouragement of their Trade of Love, that Heaven never takes cognisance of Lovers broken Vows and Oaths, and that 'tis the only Perjury that escapes the Anger of the *Gods;* But I verily believe, if it were search'd into, we should find these frequent Perjuries, that pass in the World for so many Gallantries only, to be the occasion of so many unhappy Marriages, and the cause of all those Misfortunes, which are so frequent to the Nuptiall'd Pair. For not one of a Thousand, but, either on his side, or on hers, has been perjur'd, and broke Vows made to some fond believing Wretch, whom they have abandon'd and undone. What Man that does not boast of the Numbers he has thus ruin'd, and, who does not glory in the shameful Triumph? Nay, what Woman, almost, has not a pleasure in Deceiving, taught, perhaps, at first, by some dear false one, who had fatally instructed her Youth in an Art she ever after practis'd, in Revenge on all those she could be too hard for, and conquer at their own Weapons? For, without all dispute, Women are by Nature more Constant and Just, than Men, and did not their first Lovers teach them the trick of Change, they would be *Doves*, that would never quit their Mate, and, like *Indian* Wives, would leap alive into the Graves of their deceased Lovers, and be buried quick with 'em. But Customs of Countries change even Nature her self, and long Habit takes her place: The Women are taught, by the Lives of the Men, to live up to all their Vices, and are become almost as inconstant; and 'tis but Modesty that makes the difference, and, hardly, inclination; so deprav'd the nicest Appetites grow in time, by bad Examples.

But, as there are degrees of Vows, so there are degrees of Punishments for Vows, there are solemn Matrimonial Vows, such as contract and are the most effectual Marriage, and have the most reason to be so; there are a thousand Vows and Friendships, that pass between Man and Man, on a thousand Occasions; but there is another Vow, call'd a *Sacred Vow*, made to God only; and, by which, we oblige our selves eternally to serve him with all Chastity and Devotion: This Vow is only taken, and made, by those that enter into Holy Orders, and, of all broken Vows, these are those, that receive the most severe and notorious Revenges of God; and I am almost certain, there is not one Example to be produc'd in the World, where Perjuries of this nature have past unpunish'd, nay, that have not been persu'd with the greatest and most rigorous of Punishments. I could my self, of my own knowledge, give an hundred Examples of the fatal Consequences of the Violation of Sacred Vows; and who ever make it their business, and are curious in the search of such Misfortunes, shall find, as I say, that they never go unregarded.

The young Beauty therefore, who dedicates her self to Heaven, and weds her self for ever to the service of God, ought, first, very well to consider the Self-denial she is going to put upon her youth, her fickle faithless deceiving Youth, of one Opinion to day, and of another to morrow; like Flowers, which never remain in one state or fashion, but bud to day, and blow by insensible degrees, and decay as imperceptibly. The Resolution, we promise, and believe we shall maintain, is not in our power, and nothing is so deceitful as human Hearts.

I once was design'd an humble Votary in the House of Devotion, but fancying my self not endu'd with an obstinacy of Mind, great enough to secure me from the Efforts and Vanities of the World, I rather chose to deny my self that Content I could not certainly promise my self, than to languish (as I have seen some do) in a certain Affliction ; tho' possibly, since, I have sufficiently bewailed that mistaken and inconsiderate Approbation and Preference of the false ungrateful World, (full of nothing but Nonsense, Noise, false Notions, and Contradiction) before the Innocence and Quiet of a Cloyster ; nevertheless, I could wish, for the prevention of abundance of Mischiefs and Miseries, that Nunneries and Marriages were not to be enter'd into, 'till the Maid, so destin'd, were of a mature Age to make her own Choice ; and that Parents would not make use of their justly assum'd Authority to compel their Children, neither to the one or the other ; but since I cannot alter Custom, nor shall ever be allow'd to make new Laws, or rectify the old ones, I must leave the Young Nuns inclos'd to their best Endeavours, of making a Virtue of Necessity ; and the young Wives, to make the best of a bad Market.

In *Iper*, a Town, not long since, in the Dominions of the King of *Spain*, and now in possession of the King of *France*, there liv'd a Man of Quality, of a considerable Fortune, call'd, Count *Henrick de Vallary*, who had a very beautiful Lady, by whom, he had one Daughter, call'd *Isabella*, whose Mother dying when she was about two years old to the unspeakable Grief of the Count, her Husband, he resolv'd never to partake of any Pleasure more, that this transitory World could court him with, but determin'd, with himself, to dedicate his Youth, and future Days, to Heaven, and to take upon him Holy Orders ; and, without considering, that, possibly, the young

Isabella, when she grew to Woman, might have Sentiments contrary to those that now possest him, he design'd she should also become a Nun; However, he was not so positive in that Resolution, as to put the matter wholly out of her Choice, but divided his Estate; one half he carried with him to the Monastery of *Jesuits*, of which number, he became one; and the other half, he gave with *Isabella*, to the Monastery, of which, his only Sister was Lady *Abbess*, of the Order of St. *Augustine;* but so he ordered the matter, that if, at the Age of Thirteen, *Isabella* had not a mind to take Orders, or that the Lady *Abbess* found her Inclination averse to a Monastick Life, she should have such a proportion of the Revenue, as should be fit to marry her to a Noble Man, and left it to the discretion of the Lady *Abbess*, who was a Lady of known Piety, and admirable strictness of Life, and so nearly related to *Isabella*, that there was no doubt made of her Integrity and Justice.

The little *Isabella* was carried immediately (in her Mourning for her dead Mother) into the Nunnery, and was receiv'd as a very diverting Companion by all the young Ladies, and, above all, by her Reverend Aunt, for she was come just to the Age of delighting her Parents; she was the prettiest forward Pratler in the World, and had a thousand little Charms to please, besides the young Beauties that were just budding in her little Angel Face: So that she soon became the dear lov'd Favourite of the whole House; and as she was an Entertainment to them all, so they made it their study to find all the Diversions they could for the pretty *Isabella;* and as she grew in Wit and Beauty every day, so they fail'd not to cultivate her Mind; and delicate Apprehension, in all that was advantageous to her Sex, and whatever Excellency any one abounded in, she was sure to communicate it to the young *Isabella*, if one could Dance, another Sing, another play on this Instrument, and another on that; if this spoke one

Language, and that another; if she had Wit, and she Discretion, and a third, the finest Fashion and Manners; all joyn'd to compleat the Mind and Body of this beautiful young Girl; Who, being undiverted with the less noble, and less solid, Vanities of the World, took to these Virtues, and excell'd in all; and her Youth and Wit being apt for all Impressions, she soon became a greater Mistress of their Arts, than those who taught her; so that at the Age of eight or nine Years, she was thought fit to receive and entertain all the great Men and Ladies, and the Strangers of any Nation, at the *Grate;* and that with so admirable a Grace, so quick and piercing a Wit, and so delightful and sweet a Conversation, that she became the whole Discourse of the Town, and Strangers spread her Fame, as prodigious, throughout the Christian World; for Strangers came daily to hear her talk, and sing, and play, and to admire her Beauty; and Ladies brought their Children, to shame 'em into good Fashion and Manners, with looking on the lovely young *Isabella.*

The Lady *Abbess,* her Aunt, you may believe, was not a little proud of the Excellencies and Virtues of her fair *Niece,* and omitted nothing that might adorn her Mind; because, not only of the vastness of her Parts and Fame, and the Credit she would do her House, by residing there for ever; but also, being very loth to part with her considerable Fortune, which she must resign, if she returned into the World, she us'd all her Arts and Stratagems to make her become a *Nun,* to which all the fair Sisterhood contributed their Cunning, but it was altogether needless; her Inclination, the strictness of her Devotion, her early Prayers, and those continual, and innate Stedfastness, and Calm, she was Mistress of; her Ignorance of the World's Vanities, and those that uninclos'd young Ladies count Pleasures and Diversions, being all unknown to her, she thought there was no Joy out of a *Nunnery,* and no Satisfactions on the other side of a *Grate.*

The Lady *Abbess*, seeing, that of her self she yielded faster than she could expect; to discharge her Conscience to her Brother, who came frequently to visit his Darling *Isabella*, would very often discourse to her of the Pleasures of the World, telling her, how much happier she would think her self, to be the Wife of some gallant young Cavalier, and to have Coaches and Equipages; to see the World, to behold a thousand Rarities she had never seen, to live in Splendor, to eat high, and wear magnificent Clothes, to be bow'd to as she pass'd, and have a thousand Adorers, to see in time a pretty Offspring, the products of Love, that should talk, and look, and delight, as she did, the Heart of their Parents; but to all, her Father and the Lady *Abbess* could say of the World, and its Pleasures, *Isabella* brought a thousand Reasons and Arguments, so Pious, so Devout, that the *Abbess* was very well pleased, to find her (purposely weak) Propositions so well overthrown; and gives an account of her daily Discourses to her Brother, which were no less pleasing to him; and tho' *Isabella* went already dress'd as richly as her Quality deserv'd, yet her Father, to try the utmost that the World's Vanity could do, upon her young Heart, orders the most Glorious Clothes should be bought her, and that the Lady *Abbess* should suffer her to go abroad with those Ladies of Quality, that were her Relations, and her Mother's Acquaintance; that she should visit and go on the Toore, (that is, the Hide Park there) that she should see all that was diverting, to try, whether it were not for want of Temptation to Vanity, that made her leave the World, and love an inclos'd Life.

As the Count had commanded, all things were performed; and *Isabella* arriving at her Thirteenth Year of Age, and being pretty tall of Stature, with the finest Shape that Fancy can create, with all the Adornment of a perfect brown-hair'd Beauty, Eyes black and lovely, Complexion fair; to a Miracle, all her Features of the rarest proportion, the Mouth red, the Teeth white, and a thousand Graces in her Meen and Air; she came no sooner abroad, but she had a thousand Persons fighting for love of her; the Reputation her Wit had acquir'd, got her Adorers without seeing her, but when they saw her, they found themselves conquer'd and undone; all were glad she was come into the World, of whom they had heard so much, and all the Youth of the Town dress'd only for *Isabella de Valerie*, the rose like a new Star that Eclips'd all the rest, and which set the World a-gazing. Some hop'd, and some despair'd, but all lov'd, while *Isabella* regarded not their Eyes, their distant darling Looks of Love, and their signs of Adoration; she was civil and affable to all, but so reserv'd, that none durst tell her his Passion, or name that strange and abhorr'd thing, *Love*, to her; the Relations with whom she went abroad every day, were fein to force her out, and when she went, 'twas the motive of Civility, and not Satisfaction, that made her go; whatever she saw, she beheld with no admiration, and nothing created wonder in her, tho' never so strange and Novel. She survey'd all things with an indifference, that tho' it was not sullen, was far from Transport, so that her evenness of Mind was infinitely admir'd and prais'd. And now it was, that, young as she was, her Conduct and Discretion appear'd equal to her Wit and Beauty, and she encreas'd daily in Reputation, insomuch, that the Parents of abundance of young Noble Men, made it their business to endeavour to marry their Sons to so admirable and noble a Maid, and one, whose Virtues were the Discourse of all the World; the *Father*, the Lady *Abbess*, and those who had her abroad, were solicited to make an Alliance; for the Father, he would give no answer, but left it to the discretion of *Isabella*, who could not be persuaded to hear any thing of that nature; so that for a long time she refus'd her company to all those, who propos'd any thing of Marriage to her; she said, she had seen nothing in the World that was worth her Care, or the venturing the losing of

Heaven for, and therefore was resolv'd to dedicate her self to that; that the more she saw of the World, the worse she lik'd it, and pity'd the Wretches that were condemn'd to it; that she had consider'd it, and found no one Inclination that forbad her immediate Entrance into a Religious Life; to which, her Father, after using all the Arguments he could, to make her take good heed of what she went about, to consider it well; and had urg'd all the Inconveniencies of Severe Life, Watchings, Midnight Risings in all Weathers and Seasons to Prayers, hard Lodging, course Diet, and homely Habit, with a thousand other things of Labour and Work us'd among the *Nuns*; and finding her still resolv'd and inflexible to all contrary persuasions, he consented, kiss'd her, and told her, She had argu'd according to the wish of his Soul, and that he never believ'd himself truly happy, till this moment that he was assur'd, she would become a Religious.

This News, to the Heart-breaking of a thousand Lovers, was spread all over the Town, and there was nothing but Songs of Complaint, and of her retiring, after she had shewn her self to the World, and vanquish'd so many Hearts; all Wits were at work on this Cruel Subject, and one begat another, as is usual in such Affairs. Amongst the number of these Lovers, there was a young Gentleman, Nobly born, his name was *Villenoys*, who was admirably made, and very handsom, had travell'd and accomplish'd himself, as much as was possible for one so young to do; he was about Eighteen, and was going to the Siege of *Candia*, in a very good Equipage, but, overtaken by his Fate, surpris'd in his way to Glory, he stopt at *Ipers*, so fell most passionately in love with this Maid of Immortal Fame; but being defeated in his hopes by this News, was the Man that made the softest Complaints to this fair Beauty, and whose violence of Passion oppress'd him to that degree, that he was the only Lover, who durst himself tell her, he was in love with her; he writ Billets so soft

and tender, that she had, of all her Lovers, most compassion
for *Villenoys*, and dain'd several times, in pity of him, to
send him answers to his Letters, but they were such, as
absolutely forbad him to love her; such as incited him to
follow Glory, the Mistress that could noblest reward him;
and that, for her part, her Prayers should always be, that
he might be victorious, and the Darling of that Fortune
he was going to court; and that she, for her part, had fix'd
her Mind on Heaven, and no Earthly Thought should
bring it down; but she should ever retain for him all
Sisterly Respect, and begg'd, in her Solitudes, to hear,
whether her Prayers had prov'd effectual or not, and if
Fortune were so kind to him, as she should perpetually wish.

When *Villenoys* found she was resolv'd, he design'd to
persue his Journy, but could not leave the Town, till he
had seen the fatal Ceremony of *Isabella's* being made a
Nun, which was every day expected; and while he stay'd,
he could not forbear writing daily to her, but receiv'd no
more Answers from her, she already accusing her self of
having done too much, for a Maid in her Circumstances;
but she confess'd, of all she had seen, she lik'd *Villenoys*
the best; and if she ever could have lov'd, she believ'd it
would have been *Villenoys*, for he had all the good Qualities,
and grace, that could render him agreeable to the Fair;
besides, that he was only Son to a very rich and noble
Parent, and one that might very well presume to lay claim
to a Maid of *Isabella's* Beauty and Fortune.

As the time approach'd, when he must eternally lose
all hope, by *Isabella's* taking Orders, he found himself less
able to bear the Efforts of that Despair it possess'd him
with, he languish'd with the thought, so that it was visible
to all his Friends, the decays it wrought on his Beauty and
Gaiety: So that he fell at last into a Feaver; and 'twas the
whole Discourse of the Town, That *Villenoys* was dying for
the Fair *Isabella;* his Relations, being all of Quality, were
extreamly afflicted at his Misfortune, and joyn'd their

Interests yet, to dissuade this fair young Victoress from an act so cruel, as to inclose herself in a *Nunnery*, while the finest of all the youths of Quality was dying for her, and ask'd her, If it would not be more acceptable to Heaven to save a Life, and perhaps a Soul, than to go and expose her own to a thousand Tortures? They assur'd her, *Villenoys* was dying, and dying Adoring her; that nothing could save his Life, but her kind Eyes turn'd upon the fainting Lover; a Lover, that could breath nothing, but her Name in Sighs; and find satisfaction in nothing, but weeping and crying out, 'I dye for Isabella!' This Discourse fetch'd abundance of Tears from the fair Eyes of this tender Maid; but, at the same time, she besought them to believe, these Tears ought not to give them hope, she should ever yield to save his Life, by quitting her Resolution, of becoming a *Nun;* but, on the contrary, they were Tears, that only bewail'd her own Misfortune, in having been the occasion of the death of any Man, especially, a Man, who had so many Excellencies, as might have render'd him entirely Happy and Glorious for a long race of Years, had it not been his ill fortune to have seen her unlucky Face. She believ'd, it was for her Sins of Curiosity, and going beyond the Walls of the Monastery, to wander after the Vanities of the foolish World, that had occasion'd this Misfortune to the young Count of *Villenoys*, and she would put a severe Penance on her Body, for the Mischiefs her Eyes had done him; she fears she might, by something in her looks, have intic'd his Heart, for she own'd she saw him, with wonder at his Beauty, and much more she admir'd him, when she found the Beauties of his Mind; she confess'd, she had given him hope, by answering his Letters; and that when she found her Heart grow a little more than usually tender, when she thought on him, she believ'd it a Crime, that ought to be check'd by a Virtue, such as she pretended to profess, and hop'd she should ever carry to her Grave; and she desired his Relations to implore

him, in her Name, to rest contented, in knowing he was
the first, and should be the last, that should ever make an
impression on her Heart; that what she had conceiv'd
there, for him, should remain with her to her dying day,
and that she besought him to live, that she might see, he
both deserv'd this Esteem she had for him, and to repay
it her, otherwise he would dye in her debt, and make her
Life ever after reposeless.

This being all they could get from her, they return'd
with Looks that told their Message; however, they render'd those soft things *Isabella* had said, in so moving a
manner, as fail'd not to please, and while he remain'd in
this condition, the Ceremonies were compleated, of making
Isabella a *Nun*; which was a Secret to none but *Villenoys*,
and from him it was carefully conceal'd, so that in a little
time he recover'd his lost health, at least, so well, as to
support the fatal News, and upon the first hearing it, he
made ready his Equipage, and departed immediately for
Candia; where he behav'd himself very gallantly, under
the Command of the Duke De *Beaufort*, and, with him,
return'd to *France*, after the loss of that noble City to the
Turks.

In all the time of his absence, that he might the sooner
establish his Repose, he forbore sending to the fair Cruel
Nun, and she heard no more of *Villenoys* in above two
years; so that giving her self wholly up to Devotion, there
was never seen any one, who led so Austere and Pious a
Life, as this young *Votress*; she was a Saint in the Chapel,
and an Angel at the *Grate*: She there laid by all her
severe Looks, and mortify'd Discourse, and being at perfect
peace and tranquility within, she was outwardly all gay,
sprightly, and entertaining, being satisfy'd, no Sights, no
Freedoms, could give any temptations to worldly desires;
she gave a loose to all that was modest, and that Virtue
and Honour would permit, and was the most charming
Conversation that ever was admir'd; and the whole World

that pass'd through *Iper*; of Strangers, came directed and recommended to the lovely *Isabella*; I mean, those of Quality: But however Diverting she was at the *Grate*, she was most exemplary Devout in the Cloister, doing more Penance, and imposing a more rigid Severity and Task on her self, than was requir'd, giving such rare Examples to all the *Nuns* that were less Devout, that her Life was a Proverb, and a President, and when they would express a very Holy Woman indeed, they would say, 'She was a very *ISABELLA.*'

There was in this *Nunnery*, a young *Nun*, call'd, Sister *Katteriena*, Daughter to the Grave *Vanhenault*, that is to say, an Earl, who liv'd about six Miles from the Town, in a noble *Villa*; this Sister *Katteriena* was not only a very beautiful Maid, but very witty, and had all the good qualities to make her be belov'd, and had most wonderfully gain'd upon the Heart of the fair *Isabella*, she was her Chamber-Fellow and Companion in all her Devotions and Diversions, so that where one was, there was the other, and they never went but together to the *Grate*, to the Garden, or to any place, whither their *Affairs* call'd either. This young *Katteriena* had a Brother, who lov'd her intirely, and came every day to see her, he was about twenty Years of Age, rather tall than middle Statur'd, his Hair and Eyes brown, but his Face exceeding beautiful, adorn'd with a thousand Graces, and the most nobly and exactly made, that 'twas possible for Nature to form; to the Fineness and Charms of his Person, he had an Air in his Meen and Dressing, so very agreeable, besides rich, that 'twas impossible to look on him, without wishing him happy, because he did so absolutely merit being so. His Wit and his Manner was so perfectly Obliging, a Goodness and Generosity so Sincere and Gallant, that it would even have aton'd for Ugliness. As he was eldest Son to so great a Father, he was kept at home, while the rest of his Brothers were employ'd in Wars abroad; this made him of a melancholy Temper, and fit for soft Impressions; he was very Bookish, and had the best Tutors that could be got, for Learning and Languages, and all that could compleat a Man; but was unus'd to Action, and of a temper Lazy, and given to Repose, so that his Father could hardly ever get him to use any Exercise, or so much as ride abroad, which he would call, Losing Time from his Studies: He car'd not for the Conversation of Men, because he lov'd not Debauch, as they usually did; so that for Exercise, more than any Design, he came on Horseback every day to *Iper* to the *Monastery*, and would sit at the *Grate*, entertaining his Sister the most part of the Afternoon, and, in the Evening, retire; he had often seen and convers'd with the lovely *Isabella*, and found from the first sight of her, he had more Esteem for her, than any other of her Sex: But as Love very rarely takes Birth without Hope; so he never believ'd that the Pleasure he took in beholding her, and in discoursing with her, was Love, because he regarded her, as a Thing consecrate to Heaven, and never so much as thought to wish, she were a Mortal fit for his Addresses; yet he found himself more and more fill'd with Reflections on her which was not usual with him; he found she grew upon his Memory, and oftner came there, than he us'd to do, that he lov'd his Studies less, and going to *Iper* more; and, that every time he went, he found a new Joy at his Heart that pleas'd him; he found, he could not get himself from the *Grate*, without Pain; nor part from the sight of that all-charming Object, without Sighs; and if, while he was there, any persons came to visit her, whose Quality she could not refuse the honour of her sight to, he would blush, and pant with uneasiness, especially, if they were handsom, and fit to make Impressions: And he would check this Uneasiness in himself, and ask his Heart, what it meant, by rising and beating in those Moments, and strive to assume an Indifferency in vain, and depart dissatisfy'd, and out of humour.

On the other side, *Isabella* was not so Gay as she us'd to be, but, on the sudden, retir'd her self more from the *Grate* than she us'd to do, refus'd to receive Visits every day, and her Complexion grew a little pale and languid ; she was observ'd not to sleep, or eat, as she us'd to do, nor exercise in those little Plays they made, and diverted themselves with, now and then ; she was heard to sigh often, and it became the Discourse of the whole House, that she was much alter'd : The Lady *Abbess*, who lov'd her with a most tender Passion, was infinitely concern'd at this Change, and endeavour'd to find out the Cause, and 'twas generally believ'd, she was too Devout, for now she redoubled her Austerity ; and in cold Winter Nights, of Frost and Snow, would be up at all Hours, and lying upon the cold Stones, before the Altar, prostrate at Prayers : So that she receiv'd Orders from the Lady *Abbess*, not to harass her self so very much, but to have a care of her Health, as well as her Soul ; but she regarded not these Admonitions, tho' even persuaded daily by her *Katteriena*, whom she lov'd every day more and more.

But, one Night, when they were retir'd to their Chamber, amongst a thousand things that they spoke of, to pass away a tedious Evening, they talk'd of Pictures and Likenesses, and *Katteriena* told *Isabella*, that before she was a *Nun*, in her more happy days, she was so like her Brother *Bernardo Henault*, (who was the same that visited them every day) that she would, in Men's Clothes, undertake, she should not have known one from t'other, and fetching out his *Picture*, she had in a Dressing-Box, she threw it to *Isabella*, who, at the first sight of it, turns as pale as Ashes, and, being ready to swound, she bid her take it away, and could not, for her Soul, hide the sudden surprise the *Picture* brought : *Katteriena* had too much Wit, not to make a just Interpretation of this Change, and (as a Woman) was naturally curious to pry farther, tho' Discretion should have made her been silent, for Talking, in such cases, does but make the Wound rage the more ; 'Why, my dear Sister, (said *Katteriena*) is the likeness of my Brother so offensive to you ?' *Isabella* found by this, she had discover'd too much, and that Thought put her by all power of excusing it ; she was confounded with Shame, and the more she strove to hide it, the more it disorder'd her ; so that she (blushing extremely) hung down her Head, sigh'd, and confess'd all by her Looks. At last, after a considering Pause, she cry'd, 'My dearest Sister, I do confess, I was sur-priz'd at the sight of Monsieur *Henault*, and much more than ever you have observ'd me to be at the sight of his Person, because there is scarce a day wherein I do not see that, and know beforehand I shall see him ; I am prepar'd for the Encounter, and have lessen'd my Con-cern, or rather Confusion, by that time I come to the *Grate*, so much Mistress I am of my Passions, when they give me warning of their approach, and sure I can with-stand the greatest assaults of Fate, if I can but foresee it ; but if it surprize me, I find I am as feeble a Woman, as the most unresolv'd ; you did not tell me, you had this Picture, nor say, you would shew me such a Picture ; but when I least expect to see that Face, you shew it me, even in my Chamber.'

'Ah, my dear Sister ! (reply'd *Katteriena*) I believe, that Paleness, and those Blushes, proceed from some other cause, than the Nicety of seeing the Picture of a Man in your Chamber':

'You have too much Wit, (reply'd *Isabella*) to be impos'd on by such an Excuse, if I were so silly to make it; but oh ! my dear Sister ! it was in my Thoughts to deceive you ; could I have concealed my Pain and Sufferings, you should never have known them ; but since I find it impossible, and that I am too sincere to make use of Fraud in any thing, 'tis fit I tell you, from

what cause my change of Colour proceeds, and to own to
you, I fear, 'tis Love, if ever therefore, oh gentle pitying
Maid! thou wert a Lover? If ever thy tender Heart were
touch'd with that Passion? Inform me, oh! inform me,
of the nature of that cruel Disease, and how thou found'st
a Cure?'

While she was speaking these words, she threw her
Arms about the Neck of the fair *Katteriena*, and bath'd
her Bosom (where she hid her Face) with a shower of
Tears; *Katteriena*, embracing her with all the fondness of
a dear Lover, told her, with a Sigh, that she could deny
her nothing, and therefore confess'd to her, she had been a
Lover, and that was the occasion of her being made a *Nun*,
her Father finding out the Intrigue, which fatally happen'd
to be with his own Page, a Youth of extraordinary Beauty.
'I was but Young, (said she) about Thirteen, and knew not
what to call the new-known Pleasure that I felt; when
e're I look'd upon the young *Arnaldo*, my Heart would
heave, when e're he came in view, and my disorder'd Breath
came doubly from my Bosom; a Shivering seiz'd me, and
my Face grew wan; my Thought was at a stand, and
Sense it self, for that short moment, lost its Faculties;
But when he touch'd me, oh! no hunted Deer, tir'd with
his flight, and just secur'd in Shades, pants with a nimbler
motion than my Heart; at first, I thought the Youth
had had some Magick Art, to make one faint and tremble
at his touches; but he himself, when I accus'd his
Cruelty, told me, he had no Art, but awful Passion, and
vow'd that when I touch'd him, he was so; so trembling,
so surprized, so charm'd, so pleas'd. When he was
present, nothing could displease me, but when he parted
from me; then 'twas rather a soft silent Grief, that
eas'd itself by sighing, and by hoping, that some kind
moment would restore my joy. When he was absent,
nothing could divert me, howe're I strove, howe're I
toyl'd for Mirth; no Smile, no Joy, dwelt in my Heart

or Eyes ; I could not feign, so very well I lov'd, impatient in his absence, I would count the tedious parting Hours, and pass them off like useless Visitants, whom we wish were gon; these are the Hours, where Life no business has, at least, a Lover's Life. But, oh ! what Minutes seem'd the happy Hours, when on his Eyes I gaz'd, and he on mine, and half our Conversation lost in Sighs, Sighs, the soft moving Language of a Lover ! '

'No more, no more, (reply'd *Isabella*, throwing her Arms again about the Neck of the transported *Katteriena*) thou blow'st my Flame by thy soft Words, and mak'st me know my Weakness, and my Shame : I love ! I love ! and feel those differing Passions !'—Then pausing a moment, she proceeded,—'Yet so didst thou, but hast surmounted it. Now thou hast found the Nature of my Pain, oh ! tell me thy saving Remedy ?' 'Alas ! (reply'd *Katteriena*) tho' there's but one Disease, there's many Remedies : They say, possession's one, but that to me seems a Riddle; Absence, they say, another, and that was mine ; for *Arnaldo* having by chance lost one of my Billets, discover'd the Amour, and was sent to travel, and my self forc'd into this Monastery, where at last, Time convinc'd me, I had lov'd below my Quality, and that sham'd me into Holy Orders.' 'And is it a Disease, (reply'd *Isabella*) that People often recover ?' 'Most frequently, (said *Katteriena*) and yet some dye of the Disease, but very rarely.' 'Nay then, (said *Isabella*) I fear, you will find me one of these Martyrs ; for I have already oppos'd it with the most severe Devotion in the World : But all my Prayers are vain, your lovely Brother persues me into the greatest Solitude ; he meets me at my very Midnight Devotions, and interrupts my Prayers ; he gives me a thousand Thoughts, that ought not to enter into a Soul dedicated to Heaven ; he ruins all the Glory I have achiev'd, even above my Sex, for Piety of Life, and the Observation of all Virtues.

Oh *Katteriena!* he has a Power in his Eyes, that transcends all the World besides: And, to shew the weakness of Human Nature, and how vain all our Boastings are, he has done that in one fatal Hour, that the persuasions of all my Relations and Friends, Glory, Honour, Pleasure, and all that can tempt, could not perform in Years ; I resisted all but *Henault's* Eyes, and they were Ordain'd to make me truly wretched ; But yet with thy Assistance, and a Resolution to see him no more, and my perpetual Trust in Heaven, I may, perhaps, overcome this Tyrant of my Soul, who, I thought, had never enter'd into holy Houses, or mix'd his Devotions and Worship with the true Religion ; but, oh ! no Cells, no Cloysters, no Hermitages, are secur'd from his Efforts.'

This Discourse she ended with abundance of Tears, and it was resolv'd, since she was devoted for ever to a Holy Life, That it was best for her to make it as easy to her as was possible; in order to it, and the banishing this fond and useless Passion from her Heart, it was very necessary, she should see *Henault* no more : At first, *Isabella* was afraid, that, in refusing to see him, he might mistrust her Passion ; but *Katteriena* who was both Pious and Discreet, and endeavour'd truly to cure her of so violent a Disease, which must, she knew, either end in her death or destruction, told her, She would take care of that matter, that it should not blemish her Honour ; and so leaving her a while, after they had resolved on this, she left her in a thousand Confusions, she was now another Woman than what she had hitherto been ; she was quite alter'd in every Sentiment, thought and Notion ; she now repented, she had promis'd not to see *Henault ;* she trembled and even fainted, for fear she should see him no more ; she was not able to bear that thought, it made her rage within, like one possest, and all her Virtue could not calm her ; yet since her word was past, and, as she was, she could not, without great Scandal, break it in that point, she resolv'd to dye a thousand Deaths, rather than not perform her Promise made to *Katteriena* ; but 'tis not to be express'd what she endur'd ; what Fits, Pains, and Convulsions, she sustain'd ; and how much ado she had to dissemble to Dame *Katteriena*, who soon return'd to the afflicted Maid ; the next day, about the time that *Henault* was to come, as he usually did, about two or three a Clock after Noon, 'tis impossible to express the uneasiness of *Isabella* ; she ask'd, a thousand times, 'What, is not your Brother come?' When Dame *Katteriena* would reply, 'Why do you ask?' She would say, 'Because I would be sure not to see him' : 'You need not fear, Madam, (reply'd *Katteriena*) for you shall keep your Chamber.' She need not have urg'd that, for *Isabella* was very ill without knowing it, and in a Feaver.

At last, one of the *Nuns* came up, and told Dame *Katteriena*, that her Brother was at the *Grate*, and she desired, he should be bid come about to the Private *Grate* above stairs, which he did, and she went to him, leaving *Isabella* even dead on the Bed, at the very name of *Henault*: But the more she conceal'd her Flame, the more violently it rag'd, which she strove in vain by Prayers, and those Recourses of Solitude to lessen ; all this did but augment the Pain, and was Oyl to the Fire, so that she now could hope, that nothing but Death would put an end to her Griefs, and her Infamy. She was eternally thinking on him, how handsome his Face, how delicate every Feature, how charming his Air, how graceful his Meen, how soft and good his Disposition, and how witty and entertaining his Conversation. She now fancy'd, she was at the *Grate*, talking to him as she us'd to be, and blest those happy Hours she past then, and bewail'd her Misfortune, that she is no more destin'd to be so Happy, then gives a loose to Grief; Griefs, at which, no Mortals, but Despairing Lovers, can guess, or how tormenting they are ; where the most easie Moments are, those, wherein one resolves

to kill ones self, and the happiest Thought is Damnation;
but from these Imaginations, she endeavours to fly, all
frighted with horror; but, alas! whither would she fly,
but to a Life more full of horror? She considers well, she
cannot bear Despairing Love, and finds it impossible to
cure her Despair; she cannot fly from the Thoughts of
the Charming *Henault;* and 'tis impossible to quit 'em;
and, at this rate, she found, Life could not long support
it self, but would either reduce her to Madness, and so
render her an hated Object of Scorn to the Censuring
World, or force her Hand to commit a Murder upon her
self. This she had found, this she had well consider'd, nor
could her fervent and continual Prayers, her nightly
Watchings, her Mortifications on the cold Marble in long
Winter Season, and all her Acts of Devotion abate one
spark of this shameful Feaver of Love, that was destroying
her within. When she had rag'd and struggled with this
unruly Passion, 'till she was quite tir'd and breathless,
finding all her force in vain, she fill'd her fancy with a
thousand charming *Ideas* of the lovely *Henault,* and, in
that soft fit, had a mind to satisfy her panting Heart, and
give it one Joy more, by beholding the Lord of its Desires,
and the Author of its Pains: Pleas'd, yet trembling, at
this Resolve, she rose from the Bed where she was laid,
and softly advanc'd to the Stair-Case, from whence there
open'd that Room where Dame *Katteriena* was, and where
there was a private *Grate,* at which, she was entertaining
her *Brother;* they were earnest in Discourse, and so loud,
that *Isabella* could easily hear all they said, and the first
words were from *Katteriena,* who, in a sort of Anger,
cry'd, 'Urge me no more! My Virtue is too nice, to
become an Advocate for a Passion, that can tend to nothing
but your Ruin; for, suppose I should tell the fair *Isabella,*
you dye for her, what can it avail you? What hope can
any Man have, to move the Heart of a Virgin, so averse
to Love? A Virgin, whose Modesty and Virtue is so

very curious, it would fly the very word, Love, as some monstrous Witchcraft, or the foulest of Sins, who would loath me for bringing so lewd a Message, and banish you her Sight, as the Object of her Hate and Scorn; is it unknown to you, how many of the noblest Youths of *Flanders* have address'd themselves to her in vain, when yet she was in the World? Have you been ignorant, how the young Count de *Villenoys* languished, in vain, almost to Death for her? And, that no Persuasions, no Attractions in him, no wordly Advantages, or all his Pleadings, who had a Wit and Spirit capable of prevailing on any Heart, less severe and harsh, than hers? Do you not know, that all was lost on this insensible fair one, even when she was a proper Object for the Adoration of the Young and Amorous? And can you hope, now she has so entirely wedded her future days to Devotion, and given all to Heaven; nay, lives a Life here more like a Saint, than a Woman; rather an Angel, than a mortal Creature? Do you imagin, with any Rhetorick you can deliver, now to turn the Heart, and whole Nature, of this Divine Maid, to consider your Earthly Passion? No, 'tis fondness, and an injury to her Virtue, to harbour such a Thought; quit it, quit it, my dear Brother! before it ruin your Repose.' 'Ah, Sister! (replied the dejected *Henault*) your Counsel comes too late, and your Reasons are of too feeble force, to rebate those Arrows, the Charming *Isabella's* Eyes have fix'd in my Heart and Soul; and I am undone, unless she know my Pain, which I shall dye, before I shall ever dare mention to her; but you, young Maids, have a thousand Familiarities together, can jest, and play, and say a thousand things between Railery and Earnest, that may first hint what you would deliver, and insinuate into each others Hearts a kind of Curiosity to know more; for naturally, (my dear Sister) Maids, are curious and vain; and however Divine the Mind of the fair *Isabella* may be, it bears the Tincture still of Mortal Woman.'

'Suppose this true, how could this Mortal part about her Advantage you, (said *Katteriena*) all that you can expect from this Discovery, (if she should be content to hear it, and to return you pity) would be, to make her wretched, like your self? What farther can you hope?' 'Oh! talk not, (replied *Henault*) of so much Happiness! I do not expect to be so blest, that she should pity me, or love to a degree of Inquietude; 'tis sufficient, for the ease of my Heart, that she know its Pains, and what it suffers for her; that she would give my Eyes leave to gaze upon her, and my Heart to vent a Sigh now and then; and, when I dare, to give me leave to speak, and tell her of my Passion; This, this, is all, my Sister.' And, at that word, the Tears glided down his Cheeks, and he declin'd his Eyes, and set a Look so charming, and so sad, that *Isabella*, whose Eyes were fix'd upon him, was a thousand times ready to throw her self into the Room, and to have made a Confession, how sensible she was of all she had heard and seen: But, with much ado, she contain'd and satisfy'd her self, with knowing, that she was ador'd by him whom she ador'd, and, with Prudence that is natural to her, she withdrew, and waited with patience the event of their Discourse. She impatiently long'd to know, how *Katteriena* would manage this Secret her Brother had given her, and was pleas'd, that the Friendship and Prudence of that Maid had conceal'd her Passion from her Brother; and now contented and joyful beyond imagination, to find her self belov'd, she knew she could dissemble her own Passion and make him the first Aggressor; the first that lov'd, or at least, that should seem to do so. This Thought restores her so great a part of her Peace of Mind, that she resolv'd to see him, and to dissemble with *Katteriena* so far, as to make her believe, she had subdu'd that Passion, she was really asham'd to own; she now, with her Woman's Skill, begins to practise an Art she never before understood, and has recourse to

Cunning, and resolves to seem to reassume her former
Repose: But hearing *Katteriena* approach, she laid her
self again on her Bed, where she had left her, but compos'd her Face to more chearfulness, and put on a Resolution that indeed deceiv'd the Sister, who was extreamly
pleased, she said, to see her look so well: When *Isabella*
reply'd, 'Yes, I am another Woman now; I hope Heaven
has heard, and granted, my long and humble Supplications,
and driven from my Heart this tormenting God, that has
so long disturb'd my purer Thoughts.' 'And are you sure,
(said Dame *Katteriena*) that this wanton Deity is repell'd
by the noble force of your Resolutions? Is he never to
return?' 'No, (replied *Isabella*) never to my Heart.' 'Yes,
(said *Katteriena*) if you should see the lovely Murderer of
your Repose, your Wound would bleed anew.' At this,
Isabella smiling with a little Disdain, reply'd, 'Because
you once to love, and *Henault's* Charms defenceless found
me, ah! do you think I have no Fortitude? But so in
Fondness lost, remiss in Virtue, that when I have resolv'd,
(and see it necessary for my after-Quiet) to want the power
of keeping that Resolution? No, scorn me, and despise
me then, as lost to all the Glories of my Sex, and all that
Nicety I've hitherto preserv'd.' There needed no more
from a Maid of *Isabella's* Integrity and Reputation, to
convince any one of the Sincerity of what she said, since,
in the whole course of her Life, she never could be charg'd
with an Untruth, or an Equivocation; and *Katteriena*
assur'd her, she believ'd her, and was infinitely glad she
had vanquish'd a Passion, that would have prov'd destructive to her Repose: *Isabella* reply'd, She had not altogether
vanquish'd her Passion, she did not boast of so absolute a
power over her soft Nature, but had resolv'd things great,
and Time would work the Cure; that she hop'd, *Katteriena*
would make such Excuses to her Brother, for her not
appearing at the *Grate* so gay and entertaining as she us'd,
and, by a little absence, she should retrieve the Liberty

she had lost : But she desir'd, such Excuses might be made
for her, that young *Henault* might not perceive the Reason.
At the naming him, she had much ado not to shew some
Concern extraordinary, and *Katteriena* assur'd her, She
had now a very good Excuse to keep from the *Grate*,
when he was at it; 'For, (said she) now you have resolv'd,
I may tell you, he is dying for you, raving in Love, and
has this day made me promise to him, to give you some
account of his Passion, and to make you sensible of his
Languishment: I had not told you this, (reply'd *Katteriena*)
but that I believe you fortify'd with brave Resolution and
Virtue, and that this knowledge will rather put you more
upon your Guard, than you were before.' While she spoke,
she fixed her Eyes on *Isabella*, to see what alteration it
would make in her Heart and Looks; but the Master-piece
of this young Maid's Art was shewn in this minute, for
she commanded her self so well, that her very Looks dissembled and shew'd no concern at a Relation, that made
her Soul dance with Joy; but it was, what she was prepar'd for, or else I question her Fortitude. But, with a
Calmness, which absolutely subdu'd *Katteriena*, she reply'd,
'I am almost glad he has confess'd a Passion for me, and
you shall confess to him, you told me of it, and that
I absent my self from the *Grate*, on purpose to avoid the
sight of a Man, who durst love me, and confess it; and
I assure you, my dear Sister ! (continued she, dissembling)
You could not have advanc'd my Cure by a more effectual
way, than telling me of his Presumption.' At that word,
Katteriena joyfully related to her all that had pass'd between
young *Henault* and her self, and how he implor'd her Aid
in this Amour; at the end of which Relation, *Isabella*
smil'd, and carelesly reply'd, 'I pity him': And so going
to their Devotion, they had no more Discourse of the
Lover.

In the mean time, young *Henault* was a little satisfy'd,
to know, his Sister would discover his Passion to the lovely

Isabella; and though he dreaded the return, he was pleas'd
that she should know, she had a Lover that ador'd her,
though even without hope; for though the thought of
possessing *Isabella*, was the most ravishing that could be;
yet he had a dread upon him, when he thought of it, for
he could not hope to accomplish that, without Sacrilege;
and he was a young Man, very Devout, and even bigotted
in Religion; and would often question and debate within
himself, that, if it were possible, he should come to be
belov'd by this Fair Creature, and that it were possible for
her, to grant all that Youth in Love could require, whether
he should receive the Blessing offer'd? And though he
ador'd the Maid, whether he should not abhor the *Nun*
in his Embraces? 'Twas an undetermin'd Thought, that
chill'd his Fire as often as it approach'd; but he had too
many that rekindled it again with the greater Flame and
Ardor.

His impatience to know, what Success *Katteriena* had,
with the Relation she was to make to *Isabella* in his behalf,
brought him early to *Iper* the next day. He came again
to the private *Grate*, where his Sister receiving him, and
finding him, with a sad and dejected Look, expect what
she had to say; she told him, That Look well became the
News she had for him, it being such, as ought to make
him, both Griev'd, and Penitent; for, to obey him, she
had so absolutely displeas'd *Isabella*, that she was resolv'd
never to believe her her Friend more, 'Or to see you, (said
she) therefore, as you have made me commit a Crime
against my Conscience, against my Order, against my
Friendship, and against my Honour, you ought to do some
brave thing; take some noble Resolution, worthy of your
Courage, to redeem all; for your Repose, I promis'd, I
would let Isabella know you lov'd, and, for the mitigation
of my Crime, you ought to let me tell her, you have
surmounted your Passion, as the last Remedy of Life and
Fame.'

At these her last words, the Tears gush'd from his Eyes, and he was able only, a good while, to sigh; at last, cry'd, 'What! see her no more! see the Charming *Isabella* no more!' And then vented the Grief of his Soul in so passionate a manner, as his Sister had all the Compassion imaginable for him, but thought it great Sin and Indiscretion to cherish his Flame: So that, after a while, having heard her Counsel, he reply'd, 'And is this all, my Sister, you will do to save a Brother?' 'All! (reply'd she) I would not be the occasion of making a *NUN* violate her Vow, to save a Brother's Life, no, nor my own; assure your self of this, and take it as my last Resolution: Therefore, if you will be content with the Friendship of this young Lady, and so behave your self, that we may find no longer the Lover in the Friend, we shall reassume our former Conversation, and live with you, as we ought; otherwise, your Presence will continually banish her from the *Grate*, and, in time, make both her you love, and your self, a Town Discourse.'

Much more to this purpose she said, to dissuade him, and bid him retire, and keep himself from thence, till he could resolve to visit them without a Crime; and she protested, if he did not do this, and master his foolish Passion, she would let her Father understand his Conduct, who was a Man of temper so very precise, that should he believe, his Son should have a thought of Love to a Virgin vow'd to Heaven, he would abandon him to Shame, and eternal Poverty, by disinheriting him of all he could: Therefore, she said, he ought to lay all this to his Heart, and weigh it with his unheedy Passion. While the Sister talk'd thus wisely, *Henault* was not without his Thoughts, but consider'd as she spoke, but did not consider in the right place; he was not considering, how to please a Father, and save an Estate, but how to manage the matter so, to establish himself, as he was before with *Isabella;* for he imagin'd, since already she knew his Passion, and that if after that she would be prevail'd with to see him, he might, some lucky Minute or other, have the pleasure of speaking for himself, at least, he should again see and talk to her, which was a joyful Thought in the midst of so many dreadful ones : And, as if he had known what pass'd in *Isabella's* Heart, he, by a strange sympathy, took the same measures to deceive *Katteriena*, a well-meaning young Lady, and easily impos'd on from her own Innocence, he resolv'd to dissemble Patience, since he must have that Virtue, and own'd, his Sister's Reasons were just, and ought to be persu'd ; that she had argu'd him into half his Peace, and that he would endeavour to recover the rest; that Youth ought to be pardon'd a thousand Failings, and Years would reduce him to a condition of laughing at his Follies of Youth, but that grave Direction was not yet arriv'd : And so desiring, she would pray for his Conversion, and that she would recommend him to the Devotions of the Fair *Isabella*, he took his leave, and came no more to the *Nunnery* in ten Days; in all which time, none but Impatient Lovers can guess, what Pain and Languishments *Isabella* suffer'd, not knowing the Cause of his Absence, nor daring to enquire ; but she bore it out so admirably, that Dame *Katteriena* never so much as suspected she had any Thoughts of that nature that perplex'd her, and now believ'd indeed she had conquer'd all her Uneasiness : And one day, when *Isabella* and she were alone together, she ask'd that fair Dissembler, if she did not admire at the Conduct and Resolution of her Brother ? 'Why!' (reply'd *Isabella* unconcernedly, while her Heart was fainting within, for fear of ill News :) With that, *Katteriena* told her the last Discourse she had with her Brother, and how at last she had persuaded him (for her sake) to quit his Passion ; and that he had promis'd, he would endeavour to surmòunt it; and that, that was the reason he was absent now, and they were to see him no more, till he had made a Conquest over himself. You may assure your

self, this News was not so welcom to *Isabella*, as *Katteriena*
imagin'd; yet still she dissembled, with a force, beyond
what the most cunning Practitioner could have shewn,
and carry'd her self before People, as if no Pressures had
lain upon her Heart; but when alone retir'd, in order to
her Devotion, she would vent her Griefs in the most
deplorable manner, that a distress'd distracted Maid could
do, and which, in spite of all her severe Penances, she
found no abatement of.

At last *Henault* came again to the *Monastery*, and, with
a Look as gay as he could possibly assume, he saw his Sister,
and told her, He had gain'd an absolute Victory over his
Heart; and desir'd, he might see *Isabella*, only to convince,
both her, and *Katteriena*, that he was no longer a Lover of
that fair Creature, that had so lately charm'd him; that he
had set Five thousand Pounds a Year, against a fruitless
Passion, and found the solid Gold much the. heavier in
the Scale: And he smil'd, and talk'd the whole Day of
indifferent things, with his Sister, and ask'd no more for
Isabella; nor did *Isabella* look, or ask, after him, but in her
Heart. Two Months pass'd in this Indifference, till it was
taken notice of, that Sister *Isabella* came not to the *Grate,*
when *Henault* was there, as she us'd to do; this being
spoken to Dame *Katteriena,* she told it to *Isabella,* and said,
'The *NUNS* would believe, there was some Cause for her
Absence, if she did not appear again': That if she could
trust her Heart, she was sure she could trust her Brother,
for he thought no more of her, she was confident; this, in
lieu of pleasing, was a Dagger to the Heart of *Isabella,* who
thought it time to retrieve the flying Lover, and therefore
told *Katteriena,* She would the next Day entertain at the
Low *Grate,* as she was wont to do, and accordingly, as soon
as any People of Quality came, she appear'd there, where
she had not been two Minutes, but she saw the lovely
Henault, and it was well for both, that People were in
the Room, they had else both sufficiently discover'd their

Inclinations, or rather their not to be conceal'd Passions; after the General Conversation was over, by the going away of the Gentlemen that were at the *Grate*, *Katteriena* being employ'd elsewhere, *Isabella* was at last left alone with *Henault*; but who can guess the Confusion of these two Lovers, who wish'd, yet fear'd, to know each others Thoughts? She trembling with a dismal Apprehension, that he lov'd no more; and he almost dying with fear, she should Reproach or Upbraid him with his Presumption; so that both being possess'd with equal Sentiments of Love, Fear, and Shame, they both stood fix'd with dejected Looks and Hearts, that heav'd with stifled Sighs. At last, *Isabella*, the softer and tender-hearted of the two, tho' not the most a Lover perhaps, not being able to contain her Love any longer within the bounds of Dissimulation or Discretion, being by Nature innocent, burst out into Tears, and all fainting with pressing Thoughts within, she fell languishly into a Chair that stood there, while the distracted *Henault*, who could not come to her Assistance, and finding Marks of Love, rather than Anger or Disdain, in that Confusion of *Isabella's*, throwing himself on his Knees at the *Grate*, implor'd her to behold him, to hear him, and to pardon him, who dy'd every moment for her, and who ador'd her with a violent Ardor; but yet, with such an one, as should (tho' he perish'd with it) be conformable to her Commands; and as he spoke, the Tears stream'd down his dying Eyes, that beheld her with all the tender Regard that ever Lover was capable of; she recover'd a little, and turn'd her too beautiful Face to him, and pierc'd him with a Look, that darted a thousand Joys and Flames into his Heart, with Eyes, that told him her Heart was burning and dying for him; for which Assurances, he made Ten thousand Asseverations of his never-dying Passion, and expressing as many Raptures and Excesses of Joy, to find her Eyes and Looks confess, he was not odious to her, and that the knowledge he was her Lover, did not make her hate him:

In fine, he spoke so many things all soft and moving, and so well convinc'd her of his Passion, that she at last was compell'd by a mighty force, absolutely irresistible, to speak.

'Sir, (said she) perhaps you will wonder, where I, a Maid, brought up in the simplicity of Virtue, should learn the Confidence, not only to hear of Love from you, but to confess I am sensible of the most violent of its Pain my self; and I wonder, and am amazed at my own Daring, that I should have the Courage, rather to speak, than dye, and bury it in silence; but such is my Fate. Hurried by an unknown Force, which I have endeavoured always, in vain, to resist, I am compell'd to tell you, I love you, and have done so from the first moment I saw you; and you are the only Man born to give me Life or Death, to make me Happy or Blest; perhaps, had I not been confin'd, and, as it were, utterly forbid by my Vow, as well as my Modesty, to tell you this, I should not have been so miserable to have fallen thus low, as to have confess'd my Shame; but our Opportunities of Speaking are so few, and Letters so impossible to be sent without discovery, that perhaps this is the only time I shall ever have to speak with you alone.' And, at that word the Tears flow'd abundantly from her Eyes, and gave *Henault* leave to speak. 'Ah Madam! (said he) do not, as soon as you have rais'd me to the greatest Happiness in the World, throw me with one word beneath your Scorn, much easier 'tis to dye, and know I am lov'd, than never, never, hope to hear that blessed sound again from that beautiful Mouth: Ah, Madam! rather let me make use of this one opportunity our happy Luck has given us, and contrive how we may for ever see, and speak, to each other; let us assure one another, there are a thousand ways to escape a place so rigid, as denies us that Happiness; and denies the fairest Maid in the World, the privilege of her Creation, and the end to which she was form'd so Angelical.' And seeing *Isabella* was going to speak, lest she should say something, that might dissuade from an Attempt so dangerous and wicked, he persu'd to tell her, it might be indeed the last moment Heaven would give 'em, and besought her to answer him what he implor'd, whether she would fly with him from the *Monastery?* At this Word, she grew pale, and started, as at some dreadful Sound, and cry'd, 'Hah! what is't you say? Is it possible, you should propose a thing so wicked? And can it enter into your Imagination, because I have so far forget my Virtue, and my Vow, to become a Lover, I should therefore fall to so wretched a degree of Infamy and Reprobation? No, name it to me no more, if you would see me; and if it be as you say, a Pleasure to be belov'd by me; for I will sooner dye, than yield to what . . . Alas! I but too well approve!' These last words, she spoke with a fainting Tone, and the Tears fell anew from her fair soft Eyes. 'If it be so,' said he, (with a Voice so languishing, it could scarce be heard) 'If it be so, and that you are resolv'd to try, if my Love be eternal without Hope, without expectation of any other Joy, than seeing and adoring you through the *Grate;* I am, and must, and will be contented, and you shall see, I can prefer the Sighing to these cold Irons, that separate us, before all the Possessions of the rest of the World; that I chuse rather to lead my Life here, at this cruel Distance from you, for ever, than before the Embrace of all the Fair; and you shall see, how pleas'd I will be, to languish here; but as you see me decay, (for surely so I shall) do not triumph o're my languid Looks, and laugh at my Pale and meager Face; but, Pitying, say, How easily I might have preserv'd that Face, those Eyes, and all that Youth and Vigour, now no more, from this total Ruine I now behold it in, and love your Slave that dyes, and will be daily and visibly dying, as long as my Eyes can gaze on that fair Object, and my Soul be fed and kept alive with her Charming Wit and Conversation; if Love can live on such Airy Food, (tho' rich in it self, yet unfit, alone, to sustain Life) it shall

be for ever dedicated to the lovely *ISABELLA* : But, oh !
that time cannot be long! Fate will not lend her Slave
many days, who loves too violently, to be satisfy'd to enjoy
the fair Object of his Desires, no otherwise than at a *Grate*.'

He ceas'd speaking, for Sighs and Tears stopt his Voice,
and he begg'd the liberty to sit down ; and his Looks being
quite alter'd, *ISABELLA* found her self touch'd to the
very Soul, with a concern the most tender, that ever yielding Maid was oppress'd with : She had no power to suffer
him to Languish, while she by one soft word could restore
him, and being about to say a thousand things that would
have been agreeable to him, she saw herself approach'd by
some of the *Nuns*, and only had time to say, 'If you love
me, live and hope.' The rest of the *Nuns* began to ask
Henault of News, for he always brought them all that was
Novel in the Town, and they were glad still of his Visits,
above all other, for they heard, how all Amours and Intrigues
pass'd in the World, by this young Cavalier. These last
words of *Isabella's* were a Cordial to his Soul, and he, from
that, and to conceal the present Affair, endeavour'd to
assume all the Gaity he could, and told 'em all he could
either remember, or invent, to please 'em, tho' he wish'd
them a great way off at that time.

Thus they pass'd the day, till it was a decent hour for
him to quit the *Grate*, and for them to draw the Curtain ;
all that Night did *Isabella* dedicate to Love, she went to
Bed, with a Resolution, to think over all she had to do,
and to consider, how she should manage this great Affair
of her Life : I have already said, she had try'd all that was
possible in Human Strength to perform, in the design of
quitting a Passion so injurious to her Honour and Virtue,
and found no means possible to accomplish it : She had
try'd Fasting long, Praying fervently, rigid Penances and
Pains, severe Disciplines, all the Mortification, almost to
the destruction of Life it self, to conquer the unruly
Flame ; but still it burnt and rag'd but the more ; so, at

last, she was forc'd to permit that to conquer her, she could not conquer, and submitted to her Fate, as a thing destin'd her by Heaven it self; and after all this opposition, she fancy'd it was resisting even Divine Providence, to struggle any longer with her Heart; and this being her real Belief, she the more patiently gave way to all the Thoughts that pleas'd her.

As soon as she was laid, without discoursing (as she us'd to do) to *Katteriena*, after they were in Bed, she pretended to be sleepy, and turning from her, setled her self to profound Thinking, and was resolv'd to conclude the Matter, between her Heart, and her Vow of Devotion, that Night, and she, having no more to determine, might end the Affair accordingly, the first opportunity she should have to speak to *Henault*, which was, to fly, and marry him; or, to remain for ever fix'd to her Vow of Chastity. This was the Debate; she brings Reason on both sides: Against the first, she sets the Shame of a Violated Vow, and considers, where she shall shew her Face after such an Action; to the Vow, she argues, that she was born in Sin, and could not live without it; that she was Human, and no Angel, and that, possibly, that Sin might be as soon forgiven, as another; that since all her devout Endeavours could not defend her from the Cause, Heaven ought to execute the Effect; that as to shewing her Face, so she saw that of *Henault* always turned (Charming as it was) towards her with love; what had she to do with the World, or car'd to behold any other?

Some times, she thought, it would be more Brave and Pious to dye, than to break her Vow; but she soon answer'd that, as false Arguing, for Self-Murder was the worst of Sins, and in the Deadly Number. She could, after such an Action, live to repent, and, of two Evils, she ought to chuse the least; she dreads to think, since she had so great a Reputation for Virtue and Piety, both in the *Monastery*, and in the World, what they both would say, when she should commit an Action so contrary to both these, she posest; but, after a whole Night's Debate, Love was strongest, and gain'd the Victory. She never went about to think, how she should escape, because she knew it would be easy, the keeping of the Key of the *Monastery*, [was] often intrusted in her keeping, and was, by turns, in the hands of many more, whose Virtue and Discretion was Infallible, and out of Doubt; besides, her Aunt being the Lady *Abbess*, she had greater privilege than the rest; so that she had no more to do, she thought, than to acquaint *Henault* with her Design, as soon as she should get an opportunity. Which was not quickly; but, in the mean time, *Isabella's* Father dy'd, which put some little stop to our Lover's Happiness, and gave her a short time of Grief; but Love, who, while he is new and young, can do us Miracles, soon wip'd her Eyes, and chas'd away all Sorrows from her Heart, and grew every day more and more impatient, to put her new Design in Execution, being every day more resolv'd. Her Father's Death had remov'd one Obstacle, and secur'd her from his Reproaches; and now she only wants Opportunity, first, to acquaint *Henault*, and then to fly.

She waited not long, all things concurring to her desire; for *Katteriena* falling sick, she had the good luck, as she call'd it then, to entertain *Henault* at the *Grate* oftentimes alone; the first moment she did so, she entertain'd him with the good News, and told him, She had at last vanquish'd her Heart in favour of him, and loving him above all things, Honour, her Vow or Reputation, had resolv'd to abandon her self wholly to him, to give her self up to love and serve him, and that she had no other Consideration in the World; but *Henault*, instead of returning her an Answer, all Joy and Satisfaction, held down his Eyes, and Sighing, with a dejected Look, he cry'd, 'Ah, Madam! Pity a Man so wretched and undone, as not to be sensible of this Blessing as I ought.' She grew pale at this Reply, and trembling, expected he would proceed: "'Tis not (continued he) that I want Love, tenderest Passion, and all the desire Youth and Love can inspire; But, Oh, Madam! when I consider, (for raving mad in Love as I am for your sake, I do consider) that if I should take you from this Repose, Nobly Born and Educated, as you are; and, for that Act, should find a rigid Father deprive me of all that ought to support you, and afford your Birth, Beauty, and Merits, their due, what would you say? How would you Reproach me?' He sighing, expected her Answer, when Blushes overspreading her Face, she reply'd, in a Tone all haughty and angry, 'Ah, *Henault!* Am I then refus'd, after having abandon'd all things for you? Is it thus, you reward my Sacrific'd Honour, Vows, and Virtue? Cannot you hazard the loss of Fortune to possess *Isabella*, who loses all for you!' Then bursting into Tears, at her misfortune of Loving, she suffer'd him to say, 'Oh, Charming fair one! how industrious is your Cruelty, to find out new Torments for an Heart, already press'd down with the Severities of Love? Is it possible, you can make so unhappy a Construction of the tenderest part of my Passion? And can you imagin it want of Love in me, to consider, how I shall preserve and merit the vast Blessing Heaven has given me? Is my Care a Crime? And would not the most deserving Beauty of the World hate me, if I should, to preserve my Life, and satisfy the Passion of my fond Heart, reduce her to the Extremities of Want and Misery? And is there any thing, in what I have said, but what you ought to take for the greatest Respect and tenderness!' 'Alas! (reply'd *Isabella* sighing) young as I am, all unskilful in Love I find, but what I feel, that Discretion is no part of it; and Consideration, inconsistent with the Nobler Passion, who will subsist of its own Nature, and Love unmixed with any other Sentiment? And 'tis not pure, if it be otherwise: I know, had I mix'd Discretion with mine, my Love must have been less,

I never thought of living, but my Love ; and, if I consider'd at all, it was, that Grandure and Magnificence were useless Trifles to Lovers, wholly needless and troublesom. I thought of living in some loanly Cottage, far from the noise of crowded busie Cities, to walk with thee in Groves, and silent Shades, where I might hear no Voice but thine ; and when we had been tir'd, to sit us done by some cool murmuring Rivulet, and be to each a World, my Monarch thou, and I thy Sovereign Queen, while Wreaths of Flowers shall crown our happy Heads, some fragrant Bank our Throne, and Heaven our Canopy : Thus we might laugh at Fortune, and the Proud, despise the duller World, who place their Joys in mighty Shew and Equipage. Alas ! my Nature could not bear it, I am unus'd to Wordly Vanities, and would boast of nothing but my *Henault ;* no Riches, but his Love ; no Grandure, but his Presence.' She ended speaking, with Tears, and he reply'd, 'Now, now, I find, my *Isabella* loves indeed, when she's content to abandon the World for my sake; Oh ! thou hast named the only happy Life that suits my quiet Nature, to be retir'd, has always been my Joy ! But to be so with thee ! Oh ! thou hast charm'd me with a Thought so dear, as has for ever banish'd all my Care, but how to receive thy Goodness ! Please think no more what my angry Parent may do, when he shall hear, how I have dispos'd of my self against his Will and Pleasure, but trust to Love and Providence ; no more ! be gone all Thoughts, but those of *Isabella !* '

As soon as he had made an end of expressing his Joy, he fell to consulting how, and when, she should escape ; and since it was uncertain, when she should be offer'd the Key, for she would not ask for it, she resolv'd to give him notice, either by word of Mouth, or a bit of Paper she would write in, and give him through the *Grate* the first opportunity ; and, parting for that time, they both resolv'd to get up what was possible for their Support, till Time should reconcile Affairs and Friends, and to wait the happy hour.

Isabella's dead Mother had left Jewels, of the value of 2000*l.* to her Daughter, at her Decease, which Jewels were in the possession, now, of the Lady *Abbess*, and were upon Sale, to be added to the Revenue of the *Monastery;* and as *Isabella* was the most Prudent of her Sex, at least, had hitherto been so esteem'd, she was intrusted with all that was in possession of the Lady *Abbess*, and 'twas not difficult to make her self Mistress of all her own Jewels; as also, some 3 or 400*l.* in Gold, that was hoarded up in her Ladyship's Cabinet, against any Accidents that might arrive to the *Monastery;* these *Isabella* also made her own, and put up with the Jewels; and having acquainted *Henault*, with the Day and Hour of her Escape, he got together what he could, and waiting for her, with his Coach, one Night, when no body was awake but her self, when rising softly, as she us'd to do, in the Night, to her Devotion, she stole so dexterously out of the *Monastery*, as no body knew any thing of it; she carry'd away the Keys with her, after having lock'd all the Doors, for she was intrusted often with all. She found *Henault* waiting in his Coach, and trusted none but an honest Coachman that lov'd him; he receiv'd her with all the Transports of a truly ravish'd Lover, and she was infinitely charm'd with the new Pleasure of his Embraces and Kisses.

They drove out of Town immediately, and because she durst not be seen in that Habit, (for it had been immediate Death for both) they drove into a Thicket some three Miles from the Town, where *Henault* having brought her some of his younger Sister's Clothes, he made her put off her Habit, and put on those; and, rending the other, they hid them in a Sand-pit, covered over with Broom, and went that Night forty Miles from *Iper*, to a little Town upon the River *Rhine*, where, changing their Names, they were forthwith married, and took a House in a Country Village, a Farm, where they resolv'd to live retir'd, by the name of *Beroone*, and drove a Farming Trade;

however, not forgetting to set Friends and Engines at work, to get their Pardon, as Criminals, first, that had trangress'd the Law; and, next, as disobedient Persons, who had done contrary to the Will and Desire of their Parents: *Isabella* writ to her Aunt the most moving Letters in the World, so did *Henault* to his Father; but she was a long time, before she could gain so much as an answer from her Aunt, and *Henault* was so unhappy, as never to gain one from his Father; who no sooner heard the News that was spread over all the Town and Country, that young *Henault* was fled with the so fam'd *Isabella*, a *Nun*, and singular for Devotion and Piety of Life, but he immediately setled his Estate on his younger Son, cutting *Henault* off with all his Birthright, which was 5000*l.* a Year. This News, you may believe, was not very pleasing to the young Man, who tho' in possession of the loveliest Virgin, and now Wife, that ever Man was bless'd with; yet when he reflected, he should have children by her, and these and she should come to want, (he having been magnificently Educated, and impatient of scanty Fortune) he laid it to Heart, and it gave him a thousand Uneasinesses in the midst of unspeakable Joys; and the more he strove to hide his Sentiments from *Isabella*, the more tormenting it was within; he durst not name it to her, so insuperable a Grief it would cause in her, to hear him complain; and tho' she could live hardly, as being bred to a devout and severe Life, he could not, but must let the Man of Quality shew it self; even in the disguise of an humbler Farmer: Besides all this, hs found nothing of his Industry thrive, his Cattel still dy'd in the midst of those that were in full Vigour and Health of other Peoples; his Crops of Wheat and Barly, and other Grain, tho' manág'd by able and knowing Husbandmen, were all, either Mildew'd, or Blasted, or some Misfortune still arriv'd to him; his Coach-Horses would fight and kill one another, his Barns sometimes be fir'd; so that it became a Proverb all over the

Country, if any ill Luck had arriv'd to any body, they would say, 'They had Monsieur *BEROONE'S* Luck.' All these Reflections did but add to his Melancholy, and he grew at last to be in some want, insomuch, that *Isabella*, who had by her frequent Letters, and submissive Supplications, to her Aunt, (who lov'd her tenderly) obtain'd her Pardon, and her Blessing; she now press'd her for some Money, and besought her to consider, how great a Fortune she had brought to the *Monastery*, and implor'd, she would allow her some Sallary out of it, for she had been marry'd two Years, and most of what she had was exhausted. The Aunt, who found, that what was done, could not be undone, did, from time to time, supply her so, as one might have liv'd very decently on that very Revenue; but that would not satisfy the great Heart of *Henault*. He was now about three and twenty Years old, and *Isabella* about eighteen, too young, and too lovely a Pair, to begin their Misfortunes so soon; they were both the most Just and Pious in the World; they were Examples of Goodness, and Eminent for Holy Living, and for perfect Loving, and yet nothing thriv'd they undertook; they had no Children, and all their Joy was in each other; at last, one good Fortune arriv'd to them, by the Solicitations of the Lady *Abbess*, and the *Bishop*, who was her near Kinsman, they got a Pardon for *Isabella's* quitting the *Monastery*, and marrying, so that she might now return to her own Country again. *Henault* having also his Pardon, they immediately quit the place, where they had remain'd for two Years, and came again into *Flanders*, hoping, the change of place might afford 'em better Luck.

Henault then began again to solicit his Cruel Father, but nothing would do, he refus'd to see him, or to receive any Letters from him; but, at last, he prevail'd so far with him, as that he sent a Kinsman to him, to assure him, if he would leave his Wife, and go into the *French* Campagn, he would Equip him as well as his Quality requir'd, and that, according as he behav'd himself, he should gain his Favour; but if he liv'd Idly at home, giving up his Youth and Glory to lazy Love, he would have no more to say to him, but race him out of his Heart, and out of his Memory.

He had setled himself in a very pretty House, furnished with what was fitting for the Reception of any Body of Quality that would live a private Life, and they found all the Respect that their Merits deserv'd from all the World, every body entirely loving and endeavouring to serve them; and *Isabella* so perfectly had the Ascendent over her Aunt's Heart, that she procur'd from her all that she could desire, and much more than she could expect. She was perpetually progging and saving all that she could, to enrich and advance her, and, at last, pardoning and forgiving *Henault*, lov'd him as her own Child; so that all things look'd with a better Face than before, and never was so dear and fond a Couple seen, as *Henault* and *Isabella*; but, at last, she prov'd with Child, and the Aunt, who might reasonably believe, so young a Couple would have a great many Children, and foreseeing there was a no Provision likely to be made them, unless he pleas'd his Father, for if the Aunt should chance to dye, all their Hope was gone; she therefore daily solicited him to obey his Father, and go to the Camp; and that having atchiev'd Fame and Renown, he would return a Favourite to his Father, and Comfort to his Wife: After she had solicited in vain, for he was not able to endure the thought of leaving *Isabella*, melancholy as he was with his ill Fortune; the *Bishop*, kinsman to *Isabella*, took him to task, and urg'd his Youth and Birth, and that he ought not to wast both without Action, when all the World was employ'd; and, that since his Father had so great a desire he should go into a Campagn, either to serve the *Venetian* against the *Turks*, or into the *French* Service, which he lik'd best; he besought him to think of it; and since he had satisfy'd his Love, he should and ought to satisfy his Duty, it being absolutely necessary for the wiping off the Stain of his Sacrilege, and to gain him the favour of Heaven, which, he found, had hitherto been averse to all he had undertaken: In fine, all his Friends, and all who lov'd him, joyn'd in this Design, and all thought it convenient, nor was he insensible of the Advantage it might bring him; but Love, which every day grew fonder and fonder in his Heart, oppos'd all their Reasonings, tho' he saw all the Brave Youth of the Age preparing to go, either to one Army, or the other.

At last, he lets *Isabella* know, what Propositions he had made him, both by his Father, and his Relations; at the very first Motion, she almost fainted in his Arms, while he was speaking, and it possess'd her with so intire a Grief, that she miscarry'd, to the insupportable Torment of her tender Husband and Lover, so that, to re-establish her Repose, he was forc'd to promise not to go; however, she consider'd all their Circumstances, and weigh'd the Advantages that might redound both to his Honour and Fortune, by it; and, in a matter of a Month's time, with the Persuasions and Reasons of her Friends, she suffer'd him to resolve upon going, her self determining to retire to the *Monastery*, till the time of his Return; but when she nam'd the *Monastery*, he grew pale and disorder'd, and obliged her to promise him, not to enter into it any more, for fear they should never suffer her to come forth again; so that he resolv'd not to depart, till she had made a Vow to him, never to go again within the Walls of a Religious House, which had already been so fatal to them. She promis'd, and he believ'd.

Henault, at last, overcame his Heart, which pleaded so for his Stay, and sent his Father word, he was ready to obey him, and to carry the first Efforts of his Arms against the common Foes of Christendom, the *Turks*; his Father was very well pleas'd at this, and sent him Two thousand

Crowns, his Horses and Furniture sutable to his Quality, and a Man to wait on him; so that it was not long e're he got himself in order to be gone, after a dismal parting.

He made what hast he could to the *French* Army, then under the Command of the Monsignior, the Duke of *Beaufort*, then at *Candia*, and put himself a Voluntier under his Conduct; in which Station was *Villenoys*, who, you have already heard, was so passionate a Lover of *Isabella*, who no sooner heard of *Henault's* being arriv'd, and that he was Husband to *Isabella*, but he was impatient to learn, by what strange Adventure he came to gain her, even from her Vow'd Retreat, when he, with all his Courtship, could not be so happy, tho' she was then free in the World, and Unvow'd to Heaven.

As soon as he sent his Name to *Henault*, he was sent for up, for *Henault* had heard of *Villenoys*, and that he had been a Lover of *Isabella;* they receiv'd one another with all the endearing Civility imaginable for the aforesaid Reason, and for that he was his Country-man, tho' unknown to him, *Villenoys* being gone to the Army, just as *Henault* came from the *Jesuits* College. A great deal of Endearment pass'd between them, and they became, from that moment, like two sworn Brothers, and he receiv'd the whole Relation from *Henault*, of his Amour.

It was not long before the Siege began anew, for he arriv'd at the beginning of the Spring, and, as soon as he came, almost, they fell to Action; and it happen'd upon a day, that a Party of some Four hundred Men resolv'd to sally out upon the Enemy, as, when ever they could, they did; but as it is not my business to relate the History of the War, being wholly unacquainted with the Terms of Battels, I shall only say, That these Men were led by *Villenoys*, and that *Henault* would accompany him in this Sally, and that they acted very Noble, and great Things, worthy of a Memory in the History of that Siege; but this day, particularly, they had an occasion to shew their

Valour, which they did very much to their Glory; but, venturing too far, they were ambush'd, in the persuit of the Party of the Enemies, and being surrounded, *Villenoys* had the unhappiness to see his gallant Friend fall, fighting and dealing of Wounds around him, even as he descended to the Earth, for he fell from his Horse at the same moment that he kill'd a *Turk;* and *Villenoys* could neither assist him, nor had he the satisfaction to be able to rescue his dead Body from under the Horses, but, with much ado, escaping with his own Life, got away, in spite of all that follow'd him, and recover'd the Town, before they could overtake him : He passionately bewail'd the Loss of this brave young Man, and offer'd any Recompence to those, that would have ventur'd to have search'd for his dead Body among the Slain ; but it was not fit to hazard the Living, for unnecessary Services to the Dead ; and tho' he had a great mind to have Interr'd him, he rested content with what he wish'd to pay his Friends Memory, tho' he could not : So that all the Service now he could do him, was, to write to *Isabella*, to whom he had not writ, tho' commanded by her so to do, in three Years before, which was never since she took Orders. He gave her an Account of the Death of her Husband, and how Gloriously he fell fighting for the Holy Cross, and how much Honour he had won, if it had been his Fate to have outliv'd that great, but unfortunate, Day, where, with 400 Men, they had kill'd 1500 of the Enemy. The General *Beaufort* himself had so great a Respect and Esteem for this young Man, and knowing him to be of Quality, that he did him the honour to bemoan him, and to send a Condoling Letter to *Isabella*, how much worth her Esteem he dy'd, and that he had Eterniz'd his Memory with the last Gasp of his Life.

When this News arriv'd, it may be easily imagin'd, what Impressions, or rather Ruins, it made in the Heart of this fair Mourner ; the Letters came by his Man, who saw him fall in Battel, and came off with those few that escap'd with *Villenoys;* he brought back what Money he had, a few Jewels, with *Isabella's* Picture that he carry'd with him and had left in his Chamber in the Fort at *Candia,* for fear of breaking it in Action. And now *Isabella's* Sorrow grew to the Extremity, she thought, she could not suffer more than she did by his Absence, but she now found a Grief more killing; she hung her Chamber with Black, and liv'd without the Light of Day : Only Wax Lights, that let her behold the Picture of this Charming Man, before which she sacrific'd Floods of Tears. He had now been absent about ten Months, and she had learnt just to live without him, but Hope preserv'd her then ; but now she had nothing, for which to wish to live. She, for about two Months after the News arriv'd, liv'd without seeing any Creature but a young Maid, that was her Woman ; but extream Importunity oblig'd her to give way to the Visits of her Friends, who endeavour'd to restore her Melancholy Soul to its wonted Easiness; for, however it was oppress'd within, by *Henault's* Absence, she bore it off with a modest Chearfulness; but now she found, that Fortitude and Virtue fail'd her, when she was assur'd, he was no more: She continu'd thus Mourning, and thus inclos'd, the space of a whole Year, never suffering the Visit of any Man, but of a near Relation ; so that she acquir'd a Reputation, such as never any young Beauty had, for she was now but Nineteen, and her Face and Shape more excellent than ever; she daily increas'd in Beauty, which, joyn'd to her Exemplary Piety, Charity, and all other excellent Qualities, gain'd her a wonderous Fame, and begat an Awe and Reverence in all that heard of her, and there was no Man of any Quality, that did not Adore her. After her Year was up, she went to the Churches, but would never be seen any where else abroad, but that was enough to procure her a thousand Lovers; and some, who had the boldness to send her Letters, which, if she receiv'd, she gave no Answer to, and many she sent back unread and unseal'd: So that she would encourage none, tho' their Quality was far beyond what she could hope; but she was resolv'd to marry no more, however her Fortune might require it.

It happen'd, that, about this time, *Candia* being unfortunately taken by the *Turks*, all the brave Men that escap'd the Sword, return'd, among them, *Villenoys*, who no sooner arriv'd, but he sent to let *Isabella* know of it, and to beg the Honour of waiting on her; desirous to learn what Fate befel her dear Lord, she suffer'd him to visit her, where he found her, in her Mourning, a thousand times more Fair, (at least, he fancy'd so) than ever she appear'd to be; so that if he lov'd her before, he now ador'd her; if he burnt then, he rages now; but the awful Sadness, and soft Languishment of her Eyes, hinder'd him from the presumption of speaking of his Passion to her, tho' it would have been no new thing; and his first Visit was spent in the Relation of every Circumstance of *Henault's* Death; and, at his going away, he begg'd leave to visit her sometimes, and she gave him permission: He lost no time, but made use of the Liberty she had given him; and when his Sister, who was a great Companion of *Isabella's*, went to see her, he would still wait on her; so that, either with his own Visits, and those of his Sister's, he saw *Isabella* every day, and had the good luck to see, he diverted her, by giving her Relations of Transactions of the Siege, and the Customs and Manners of the *Turks*: All he said, was with so good a Grace, that he render'd every thing agreeable; he was, besides, very Beautiful, well made, of Quality and Fortune, and fit to inspire Love.

He made his Visits so often, and so long, that, at last, he took the Courage to speak of his Passion, which, at first, *Isabella* would by no means hear of, but, by degrees, she yielded more and more to listen to his tender Discourse; and he liv'd thus with her two Years, before he could

gain any more upon her Heart, than to suffer him to speak
of Love to her; but that, which subdu'd her quite was,
That her Aunt, the Lady *Abbess*, dy'd, and with her, all
the Hopes and Fortune of *Isabella*, so that she was left
with only a Charming Face and Meen, a Virtue, and a
Discretion above her Sex, to make her Fortune within
the World; into a Religious House, she was resolv'd not
to go, because her Heart deceiv'd her once, and she durst
not trust it again, whatever it promis'd.

The death of this Lady made her look more favourably
on *Villenoys*; but yet, she was resolv'd to try his Love to
the utmost, and keep him off, as long as 'twas possible
she could subsist, and 'twas for Interest she married again,
tho' she lik'd the Person very well; and since she was
forc'd to submit her self to be a second time a Wife, she
thought, she could live better with *Villenoys*, than any other,
since for him she ever had a great Esteem; and fancy'd
the Hand of Heaven had pointed out her Destiny, which
she could not avoid, without a Crime.

So that when she was again importun'd by her impatient
Lover, she told him, She had made a Vow to remain three
Years, at least, before she would marry again, after the
Death of the best of Men and Husbands, and him who
had the Fruits of her early Heart; and, notwithstanding
all the Solicitations of *Villenoys*, she would not consent to
marry him, till her Vow of Widowhood was expir'd.

He took her promise, which he urg'd her to give him,
and to shew the height of his Passion in his obedience;
he condescends to stay her appointed time, tho' he saw
her every day, and all his Friends and Relations made
her Visits upon this new account, and there was nothing
talk'd on, but this design'd Wedding, which, when the
time was expir'd, was perform'd accordingly with great
Pomp and Magnificence, for *Villenoys* had no Parents to
hinder his Design; or if he had, the Reputation and
Virtue of this Lady would have subdu'd them.

The Marriage was celebrated in this House, where she liv'd ever since her Return from *Germany*, from the time she got her Pardon; and when *Villenoys* was preparing all things in a more magnificent Order at his Villa, some ten Miles from the City, she was very melancholy, and would often say, She had been us'd to such profound Retreat, and to live without the fatigue of Noise and Equipage, that, she fear'd, she should never endure that Grandeur, which was proper for his Quality; and tho' the House, in the Country, was the most beautifully Situated in all *Flanders*, she was afraid of a numerous Train, and kept him, for the most part, in this pretty City Mansion, which he Adorn'd and Enlarg'd, as much as she would give him leave; so that there wanted nothing, to make this House fit to receive the People of the greatest Quality, little as it was: But all the Servants and Footmen, all but one *Valet*, and the Maid, were lodg'd abroad, for *Isabella*, not much us'd to the sight of Men about her, suffer'd them as seldom as possible, to come in her Presence, so that she liv'd more like a *Nun* still, than a Lady of the World; and very rarely any Maids came about her, but *Maria*, who had always permission to come, when ever she pleas'd, unless forbidden.

As *Villenoys* had the most tender and violent Passion for his Wife, in the World, he suffer'd her to be pleas'd at any rate, and to live in what Method she best lik'd, and was infinitely satisfy'd with the Austerity and manner of her Conduct, since in his Arms, and alone, with him, she wanted nothing that could Charm; so that she was esteemed the fairest and best of Wives, and he the most happy of all Mankind. When she would go abroad, she had her Coaches Rich and Gay, and her Livery ready to attend her in all the Splendour imaginable; and he was always buying one rich Jewel, or Necklace, or some great Rarity or other, that might please her; so that there was nothing her Soul could desire, which it had not, except the Assurance of Eternal Happiness, which she labour'd incessantly to gain. She had no Discontent, but because she was not bless'd with a Child; but she submits to the pleasure of Heaven, and endeavour'd, by her good Works, and her Charity, to make the Poor her Children, and was ever doing Acts of Virtue, to make the Proverb good, *That more are the Children of the Barren, than the Fruitful Woman.* She liv'd in this Tranquility, belov'd by all, for the space of five Years, and Time (and perpetual Obligations from *Villenoys,* who was the most indulgent and indearing Man in the World) had almost worn out of her Heart the Thought of *Henault,* or if she remember'd him, it was in her Prayers, or sometimes with a short sigh, and no more, tho' it was a great while, before she could subdue her Heart to that Calmness; but she was prudent, and wisely bent all her Endeavours to please, oblige, and caress, the deserving Living, and to strive all she could, to forget the unhappy Dead, since it could not but redound to the disturbance of her Repose, to think of him; so that she had now transferr'd all that Tenderness she had for him, to *Villenoys.*

Villenoys, of all Diversions, lov'd Hunting, and kept, at his Country House, a very famous Pack of Dogs, which he us'd to lend, sometimes, to a young Lord, who was his dear Friend, and his Neighbour in the Country, who would often take them, and be out two or three days together, where he heard of Game, and oftentimes *Villenoys* and he would be a whole Week at a time exercising in this Sport, for there was no Game near at hand. This young Lord had sent him a Letter, to invite him fifteen Miles farther than his own *Villa,* to hunt, and appointed to meet him at his Country House, in order to go in search of this promis'd Game; So that *Villenoys* got about a Week's Provision, of what Necessaries he thought he should want in that time; and taking only his *Valet,* who lov'd the Sport, he left *Isabella* for a Week to her Devotion, and her other innocent Diversions of fine Work, at which she was Excellent, and left the Town to go meet this young Challenger.

When *Villenoys* was at any time out, it was the custom of *Isabella* to retire to her Chamber, and to receive no Visits, not even the Ladies, so absolutely she devoted her self to her Husband: All the first day she pass'd over in this manner, and Evening being come, she order'd her Supper to be brought to her Chamber, and, because it was Washing-day the next day, she order'd all her Maids to go very early to Bed, that they might be up betimes, and to leave only *Maria* to attend her; which was accordingly done. This *Maria* was a young Maid, that was very discreet, and, of all things in the World, lov'd her Lady, whom she had liv'd with, ever since she came from the *Monastery*.

When all were in Bed, and the little light Supper just carry'd up to the Lady, and only, as I said, *Maria* attending, some body knock'd at the Gate, it being about Nine of the Clock at Night; so *Maria* snatching up a Candle, went to the Gate, to see who it might be; when she open'd the Door, she found a Man in a very odd Habit, and a worse Countenance, and asking, Who he would speak with? He told her, Her Lady: My Lady (reply'd *Maria*) does not use to receive Visits at this hour; Pray, what is your Business? He reply'd, That which I will deliver only to your Lady, and that she may give me Admittance, pray, deliver her this Ring: And pulling off a small Ring, with *Isabella's* Name and Hair in it, he gave it *Maria*, who, shutting the Gate upon him, went in with the Ring; as soon as *Isabella* saw it, she was ready to swound on the Chair where she sate, and cry'd, Where had you this? *Maria* reply'd, An old rusty Fellow at the Gate gave it me, and desired, it might be his Pasport to you; I ask'd his Name, but he said, You knew him not, but he had great News to tell you. *Isabella* reply'd,

(almost swounding again) Oh, *Maria!* I am ruin'd. The
Maid, all this while, knew not what she meant, nor, that
that was a Ring given to *Henault* by her Mistress, but
endeavouring to recover her, only ask'd her, What she
should say to the old Messenger? *Isabella* bid her bring
him up to her, (she had scarce Life to utter these last
words) and before she was well recover'd, *Maria* enter'd
with the Man; and *Isabella* making a Sign to her, to
depart the Room, she was left alone with him.

Henault (for it was he) stood trembling and speechless
before her, giving her leisure to take a strict Survey of
him; at first finding no Feature nor Part of *Henault* about
him, her Fears began to lessen, and she hop'd, it was not
he, as her first Apprehensions had suggested; when he
(with the Tears of Joy standing in his Eyes, and not
daring suddenly to approach her, for fear of encreasing
that Disorder he saw in her pale Face) began to speak to
her, and cry'd, Fair Creature! is there no Remains of
your *Henault* left in this Face of mine, all o'regrown with
Hair? Nothing in these Eyes, sunk with eight Years
Absence from you, and Sorrows? Nothing in this Shape,
bow'd with Labour and Griefs, that can inform you? I
was once that happy Man you lov'd! At these words,
Tears stop'd his Speech, and *Isabella* kept them Company,
for yet she wanted Words. Shame and Confusion fill'd
her Soul, and she was not able to lift her Eyes up, to
consider the Face of him, whose Voice she knew so perfectly well. In one moment, she run over a thousand
Thoughts. She finds, by his Return, she is not only
expos'd to all the Shame imaginable; to all the Upbraiding,
on his part, when he shall know she is marry'd to another;
but all the Fury and Rage of *Villenoys*, and the Scorn of
the Town, who will look on her as an Adulteress: She
sees *Henault* poor, and knew, she must fall from all the
Glory and Tranquility she had for five happy Years
triumph'd in; in which time, she had known no Sorrow,

or Care, tho' she had endur'd a thousand with *Henault*.
She dyes, to think, however, that he should know, she
had been so lightly in Love with him, to marry again;
and she dyes, to think, that *Villenoys* must see her again
in the Arms of *Henault*; besides, she could not recal her
Love, for Love, like Reputation, once fled, never returns
more. 'Tis impossible to love, and cease to love, (and
love another) and yet return again to the first Passion,
tho' the Person have all the Charms, or a thousand times
more than it had, when it first conquer'd. This Mistery
in Love, it may be, is not generally known, but nothing
is more certain. One may a while suffer the Flame to
languish, but there may be a reviving Spark in the Ashes,
rak'd up, that may burn anew; but when 'tis quite
extinguish'd, it never returns or rekindles.

'Twas so with the Heart of *Isabella*; had she believ'd,
Henault had been living, she had lov'd to the last moment
of their Lives; but, alas! the Dead are soon forgotten,
and she now lov'd only *Villenoys*.

After they had both thus silently wept, with very different
sentiments, she thought 'twas time to speak; and dissembling as well as she could, she caress'd him in her
Arms, and told him, She could not express her Surprize
and Joy for his Arrival. If she did not Embrace him
heartily, or speak so Passionately as she us'd to do, he
fancy'd it her Confusion, and his being in a condition not
so fit to receive Embraces from her; and evaded them as
much as 'twas possible for him to do, in respect to her,
till he had dress'd his Face, and put himself in order; but
the Supper being just brought up, when he knock'd, she
order'd him to sit down and Eat, and he desir'd her not
to let *Maria* know who he was, to see how long it would
be, before she knew him or would call him to mind. But
Isabella commanded *Maria*, to make up a Bed in such a
Chamber, without disturbing her Fellows, and dismiss'd
her from waiting at Table. The Maid admir'd, what

strange, good, and joyful News, this Man had brought her Mistress, that he was so Treated, and alone with her, which never any Man had yet been; but she never imagin'd the Truth, and knew her Lady's Prudence too well, to question her Conduct. While they were at Supper, *Isabella* oblig'd him to tell her, How he came to be reported Dead; of which, she receiv'd Letters, both from Monsieur *Villenoys*, and the Duke of *Beaufort*, and by his Man the News, who saw him Dead? He told her, That, after the Fight, of which, first, he gave her an account, he being left among the Dead, when the Enemy came to Plunder and strip 'em, they found, he had Life in him, and appearing as an Eminent Person, they thought it better Booty to save me, (continu'd he) and get my Ransom, than to strip me, and bury me among the Dead; so they bore me off to a Tent, and recover'd me to Life; and, after that, I was recover'd of my Wounds, and sold, by the Soldier that had taken me, to a Spahee, who kept me a Slave, setting a great Ransom on me, such as I was not able to pay. I writ several times, to give you, and my Father, an account of my Misery, but receiv'd no Answer, and endur'd seven Years of Dreadful Slavery: When I found, at last, an opportunity to make my Escape, and from that time, resolv'd, never to cut the Hair of this Beard, till I should either see my dearest *Isabella* again, or hear some News of her. All that I fear'd, was, That she was Dead; and, at that word, he fetch'd a deep Sigh; and viewing all things so infinitely more Magnificent than he had left 'em, or, believ'd, she could afford; and, that she was far more Beautiful in Person, and Rich in Dress, than when he left her: He had a thousand Torments of Jealousie that seiz'd him, of which, he durst not make any mention, but rather chose to wait a little, and see, whether she had lost her Virtue: He desir'd, he might send for a Barber, to put his Face in some handsomer Order, and more fit for the Happiness 'twas that Night to receive; but she told him, No Dress, no Disguise, could render him more Dear and Acceptable to her, and that to morrow was time enough, and that his Travels had render'd him more fit for Repose, than Dressing. So that after a little while, they had talk'd over all they had a mind to say, all that was very indearing on his side, and as much Concern as she could force, on hers; she conducted him to his Chamber, which was very rich, and which gave him a very great addition of Jealousie: However, he suffer'd her to help him to Bed, which she seem'd to do, with all the tenderness in the World; and when she had seen him laid, she said, She would go to her Prayers, and come to him as soon as she had done, which being before her usual Custom, it was not a wonder to him she stay'd long, and he, being extreamly tir'd with his Journy, fell asleep. 'Tis true, *Isabella* essay'd to Pray, but alas! it was in vain, she was distracted with a thousand Thoughts what to do, which the more she thought, the more it distracted her; she was a thousand times about to end her Life, and, at one stroke, rid her self of the Infamy, that, she saw, must inevitably fall upon her; but Nature was frail, and the Tempter strong: And after a thousand Convulsions, even worse than Death it self, she resolv'd upon the Murder of *Henault*, as the only means of removing all Obstacles to her future Happiness; she resolv'd on this, but after she had done so, she was seiz'd with so great Horror, that she imagin'd, if she perform'd it, she should run Mad; and yet, if she did not, she should be also Frantick, with the Shames and Miseries that would befal her; and believing the Murder the least Evil, since she could never live with him, she fix'd her Heart on that; and causing her self to be put immediately to Bed, in her own Bed, she made *Maria* go to hers, and when all was still, she softly rose, and taking a Candle with her, only in her Night-Gown and Slippers, she goes to the Bed of the Unfortunate *Henault*, with a Penknife in her hand; but considering, she knew not how to conceal the Blood, should she cut his Throat, she resolves to Strangle him, or Smother him with a Pillow; that last thought was no sooner borne, but put in Execution; and, as he soundly slept, she smother'd him without any Noise, or so much as his Strugling; But when she had done this dreadful Deed, and saw the dead Corps of her once-lov'd Lord, lye Smiling (as it were) upon her, she fell into a Swound with the Horror of the Deed, and it had been well for her she had there dy'd; but she reviv'd again, and awaken'd to more and new Horrors, she flyes all frighted from the Chamber, and fancies, the Phantom of her dead Lord persues her; she runs from Room to Room, and starts and stares, as if she saw him continually before her. Now all that was ever Soft and Dear to her, with him, comes into her Heart, and, she finds, he conquers anew, being Dead, who could not gain her Pity, while Living.

While she was thus flying from her Guilt, in vain, she hears one knock with Authority at the Door: She is now more affrighted, if possible, and knows not whither to fly for Refuge; she fancies, they are already the Officers of Justice, and that Ten thousand Tortures and Wrecks are fastening on her, to make her confess the horrid Murder; the knocking increases, and so loud, that the Laundry Maids believing it to be the Woman that us'd to call them up, and help them to Wash, rose, and, opening the Door, let in *Villenoys;* who having been at his Country *Villa,* and finding there a Footman, instead of his Friend, who waited to tell him, His Master was fallen sick of the Small Pox, and could not wait on him, he took Horse, and came back to his lovely *Isabella;* but running up, as he us'd to do, to her Chamber, he found her not, and seeing a Light in another Room, he went in, but found *Isabella* flying from him, out at another Door, with all the speed she could, he admires at this Action, and the more,

because his Maid told him Her Lady had been a Bed a
good while; he grows a little Jealous, and persues her,
but still she flies; at last he caught her in his Arms,
where she fell into a swound, but quickly recovering, he
set her down in a Chair, and, kneeling before her, implor'd
to know what she ayl'd, and why she fled from him, who
ador'd her? She only fix'd a ghastly Look upon him, and
said, She was not well: 'Oh! (said he) put not me off
with such poor Excuses, *Isabella* never fled from me, when
Ill, but came to my Arms, and to my Bosom, to find a
Cure; therefore, tell me, what's the matter?' At that,
she fell a weeping in a most violent manner, and cry'd,
She was for ever undone: He, being mov'd with Love
and Compassion, conjur'd her to tell what she ayl'd: 'Ah!
(said she) thou and I, and all of us, are undone!' At this,
he lost all Patience, and rav'd, and cry'd, Tell me, and
tell me immediately, what's the matter? When she saw
his Face pale, and his Eyes fierce, she fell on her knees,
and cry'd, 'Oh! you can never Pardon me, if I should
tell you, and yet, alas! I am innocent of Ill, by all that's
good, I am.' But her Conscience accusing her at that
word, she was silent. If thou art Innocent, said *Villenoys*,
taking her up in his Arms, and kissing her wet Face, 'By
all that's Good, I Pardon thee, what ever thou hast done.'
'Alas! (said she) Oh! but I dare not name it, 'till you
swear.' 'By all that's Sacred, (reply'd he) and by whatever Oath you can oblige me to; by my inviolable Love
to thee, and by thy own dear Self, I swear, whate're it
be, I do forgive thee; I know, thou art too good to commit a Sin I may not with Honour, pardon.'

With this, and hearten'd by his Caresses, she told him,
That *Henault* was return'd; and repeating to him his
Escape, she said, She had put him to Bed, and when he
expected her to come, she fell on her Knees at the Bed-
side, and confess'd, She was married to *Villenoys*; at that
word (said she) he fetch'd a deep Sigh or two, and presently

after, with a very little struggling, dy'd; and, yonder, he lyes still in the Bed. After this, she wept so abundantly, that all *Villenoys* could do, could hardly calm her Spirits; but after, consulting what they should do in this Affair, *Villenoys* ask'd her, Who of the House saw him? She said, Only *Maria*, who knew not who he was; so that, resolving to save *Isabella's* Honour, which was the only Misfortune to come, *Villenoys* himself propos'd the carrying him out to the Bridge, and throwing him into the River, where the Stream would carry him down to the Sea, and lose him; or, if he were found, none could know him. So *Villenoys* took a Candle, and went and look'd on him, and found him altogether chang'd, that no Body would know who he was; he therefore put on his Clothes, which was not hard for him to do, for he was scarce yet cold, and comforting again *Isabella*, as well as he could, he went himself into the Stable, and fetched a Sack, such as they us'd for Oats, a new Sack, whereon stuck a great Needle, with a Pack-thread in it; this Sack he brings into the House, and shews to *Isabella*, telling her, He would put the Body in there, for the better convenience of carrying it on his Back. *Isabella* all this while said but little, but, fill'd with Thoughts all Black and Hellish, she ponder'd within, while the Fond and Passionate *Villenoys* was endeavouring to hide her Shame, and to make this an absolute Secret: She imagin'd, that could she live after a Deed so black, *Villenoys* would be eternal reproaching her, if not with his Tongue, at least with his Heart, and embolden'd by one Wickedness, she was the readier for another, and another of such a Nature, as has, in my Opinion, far less Excuse, than the first; but when Fate begins to afflict, she goes through stitch with her Black Work.

When *Villenoys*, who would, for the Safety of *Isabella's* Honour, be the sole Actor in the disposing of this Body; and since he was Young, Vigorous, and Strong, and able

to bear it, would trust no one with the Secret, he having
put up the Body, and ty'd it fast, set it on a Chair, turning
his Back towards it, with the more conveniency to take
it upon his Back, bidding *Isabella* give him the two
Corners of the Sack in his Hands; telling her, They
must do this last office for the Dead, more, in order to
the securing their Honour and Tranquility hereafter, than
for any other Reason, and bid her be of good Courage,
till he came back, for it was not far to the Bridge, and it
being the dead of the Night, he should pass well enough.
When he had the Sack on his Back, and ready to go
with it, she cry'd, Stay, my Dear, some of his Clothes
hang out, which I will put in; and, with that, taking the
Pack-needle with the Thread, sew'd the Sack, with several
strong Stitches, to the Collar of *Villenoy's* Coat, without
his perceiving it, and bid him go now; and when you
come to the Bridge, (said she) and that you are throwing
him over the Rail, (which is not above Breast high) be
sure you give him a good swing, least the Sack should
hang on any thing at the side of the Bridge, and not fall
into the Stream; I'le warrant you, (said *Villenoys*) I know
how to secure his falling. And going his way with it,
Love lent him Strength, and he soon arriv'd at the Bridge;
where, turning his Back to the Rail, and heaving the
Body over, he threw himself with all his force backward,
the better to swing the Body into the River, whose weight
(it being made fast to his Collar) pull'd *Villenoys* after it,
and both the live and the dead Man falling into the
River, which, being rapid at the Bridge, soon drown'd
him, especially when so great a weight hung to his Neck;
so that he dy'd, without considering what was the occasion
of his Fate.

Isabella remain'd the most part of the Night sitting in
her Chamber, without going to Bed, to see what would
become of her Damnable Design; but when it was towards
Morning, and she heard no News, she put herself into

Bed, but not to find Repose or Rest there, for that she thought impossible, after so great a Barbarity as she had committed; No, (said she) it is but just I should for ever wake, who have, in one fatal Night, destroy'd two such Innocents. Oh! what Fate, what Destiny, is mine? Under what cursed Planet was I born, that Heaven it self could not divert my Ruine? It was not many Hours since I thought my self the most happy and blest of Women, and now am fallen to the Misery of one of the worst Fiends of Hell.

Such were her Thoughts, and such her Cryes, till the Light brought on new Matter for Grief; for, about Ten of the Clock, News was brought, that Two Men were found dead in the River, and that they were carry'd to the Town-Hall, to lye there, till they were own'd: Within an hour after, News was brought in, that one of these Unhappy Men was *Villenoys;* his *Valet,* who, all this while, imagin'd him in Bed with his Lady, ran to the Hall, to undeceive the People, for he knew, if his Lord were gone out, he should have been call'd to Dress him; but finding it, as 'twas reported, he fell a weeping, and wringing his Hands, in a most miserable manner, he ran home with the News; where, knocking at his Lady's Chamber Door, and finding it fast lock'd, he almost hop'd again, he was deceiv'd; but *Isabella* rising, and opening the Door, *Maria* first enter'd weeping, with the News, and then brought the *Valet,* to testify the fatal Truth of it. *Isabella,* tho' it were nothing but what she expected to hear, almost swounded in her Chair; nor did she feign it, but felt really all the Pangs of Killing Grief; and was so alter'd with her Night's Watching and Grieving, that this new Sorrow look'd very Natural in her. When she was recover'd, she asked a thousand Questions about him, and question'd the Possibility of it; for (said she) he went out this Morning early from me, and had no signs, in his Face, of any Grief or Discontent. Alas! (said the *Valet*)

Madam, he is not his own Murderer, some one has done
it in Revenge; and then told her, how he was found
fasten'd to a Sack, with a dead strange Man ty'd up
within it; and every body concludes, that they were both
first murder'd, and then drawn to the River, and thrown
both in. At the Relation of this Strange Man, she seem'd
more amaz'd than before, and commanding the *Valet* to go
to the Hall, and to take Order about the Coroner's sitting
on the Body of *Villenoys*, and then to have it brought
home: She called *Maria* to her, and, after bidding her
shut the Door, she cry'd, Ah, *Maria!* I will tell thee
what my Heart imagins; but first, (said she) run to the
Chamber of the Stranger, and see, if he be still in Bed,
which I fear he is not; she did so, and brought word, he
was gone; then (said she) my Forebodings are true. When
I was in Bed last night, with *Villenoys* (and at that word,
she sigh'd as if her Heart-Strings had broken) I told him,
I had lodg'd a Stranger in my House, who was by, when
my first Lord and Husband fell in Battel; and that, after
the Fight, finding him yet alive, he spoke to him, and
gave him that Ring you brought me last Night; and
conjur'd him, if ever his Fortune should bring him to
Flanders, to see me, and give me that Ring, and tell me
—(with that, she wept, and could scarce speak) a thousand
tender and endearing things, and then dy'd in his Arms.
For my dear *Henault's* sake (said she) I us'd him nobly,
and dismiss'd you that Night, because I was asham'd to
have any Witness of the Griefs I paid his Memory: All
this I told to *Villenoys*, whom I found disorder'd; and,
after a sleepless Night, I fancy he got up, and took this
poor Man, and has occasion'd his Death: At that, she
wept anew, and *Maria*, to whom, all that her Mistress
said, was Gospel, verily believ'd it so, without examining
Reason; and *Isabella* conjuring her, since none of the
House knew of the old Man's being there, (for Old he
appear'd to be) that she would let it for ever be a Secret,

and, to this she bound her by an Oath; so that none knowing *Henault*, altho' his Body was expos'd there for three Days to Publick View: When the Coroner had Set on the Bodies, he found, they had been first Murder'd some way or other, and then afterwards tack'd together, and thrown into the River, they brought the Body of *Villenoys* home to his House, where, it being laid on a Table, all the House infinitely bewail'd it; and *Isabella* did nothing but swound away, almost as fast as she recover'd Life; however, she would, to compleat her Misery, be led to see this dreadful Victim of her Cruelty, and, coming near the Table, the Body, whose Eyes were before close shut, now open'd themselves wide, and fix'd them on *Isabella*, who, giving a great Schreek, fell down in a swound, and the Eyes clos'd again; they had much ado to bring her to Life, but, at last, they did so, and led her back to her Bed, where she remain'd a good while. Different Opinions and Discourses were made, concerning the opening of the Eyes of the Dead Man, and viewing *Isabella*; but she was a Woman of so admirable a Life and Conversation, of so undoubted a Piety and Sanctity of Living, that not the least Conjecture could be made, of her having a hand in it, besides the improbability of it; yet the whole thing was a Mystery, which, they thought, they ought to look into: But a few Days after, the Body of *Villenoys* being interr'd in a most magnificent manner, and, by Will all he had, was long since setled on *Isabella*, the World, instead of Suspecting her, Ador'd her the more, and every Body of Quality was already hoping to be next, tho' the fair Mourner still kept her Bed, and Languish'd daily.

It happen'd, not long after this, there came to the Town a *French* Gentleman, who was taken at the Siege of *Candia*, and was Fellow-Slave with *Henault*, for seven Years, in *Turky*, and who had escap'd with *Henault*, and came as far as *Liege* with him, where, having some

Business and Acquaintance with a Merchant, he stay'd
some time; but when he parted with *Henault*, he ask'd
him, Where he should find him in *Flanders?* *Henault*
gave him a Note, with his Name, and Place of Abode, if
his Wife were alive; if not, to enquire at his Sister's, or
his Father's. This *French* Man came at last, to the very
House of *Isabella*, enquiring for this Man, and receiv'd a
strange Answer, and was laugh'd at; He found, that was
the House, and that the Lady; and enquiring about the
Town, and speaking of *Henault's* Return, describing the
Man, it was quickly discover'd, to be the same that was
in the Sack: He had his Friend taken up (for he was
buried) and found him the same, and, causing a *Barber*
to Trim him, when his bushy Beard was off, a great
many People remember'd him; and the *French* Man
affirming, he went to his own Home, all *Isabella's* Family,
and her self, were cited before the Magistrate of Justice,
where, as soon as she was accus'd, she confess'd the
whole Matter of Fact, and, without any Disorder, deliver'd her self in the Hands of Justice, as the Murderess
of two Husbands (both belov'd) in one Night: The whole
World stood amaz'd at this; who knew her Life a Holy
and Charitable Life, and how dearly and well she had
liv'd with her Husbands, and every one bewail'd her
Misfortune, and she alone was the only Person, that was
not afflicted for her self; she was Try'd, and Condemn'd
to lose her Head; which Sentence, she joyfully receiv'd,
and said, Heaven, and her Judges, were too Merciful to
her, and that her Sins had deserv'd much more.

While she was in Prison, she was always at Prayers, and
very Chearful and Easie, distributing all she had amongst,
and for the Use of, the Poor of the Town, especially to
the Poor Widows; exhorting daily, the Young, and the
Fair, that came perpetually to visit her, never to break a
Vow; for that was first the Ruine of her, and she never
since prosper'd, do whatever other good Deeds she could.

When the day of Execution came, she appear'd on the Scaffold all in Mourning, but with a Meen so very Majestick and Charming, and a Face so surprizing Fair, where no Languishment or Fear appear'd, but all Chearful as a Bride, that she set all Hearts a flaming, even in that mortifying Minute of Preparation for Death : She made a Speech of half an Hour long, so Eloquent, so admirable a warning to the *Vow-Breakers*, that it was as amazing to hear her, as it was to behold her.

After she had done with the help of *Maria*, she put off her Mourning Vail, and, without any thing over her Face, she kneel'd down, and the Executioner, at one Blow, sever'd her Beautiful Head from her Delicate Body, being then in her Seven and Twentieth Year. She was generally Lamented, and Honourably Bury'd.

F I N I S .

THE NUN; OR,
THE PERJUR'D BEAUTY.

THE NUN:

or, The Perjur'd Beauty.

A True Novel.

Don *Henrique* was a Person of great Birth, of a great
Estate, of a Bravery equal to either, of a most generous
Education, but of more Passion than Reason: He was
besides of an opener and freer Temper than generally
his Countrymen are (I mean, the *Spaniards*) and always
engag'd in some Love-Intrigue or other.

One Night as he was retreating from one of those
Engagements, Don *Sebastian*, whose Sister he had abus'd
with a Promise of Marriage, set upon him at the Corner of
a Street, in *Madrid*, and by the Help of three of his
Friends, design'd to have dispatch'd him on a doubtful
Embassy to the Almighty Monarch: But he receiv'd their
first Instructions with better Address than they expected,
and dismiss'd his Envoy first, killing one of Don *Sebastian's*
Friends. Which so enrag'd the injur'd Brother, that his
Strength and Resolution seem'd to be redoubled, and so
animated his two surviving Companions, that (doubtless)
they had gain'd a dishonourable Victory, had not Don
Antonio accidentally come in to the Rescue ; who after a
short Dispute, kill'd one of the two who attack'd him
only ; whilst Don *Henrique*, with the greatest Difficulty,
defended his Life, for some Moments, against *Sebastian*,
whose Rage depriv'd him of Strength, and gave his
Adversary the unwish'd Advantage of his seeming Death,
tho' not without bequeathing some bloody Legacies to
Don *Henrique*. *Antonio* had receiv'd but one slight Wound
in the left Arm, and his surviving Antagonist none ; who
however thought it not adviseable to begin a fresh Dispute
against two, of whose Courage he had but too fatal a

Proof, tho' one of 'em was sufficiently disabled. The Conquerors, on the other Side, politickly retreated, and quitting the Field to the Conquer'd, left the Living to bury the Dead, if he could, or thought convenient.

As they were marching off, Don *Antonio*, who all this while knew not whose Life he had so happily preserv'd, told his Companion in Arms, that he thought it indispensibly necessary that he should quarter with him that Night, for his further Preservation. To which he prudently consented, and went, with no little Uneasiness, to his Lodgings; where he surpriz'd *Antonio* with the Sight of his dearest Friend. For they had certainly the nearest Sympathy in all their Thoughts, that ever made two brave Men unhappy: And, undoubtedly, nothing but Death, or more fatal Love, could have divided them. However, at present, they were united and secure.

In the mean time, Don *Sebastian's* Friend was just going to call Help to carry off the Bodies, as the — came by; who seeing three Men lie dead, seiz'd the fourth; who as he was about to justify himself, by discovering one of the Authors of so much Blood-shed, was interrupted by a Groan from his supposed dead Friend Don *Sebastian*; whom, after a brief Account of some Part of the Matter, and the Knowledge of his Quality, they took up, and carried to his House; where, within a few Days, he was recovered past the Fear of Death. All this While *Henrique* and *Antonio* durst not appear, so much as by Night; nor could be found, tho' diligent and daily Search was made after the first; but upon Don *Sebastian's* Recovery, the Search ceasing, they took the Advantage of the Night, and, in Disguise, retreated to *Seville*. 'Twas there they thought themselves most secure, where indeed they were in the greatest Danger; for tho' (haply) they might there have escap'd the murderous Attempt of Don *Sebastian*, and his Friends, yet they could not there avoid the malicious Influence of their Stars.

This City gave Birth to *Antonio*, and to the Cause of his greatest Misfortunes, as well as of his Death. Dona *Ardelia* was born there, a Miracle of Beauty and Falshood. 'Twas more than a Year since Don *Antonio* had first seen and loved her. For 'twas impossible any Man should do one without the other. He had had the unkind Opportunity of speaking and conveying a Billet to her at Church; and to his greater Misfortune, the next Time he found her there, he met with too Kind a Return both from her Eyes and from her Hand, which privately slipt a Paper into his; in which he found abundantly more than he expected, directing him in that, how he should proceed, in order to carry her off from her Father with the least Danger he could look for in such an Attempt; since it would have been vain and fruitless to have asked her of her Father, because their Families had been at Enmity for several Years; tho' *Antonio* was as well descended as she, and had as ample a Fortune; nor was his Person, according to his Sex, any way inferior to her's; and certainly, the Beauties of his Mind were more excellent, especially if it be an Excellence to be constant.

He had made several Attempts to take Possession of her; but all prov'd ineffectual; however, he had the good Fortune not to be known, tho' once or twice he narrowly escap'd with Life, bearing off his Wounds with Difficulty. —(Alas, that the Wounds of Love should cause those of Hate!) Upon which she was strictly confin'd to one Room, whose only Window was towards the Garden, and that too was grated with Iron; and, once a Month, when she went to Church, she was constantly and carefully attended by her Father, and a Mother-in-Law, worse than a *Duegna*. Under this miserable Confinement *Antonio* understood she still continued, at his Return to *Seville*, with Don *Henrique*, whom he acquainted with his invincible Passion for her; lamenting the Severity of her present Circumstances, that admitted of no Prospect of Relief; which caus'd a generous Concern in Don *Henrique*, both for the Sufferings of his Friend, and of the Lady. He proposed several Ways to Don *Antonio*, for the Release of the fair Prisoner; but none of them was thought practicable, or at least likely to succeed. But *Antonio*, who (you may believe) was then more nearly engag'd, bethought himself of an Expedient that would undoubtedly reward their Endeavours. 'Twas, that Don *Henrique*, who was very well acquainted with *Ardelia's* Father, should make him a Visit, with Pretence of begging his Consent and Admission to make his Addresses to his Daughter; which, in all Probability, he could not refuse to Don *Henrique's* Quality and Estate; and then this Freedom of Access to her would give him the Opportunity of delivering the Lady to his Friend. This was thought so reasonable, that the very next Day it was put in Practice; and with so good Success, that Don *Henrique* was received by the Father of *Ardelia* with the greatest and most respectful Ceremony imaginable: And when he made the Proposal to him of marrying his Daughter, it was embraced with a visible Satisfaction and Joy in the Air of his Face. This their first Conversation ended with all imaginable Content on both Sides; Don *Henrique* being invited by the Father to Dinner the next Day, when Dona *Ardelia* was to be present; who, at that Time, was said to be indispos'd, (as 'tis very probable she was, with so close an Imprisonment.) *Henrique* returned to *Antonio*, and made him happy with the Account of his Reception; which could not but have terminated in the perfect Felicity of *Antonio*, had his Fate been just to the Merits of his Love. The Day and Hour came which brought *Henrique*, with a private Commission from his Friend, to *Ardelia*. He saw her;—(ah! would he had only seen her veil'd!) and, with the first Opportunity, gave her the Letter, which held so much Love, and so much Truth, as ought to have preserved him in the Empire of her Heart. It

contained, besides, a Discovery of his whole Design upon
her Father, for the compleating of their Happiness; which
nothing then could obstruct but her self. But *Henrique*
had seen her; he had gaz'd, and swallowed all her Beauties
at his Eyes. How greedily his Soul drank the strong
Poison in! But yet his Honour and his Friendship were
strong as ever, and bravely fought against the Usurper
Love, and got a noble Victory; at least he thought and
wish'd so. With this, and a short Answer to his Letter,
Henrique return'd to the longing *Antonio;* who, receiving
the Paper with the greatest Devotion, and kissing it with
the greatest Zeal, open'd and read these Words to himself:

Don Antonio,

*YOU have, at last, made Use of the best and only Expedient
for my Enlargement; for which I thank you, since I know it
is purely the Effect of your Love. Your Agent has a mighty
Influence on my Father: And you may assure yourself, that
as you have advis'd and desir'd me, he shall have no less on
me, who am*

Your's entirely,

And only your's,

ARDELIA.

Having respectfully and tenderly kiss'd the Name, he
could not chuse but shew the *Billet* to his Friend; who
reading that Part of it which concern'd himself, started
and blush'd: Which *Antonio* observing, was curious to
know the Cause of it. *Henrique* told him, That he was
surpriz'd to find her express so little Love, after so long
an Absence. To which his Friend reply'd for her, That,
doubtless, she had not Time enough to attempt so great
a Matter as a perfect Account of her Love; and added,
that it was Confirmation enough to him of its Continuance, since she subscrib'd her self his entirely, and only
his.—How blind is Love! Don *Henrique* knew how to
make it bear another Meaning; which, however, he had

the Discretion to conceal. *Antonio*, who was as real in his Friendship, as constant in his Love, ask'd him what he thought of her Beauty ? To which the other answer'd, that he thought it irresistable to any, but to a Soul pre-posses'd, and nobly fortify'd with a perfect Friendship :— Such as is thine, my *Henrique*, (added *Antonio ;*) yet as sincere and perfect as that is, I know you must, nay, I know you do love her. As I ought to do, (reply'd *Henrique*.) Yes, yes, (return'd his Friend) it must be so ; otherwise the Sympathy which unites our Souls would be wanting, and consequently our Friendship were in a State of Imper-fection. How industriously you would argue me into a Crime, that would tear and destroy the Foundation of the strongest Ties of Truth and Honour ! (said *Henrique*.) But (he continu'd) I hope within a few Days, to put it out of my Power to be guilty of so great a Sacrilege. I can't determine (said *Antonio*) if I knew that you lov'd one another, whether I could easier part with my Friend, or my Mistress. Tho' what you say, is highly generous, (reply'd *Henrique*) yet give me Leave to urge, that it looks like a Trial of Friendship, and argues you inclinable to Jealousy : But, pardon me, I know it to be sincerely meant by you ; and must therefore own, that 'tis the best, because 'tis the noblest Way of securing both your Friend and Mistress. I need not make use of any Arts to secure me of either, (reply'd *Antonio*) but expect to enjoy 'em both in a little Time.

Henrique, who was a little uneasy with a Discourse of this Nature, diverted it, by reflecting on what had pass'd at *Madrid*, between them two and Don *Sebastian* and his Friends ; which caus'd *Antonio* to bethink himself of the Danger to which he expos'd his Friend, by appearing daily, tho' in Disguise : For, doubtless, Don *Sebastian* would pursue his Revenge to the utmost Extremity. These Thoughts put him upon desiring his Friend, for his own Sake, to hasten the Performance of his Attempt ; and accordingly, each Day Don *Henrique* brought *Antonio* nearer the Hopes of Happiness, while he himself was hourly sinking into the lowest State of Misery. The last Night before the Day in which *Antonio* expected to be bless'd in her Love, Don *Henrique* had a long and fatal Conference with her about her Liberty. Being then with her alone in an Arbour of the Garden, which Privilege he had had for some Days; after a long Silence, and observing Don *Henrique* in much Disorder, by the Motion of his Eyes, which were sometimes stedfastly fix'd on the Ground, then lifted up to her or Heaven, (for he could see nothing more beautiful on Earth) she made use of the Privilege of her Sex, and began the Discourse first, to this Effect:—Has any Thing happened, Sir, since our Retreat hither, to occasion that Disorder which is but too visible in your Face, and too dreadful in your continued Silence? Speak, I beseech you, Sir, and let me know if I have any Way unhappily contributed to it! No, Madam, (replyed he) my Friendship is now likely to be the only Cause of my greatest Misery; for To-morrow I must be guilty of an unpardonable Crime, in betraying the generous Confidence which your noble Father has plac'd in me: To-morrow (added he, with a piteous Sigh) I must deliver you into the Hands of one whom your Father hates even to Death, instead of doing myself the Honour of becoming his Son-in-law within a few Days more.—But—I will consider and remind myself, that I give you into the Hands of my Friend; of my Friend, that loves you better than his Life, which he has often expos'd for your Sake; and what is more than all, to my Friend, whom you love more than any Consideration on Earth.—And must this be done? (she ask'd.) Is it inevitable as Fate?—Fix'd as the Laws of Nature, Madam, (reply'd he) don't you find the Necessity of it, *Ardelia*? (continued he, by Way of Question:) Does not your Love require it? Think, you are going to your dear *Antonio*, who alone can merit you, and whom only you can love. Were your last Words true (returned she) I should yet be unhappy in the Displeasure of a dear and tender Father, and infinitely more, in being the Cause of your Infidelity to him : No, Don *Henrique* (continued she) I could with greater Satisfaction return to my miserable Confinement, than by any Means disturb the Peace of your Mind, or occasion one Moment's Interruption of your Quiet.—Would to Heaven you did not, (sigh'd he to himself.)   Then addressing his Words more distinctly to her, cry'd he, Ah, cruel ! ah, unjust *Ardelia !* these Words belong to none but *Antonio ;* why then would you endeavour to persuade me, that I do, or even can merit the Tenderness of such an Expression ? — Have a Care ! (pursued he) have a Care, *Ardelia !* your outward Beauties are too powerful to be resisted ; even your Frowns have such a Sweetness that they attract the very Soul that is not strongly prepossessed with the noblest Friendship, and the highest Principles of Honour : Why then, alas ! did you add such sweet and Charming Accents ? Why—ah, Don *Henrique !* (she interrupted) why did you appear to me so charming in your Person, so great in your Friendship, and so illustrious in your Reputation ? Why did my Father, ever since your first Visit, continually fill my Ears and Thoughts with noble Characters and glorious Ideas, which yet but imperfectly and faintly represent the inimitable Original !—But—(what is most severe and cruel) why, Don *Henrique*, why will you defeat my Father in his Ambition of your Alliance, and me of those glorious Hopes with which you had bless'd my Soul, by casting me away from you to *Antonio !*—Ha ! (cry'd he, starting) what said you, Madam ? What did *Ardelia* say ? That I had bless'd your Soul with Hopes ! That I would cast you away to *Antonio !*—Can they who safely arrive in their wish'd-for Port, be said to be shipwreck'd ? Or, can an abject indigent Wretch make a King ?—These are more than Riddles, Madam; and I must not think to expound 'em.

No, (said she) let it alone, Don *Henrique;* I'll ease you of that Trouble, and tell you plainly that I love you. Ah! (cry'd he) now all my Fears are come upon me!—How! (ask'd she) were you afraid I should love you? Is my Love so dreadful then? Yes, when misplac'd (reply'd he;) but 'twas your Falshood that I fear'd: Your Love was what I would have sought with the utmost Hazard of my Life, nay, even of my future Happiness, I fear, had you not been engag'd: strongly oblig'd to love elsewhere, both by your own Choice and Vows, as well as by his dangerous Services, and matchless Constancy. For which (said she) I do not hate him, tho' his Father kill'd my Uncle: Nay, perhaps (continu'd she) I have a Friendship for him, but no more. No more, said you, Madam? (cry'd he;)—but tell me, did you never love him? Indeed, I did, (reply'd she;) but the Sight of you has better instructed me, both in my Duty to my Father, and in causing my Passion for you, without whom I shall be eternally miserable. Ah, then pursue your honourable Proposal, and make my Father happy in my Marriage! It must not be (return'd Don *Henrique*) my Honour, my Friendship forbids it. No (she return'd) your Honour requires it; and if your Friendship opposes your Honour, it can have no sure and solid Foundation. Female Sophistry! (cry'd *Henrique;*) but you need no Art nor Artifice, *Ardelia*, to make me love you: Love you! (pursu'd he:) By that bright Sun, the Light and Heat of all the World, you are my only Light and Heat—Oh, Friendship! Sacred Friendship, now assist me!—[Here for a Time he paus'd, and then afresh proceeded thus,]—You told me, or my Ears deceiv'd me, that you lov'd me, *Ardelia*. I did, she reply'd; and that I do love you, is as true as that I told you so. 'Tis well;—But would it were not so! Did ever Man receive a Blessing thus?—Why, I could wish I did not love you, *Ardelia!* But that were impossible—At least unjust, (interrupted she.) Well then (he went on) to shew you that I do sincerely consult your particular Happiness, without any regard to my own, To-morrow I will give you to Don *Antonio*; and as a Proof of your Love to me, I expect your ready Consent to it. To let you see, Don *Henrique*, how perfectly and tenderly I love you, I will be sacrificed To-morrow to Don *Antonio*, and to your Quiet. Oh, strongest, dearest Obligation !—cry'd *Henrique*: To-morrow then, as I have told your Father, I am to bring you to see the dearest Friend I have on Earth, who dares not appear within this City for some unhappy Reasons, and therefore cannot be present at our Nuptials; for which Cause, I could not but think it my Duty to one so nearly related to my Soul, to make him happy in the Sight of my beautiful Choice, e'er yet she be my Bride. I hope (said she) my loving Obedience may merit your Compassion; and that at last, e'er the Fire is lighted that must consume the Offering, I mean the Marriage-Tapers (alluding to the old *Roman* Ceremony) that you or some other pitying Angel, will snatch me from the Altar. Ah, no more, *Ardelia!* say no more (cry'd he) we must be cruel, to be just to our selves. [Here their Discourse ended, and they walked into the House, where they found the good old Gentleman and his Lady, with whom he stay'd till about an Hour after Supper, when he returned to his Friend with joyful News, but a sorrowful Heart.]

Antonio was all Rapture with the Thoughts of the approaching Day; which tho' it brought Don *Henrique* and his dear *Ardelia* to him, about five o'Clock in the Evening, yet at the same Time brought his last and greatest Misfortune. He saw her then at a She Relation's of his, above three Miles from *Seville*, which was the Place assigned for their fatal Interview. He saw her, I say; but ah! how strange! how altered from the dear, kind *Ardelia* she was when last he left her! 'Tis true, he flew to her with Arms expanded, and with so swift and eager a Motion, that she could not avoid, nor get loose from

his Embrace, till he had kissed, and sighed, and dropt
some Tears, which all the Strength of his Mind could
not restrain; whether they were the Effects of Joy, or
whether (which rather may be feared) they were the
Heat-drops which preceded and threaten'd the Thunder
and Tempest that should fall on his Head, I cannot
positively say; yet all this she was then forced to endure,
e'er she had Liberty to speak, or indeed to breathe. But
as soon as she had freed herself from the loving Circle
that should have been the dear and lov'd Confinement or
Centre of a Faithful Heart, she began to dart whole
Showers of Tortures on him from her Eyes; which that
Mouth that he had just before so tenderly and sacredly
kiss'd, seconded with whole Volleys of Deaths crammed
in every Sentence, pointed with the keenest Affliction that
ever pierc'd a Soul. *Antonio*, (she began) you have treated
me now as if you were never like to see me more: and
would to Heaven you were not!—Ha! (cry'd he, starting
and staring wildly on her;) What said you, Madam?
What said you, my *Ardelia?* If you like the Repetition,
take it? (reply'd she, unmoved) *Would to Heaven you were
never like to see me more!* Good! very Good! (cry'd he,
with a Sigh that threw him trembling into a Chair behind
him, and gave her the Opportunity of proceeding thus:)
—Yet, *Antonio*, I must not have my Wish; I must continue with you, not out of Choice, but by Command, by
the strictest and severest Obligation that ever bound
Humanity; Don *Henrique*, your Friend, commands it;
Don *Henrique*, the dearest Object of my Soul, enjoins it;
Don *Henrique*, whose only Aversion I am, will have it so.
Oh, do not wrong me, Madam! (cry'd Don *Henrique*.)
Lead me, lead me a little more by the Light of your Discourse, I beseech you (said Don *Antonio*) that I may see
your Meaning! for hitherto 'tis Darkness all to me. Attend therefore with your best Faculties (pursu'd *Ardelia*)
and know, That I do most sincerely and most passionately

love Don *Henrique;* and as a Proof of my Love to him,
I have this Day consented to be delivered up to you by
him; not for your Sake in the least, *Antonio,* but purely
to sacrifice all the Quiet of my Life to his Satisfaction.
And now, Sir (continued she, addressing her self to Don
Henrique) now, Sir, if you can be so cruel, execute your
own most dreadful Decree, and join our Hands, though
our Hearts never can meet. All this to try me! It's too
much, *Ardelia*—(said *Antonio :*) And then turning to Don
Henrique, he went on, Speak thou! if yet thou art not
Apostate to our Friendship! Yet speak, however! Speak,
though the Devil has been tampering with thee too! Thou
art a Man, a Man of Honour once. And when I forfeit
my just Title to that (interrupted Don *Henrique*) may I
be made most miserable!—May I lose the Blessings of thy
Friendship!—May I lose thee!—Say on then, *Henrique!*
(cry'd *Antonio :*) And I charge thee, by all the sacred Ties
of Friendship, say, Is this a Trial of me? Is't Illusion,
Sport, or shameful murderous Truth?—Oh, my Soul burns
within me, and I can bear no longer!—Tell! Speak! Say
on!—[Here, with folded Arms, and Eyes fixed stedfastly
on *Henrique,* he stood like a Statue, without Motion;
unless sometimes, when his swelling Heart raised his over-
charged Breast.] After a little Pause, and a hearty Sigh
or two, *Henrique* began;—Oh, *Antonio!* Oh my Friend!
prepare thy self to hear yet more dreadful Accents!—I
am (pursu'd he) unhappily the greatest and most innocent
Criminal that e'er till now offended :—I love her, *Antonio,*
—I love *Ardelia* with a Passion strong and violent as thine!
—Oh! summon all that us'd to be more than Man about
thee, to suffer to the End of my Discourse, which nothing
but a Resolution like thine can bear! I know it by myself.
—Tho' there be Wounds, Horror, and Death in each
Syllable (interrupted *Antonio*) yet prithee now go on, but
with all Haste. I will, (returned Don *Henrique*) tho' I
feel my own Words have the same cruel Effects on me.

I say, again, my Soul loves *Ardelia :* And how can it be otherwise? Have we not both the self-same Appetites, the same Disgusts? How then could I avoid my Destiny, that has decreed that I should love and hate just as you do? Oh, hard Necessity! that obliged you to use me in the Recovery of this Lady! Alas, can you think that any Man of Sense or Passion could have seen, and not have lov'd her! Then how should I, whose Thoughts are Unisons to yours, evade those Charms that had prevail'd on you?— And now, to let you know, 'tis no Illusion, no Sport, but serious and amazing woeful Truth, *Ardelia* best can tell you whom she loves. What I have already said, is true, by Heaven (cry'd she) 'tis you, Don *Henrique,* whom I only love, and who alone can give me Happiness: Ah, would you would!—With you, *Antonio,* I must remain unhappy, wretched, cursed: Thou art my Hell; Don *Henrique* is my Heaven. And thou art mine, (returned he) which here I part with to my dearest Friend. Then taking her Hand, Pardon me, *Antonio,* (pursued he) that I thus take my last Farewel of all the Tastes of Bliss from your *Ardelia,* at this Moment. [At which Words he kiss'd her Hand, and gave it to Don *Antonio;* who received it, and gently pressed it close to his Heart, as if he would have her feel the Disorders she had caus'd there.] Be happy, *Antonio,* (cry'd *Henrique :*) Be very tender of her ; To-morrow early I shall hope to see thee.—*Ardelia* (pursued he) All Happiness and Joy surround thee! May'st thou ne'er want those Blessings thou can'st give *Antonio!*— Farewel to both! (added he, going out.) Ah (cry'd she) Farewel to all Joys, Blessings, Happiness, if you forsake me.—Yet do not go!—Ah, cruel! (continu'd she, seeing him quit the Room) but you shall take my Soul with you. Here she swooned away in Don *Antonio's* Arms; who, though he was happy that he had her fast there, yet was obliged to call in his Cousin, and *Ardelia's* Attendants, e'er she could be perfectly recovered. In the mean while Don

Henrique had not the Power to go out of Sight of the House, but wandred to and fro about it, distracted in his Soul; and not being able longer to refrain her Sight, her last Words still resounding in his Ears, he came again into the Room where he left her with Don *Antonio*, just as she revived, and called him, exclaiming on his Cruelty, in leaving her so soon. But when, turning her Eyes towards the Door, she saw him; Oh! with what eager Haste she flew to him! then clasped him round the Waist, obliging him, with all the tender Expressions that the Soul of a Lover, and a Woman's too, is capable of uttering, not to leave her in the Possession of Don *Antonio*. This so amaz'd her slighted Lover, that he knew not, at first, how to proceed in this tormenting Scene; but at last, summoning all his wonted Resolution, and Strength of Mind, he told her, He would put her out of his Power, if she would consent to retreat for some few Hours to a Nunnery that was not above half a Mile distant from thence, till he had discoursed his Friend, Don *Henrique* something more particularly than hitherto, about this Matter: To which she readily agreed, upon the Promise that Don *Henrique* made her, of seeing her with the first Opportunity. They waited on her then to the Convent, where she was kindly and respectfully received by the Lady Abbess; but it was not long before her Grief renewing with greater Violence, and more afflicting Circumstances, had obliged them to stay with her till it was almost dark, when they once more begged the Liberty of an Hour's Absence; and the better to palliate their Design, *Henrique* told her, that he would make use of her Father Don *Richardo's* Coach, in which they came to Don *Antonio's*, for so small a Time: which they did, leaving only *Eleonora* her Attendant with her, with out whom she had been at a Loss, among so many fair Strangers; Strangers, I mean, to her unhappy Circumstances: Whilst they were carry'd near a Mile farther, where, just as 'twas dark, they lighted from the Coach,

Don *Henrique*, ordering the Servants not to stir thence till their Return from their private Walk, which was about a Furlong, in a Field that belong'd to the Convent. Here Don *Antonio* told Don *Henrique*, That he had not acted honourably ; That he had betray'd him, and robb'd him at once both of a Friend and Mistress. To which t'other returned, That he understood his Meaning, when he proposed a particular Discourse about this Affair, which he now perceived must end in Blood : But you may remind your self (continued he) that I have kept my Promise in delivering her to you. Yes, (cry'd *Antonio*) after you had practis'd foully and basely on her. Not at all ! (returned *Henrique*) It was her Fate that brought this Mischief on her ; for I urged the Shame and Scandal of Inconstancy, but all in vain, to her. But don't you love her, *Henrique ?* (the other ask'd.) Too well, and cannot live without her, though I fear I may feel the cursed Effects of the same Inconstancy : However, I had quitted her all to you, but you see how she resents it. And you shall see, Sir, (cry'd *Antonio*, drawing his Sword in a Rage) how I resent it. Here, without more Words, they fell to Action ; to bloody Action. (Ah ! how wretched are our Sex, in being the unhappy Occasion of so many fatal Mischiefs, even between the dearest Friends !) They fought on each Side with the greatest Animosity of Rivals, forgetting all the sacred Bonds of their former Friendship ; till Don *Antonio* fell, and said, dying, 'Forgive me, *Henrique !* I was to blame ; I could not live without her :—I fear she will betray thy Life, which haste and preserve, for my sake— Let me not die all at once !—Heaven pardon both of us ! —Farewel ! Oh, haste ! Farewel ! (*returned Don* Henrique) Farewel, thou bravest, truest Friend ! Farewel thou noblest Part of me !—And Farewel all the Quiet of my Soul.' Then stooping, he kissed his Cheek ; but, rising, he found he must retire in time, or else must perish through Loss of Blood, for he had received two or three dangerous

Wounds, besides others of less Consequence : Wherefore he made all the convenient Haste he could to the Coach, into which, by the Help of the Footmen, he got, and order'd 'em to drive him directly to Don *Richardo*'s with all imaginable Speed ; where he arriv'd in little more than half an Hour's Time, and was received by *Ardelia*'s Father with the greatest Confusion and Amazement that is expressible, seeing him return'd without his Daughter, and so desperately wounded. Before he thought it convenient to ask him any Question more than to enquire of his Daughter's Safety, to which he receiv'd a short but satisfactory Answer, Don *Richardo* sent for an eminent and able Surgeon, who probed and dress'd Don *Henrique*'s Wounds, who was immediately put to Bed ; not without some Despondency of his Recovery ; but (thanks to his kind Stars, and kinder Constitution !) he rested pretty well for some Hours that Night, and early in the Morning, *Ardelia*'s Father, who had scarce taken any Rest all that Night, came to visit him, as soon as he understood from the Servants who watched with him, that he was in a Condition to suffer a short Discourse ; which, you may be sure, was to learn the Circumstances of the past Night's Adventure ; of which Don *Henrique* gave him a perfect and pleasant Account, since he heard that Don *Antonio*, his mortal Enemy, was killed ; the Assurance of whose Death was the more delightful to him, since, by this Relation, he found that *Antonio* was the Man, whom his Care of his Daughter had so often frustrated. Don *Henrique* had hardly made an End of his Narration, e'er a Servant came hastily to give *Richardo* Notice, that the Officers were come to search for his Son-in-Law that should have been ; whom the Old Gentleman's wise Precaution had secured in a Room so unsuspected, that they might as reasonably have imagined the entire Walls of his House had a Door made of Stones, as that there should have been one to that close Apartment : He went therefore boldly to the Officers, and gave them all the Keys of his House, with free Liberty to examine every Room and Chamber; which they did, but to no Purpose; and Don *Henrique* lay there undiscover'd, till his Cure was perfected.

In the mean time *Ardelia*, who that fatal Night but too rightly guess'd that the Death of one or both her Lovers was the Cause that they did not return to their Promise, the next Day fell into a high Fever, in which her Father found her soon after he had clear'd himself of those who come to search for a Lover. The Assurance which her Father gave her of *Henrique's* Life, seemed a little to revive her; but the Severity of *Antonio's* Fate was no Way obliging to her, since she could not but retain the Memory of his Love and Constancy; which added to her Afflictions, and heightned her Distemper, insomuch that *Richardo* was constrain'd to leave her under the Care of the good Lady Abbess, and to the diligent Attendance of *Eleonora*, not daring to hazard her Life in a Removal to his own House. All their Care and Diligence was however ineffectual; for she languished even to the least Hope of Recovery, till immediately after the first Visit of Don *Henrique*, which was the first he made in a Month's Time, and that by Night *incognito*, with her Father, her Distemper visibly retreated each Day: Yet when at last she enjoy'd a perfect Health of Body, her Mind grew sick, and she plunged into a deep Melancholy; which made her entertain a positive Resolution of taking the Veil at the End of her Novitiate; which accordingly she did, notwithstanding all the Intreaties, Prayers, and Tears both of her Father and Lover. But she soon repented her Vow, and often wish'd that she might by any Means see and speak to Don *Henrique*, by whose Help she promised to her self a Deliverance out of her voluntary Imprisonment: Nor were his Wishes wanting to the same Effect, tho' he was forced to fly into *Italy*, to avoid the Prosecution of *Antonio's* Friends. Thither she pursu'd him; nor could he any way shun her, unless he could have left his Heart at a Distance from his Body : Which made him take a fatal Resolution of returning to S*eville* in Disguise, where he wander'd about the Convent every Night like a Ghost (for indeed his Soul was within, while his inanimate Trunk was without) till at last he found Means to convey a Letter to her, which both surprized and delighted her. The Messenger that brought it her was one of her Mother-in-Law's Maids, whom he had known before, and met accidentally one Night as he was going his Rounds, and she coming out from *Ardelia;* with her he prevail'd, and with Gold obliged her to Secrecy and Assistance : Which proved so successful, that he understood from *Ardelia* her strong Desire of Liberty, and the Continuance of her Passion for him, together with the Means and Time most convenient and likely to succeed for her Enlargement. The Time was the fourteenth Night following, at twelve o'Clock, which just compleated a Month since his Return thither ; at which Time they both promised themselves the greatest Happiness on Earth. But you may observe the Justice of Heaven, in their Disappointment.

Don *Sebastian,* who still pursu'd him with a most implacable Hatred, had traced him even to *Italy,* and there narrowly missing him, posted after him to *Toledo;* so sure and secret was his Intelligence ! As soon as he arriv'd, he went directly to the Convent where his Sister *Elvira* had been one of the Profess'd, ever since Don *Henrique* had forsaken her, and where *Ardelia* had taken her repented Vow. *Elvira* had all along conceal'd the Occasion of her coming thither from *Ardelia;* and tho' she was her only Confident, and knew the whole Story of her Misfortunes, and heard the Name of Don *Henrique* repeated a hundred Times a Day, whom still she lov'd most perfectly, yet never gave her beautiful Rival any Cause of Suspicion that she lov'd him, either by Words or Looks : Nay more, when she understood that Don *Henrique* came to the Convent

with *Ardelia* and *Antonio*, and at other Times with her
Father; yet she had so great a Command of her self, as to
refrain seeing him, or to be seen by him; nor ever intended
to have spoken or writ to him, had not her Brother Don
Sebastian put her upon the cruel Necessity of doing the
last; who coming to visit his Sister (as I have said before)
found her with Dona *Ardelia*, whom he never remembred
to have seen, nor who ever had seen him but twice, and
that was about six Years before, when she was but ten
Years of Age, when she fell passsionately in Love with
him, and continu'd her Passion till about the fourteenth
Year of her Empire, when unfortunate *Antonio* first began
his Court to her. Don *Sebastian* was really a very desirable
Person, being at that time very beautiful, his Age not
exceeding six and twenty, of a sweet Conversation, very
brave, but revengeful and irreconcilable (like most of his
Countrymen) and of an honourable Family. At the Sight
of him *Ardelia* felt her former Passion renew; which proceeded and continued with such Violence, that it utterly
defac'd the Ideas of *Antonio* and *Henrique*. (No Wonder
that she who could resolve to forsake her God for Man,
should quit one Lover for another.) In short, she then
only wished that he might love her equally, and then she
doubted not of contriving the Means of their Happiness
betwixt 'em. She had her Wish, and more, if possible;
for he lov'd her beyond the Thought of any other present
or future Blessing, and fail'd not to let her know it, at the
second Interview; when he receiv'd the greatest Pleasure
he could have wish'd, next to the Joys of a Bridal Bed:
For she confessed her Love to him, and presently put him
upon thinking on the Means of her Escape; but not
finding his Designs so likely to succeed, as those Measures
she had sent to Don *Henrique*, she communicates the very
same to Don *Sebastian*, and agreed with him to make use
of them on that very Night, wherein she had obliged Don
Henrique to attempt her Deliverance: The Hour indeed

was different, being determined to be at eleven. *Elvira*, who was present at the Conference, took the Hint; and not being willing to disoblige a Brother who had so hazarded his Life in Vindication of her, either does not, or would not seem to oppose his Inclinations at that Time : However, when he retired with her to talk more particularly of his intended Revenge on Don *Henrique*, who he told her lay somewhere absconded in *Toledo*, and whom he had resolved, as he assured her, to sacrifice to her injur'd Honour, and his Resentments; she oppos'd that his vindictive Resolution with all the forcible Arguments in a virtuous and pious Lady's Capacity, but in vain : so that immediately upon his Retreat from the Convent, she took the Opportunity of writing to Don *Henrique* as follows, the fatal Hour not being then seven Nights distant.

Don *Henrique*,

MY Brother is now in Town, in Pursuit of your Life ; nay more, of your Mistress, who has consented to make her Escape from the Convent, at the same Place of it, and by the same Means on which she had agreed to give her self entirely to you, but the Hour is eleven. I know, Henrique, your Ardelia is dearer to you than your Life : But your Life, your dear Life, is more desired than any Thing in this World, by

Your injur'd and forsaken

ELVIRA.

This she delivered to *Richardo's* Servant, whom *Henrique* had gained that Night, as soon as she came to visit *Ardelia*, at her usual Hour, just as she went out of the Cloister.

Don *Henrique* was not a little surprized with this *Billet ;* however, he could hardly resolve to forbear his accustom'd Visits to *Ardelia*, at first : But upon more mature Consideration, he only chose to converse with her by Letters, which still press'd her to be mindful of her Promise, and of the Hour, not taking notice of any Caution that he had received of her Treachery. To which she still return'd in Words that might assure him of her Constancy.

The dreadful Hour wanted not a Quarter of being perfect, when Don *Henrique* came; and having fixed his Rope-Ladder to that Part of the Garden-Wall, where he was expected, *Ardelia*, who had not stir'd from that very Place for a Quarter of an Hour before, prepar'd to ascend by it; which she did, as soon as his Servant had returned and fixed it on the inner-side of the Wall: On the Top of which, at a little Distance, she found another fasten'd, for her to descend on the out-side, whilst Don *Henrique* eagerly waited to receive her. She came at last, and flew into his Arms; which made *Henrique* cry out in a Rapture, *Am I at last once more happy in having my* Ardelia *in my Possession!* She, who knew his Voice, and now found she was betray'd, but knew not by whom, shriek'd out, *I am ruin'd! help! help!*—*Loose me, I charge you,* Henrique! *Loose me!* At that very Moment, and at those very Words, came *Sebastian*, attended by only one Servant; and hearing *Henrique* reply, *Not all the Powers of Hell shall snatch you from me,* drawing his Sword, without one Word, made a furious Pass at him: But his Rage and Haste misguided his Arm, for his Sword went quite through *Ardelia's* Body, who only said, *Ah, wretched Maid!* and drop'd from *Henrique's* Arms, who then was obliged to quit her, to preserve his own Life, if possible: however he had not had so much Time as to draw, had not *Sebastian* been amazed at this dreadful Mistake of his Sword; but presently recollecting himself, he flew with redoubled Rage to attack *Henrique;* and his Servant had seconded him, had not *Henrique's*, who was now descended, otherwise diverted him. They fought with the greatest Animosity on both Sides, and with equal Advantage; for they both fell together: *Ah, my* Ardelia, *I come to thee now!* (*Sebastian* groan'd out,)—*'Twas this unlucky Arm, which now embraces thee, that killed thee. Just Heaven!* (she sigh'd out,)—*Oh, yet have Mercy!* [Here they both dy'd.] *Amen,* (cry'd *Henrique*, dying) *I want it most*—*Oh,* Antonio! *Oh,* Elvira! *Ah, there's the Weight that sinks me down.*—*And yet I wish For-giveness.*—*Once more, sweet Heaven, have Mercy!* He could not out-live that last Word; which was echo'd by *Elvira*, who all this while stood weeping, and calling out for Help, as she stood close to the Wall in the Garden.

This alarmed the Rest of the Sisters, who rising, caus'd the Bell to be rung out, as upon dangerous Occasions it used to be; which rais'd the Neighbourhood, who came time enough to remove the dead Bodies of the two Rivals, and of the late fallen Angel *Ardelia*. The injur'd and neglected *Elvira*, whose Piety designed quite contrary Effects, was immediately seiz'd with a violent Fever; which, as it was violent, did not last long: for she dy'd within four and twenty Hours, with all the happy Symptoms of a departing Saint.

THE LUCKY MISTAKE.

TO GEORGE GREENVIEL, ESQ;

Sir,

At this Critical Juncture, I find the Authors will have need of a Protector, as well as the Nation, we having peculiar Laws and Liberties to be defended as well as that, but of how different a Nature, none but such Judges as you are fit to determine; whatever our Province be, I am sure it should be Wit, and you know what Ellevated *Ben* says, *That none can judge of Wit but Wit*. Let the *Heroes* toyl for Crowns and Kingdoms and with what pretences they please. Let the Slaves of State drudge on for false and empty Glories, troubling the repose of the World and ruining their own to gain uneasy Grandure, whilst you, oh! happyer Sir, great enough by your Birth, yet more Illustrious by your Wit, are capable of enjoying alone that true Felicity of Mind, which belongs to an absolutely Vertuous and Gallant Man, by that, and the lively Notions of Honour Imprinted in your Soul, you are above Ambition, and can Form *Kings* and *Heroes*, when 'ere your delicate Fancy shall put you upon the Poetical Creation.

You can make those *Heroes* Lovers too, and inspire 'em with a Language so Irresistable as may instruct the Fair, how easily you may Conquer when it comes to your turn, to plead for a Heart, nor is your delicate Wit the only Charm; your Person claims an equal share of Graces with those of your Mind, and both together are capable of rendering you Victorious, whereever you shall please to Address 'em, but your Vertue keeps you from those Ravages of Beauty, which so wholly imploy the hours of the Rest of the Gay and Young, whilst you have business more sollid, and more noble for yours.

I would not by this have the World imagine you are therefore exempt from the tenderness of Love, it rather seems you were on purpose form'd for that Soft Entertainment, such an Agreement there is between the Harmony of your Soul and your Person, and sure the *Muses* who have so divinely inspir'd you with Poetic Fires, have furnish you with that Necessary Material (Love) to maintain it, and to make it burn with the more Ellevated Flame.

'Tis therefore, Sir, I expect you will the more easily Pardon the Dedicating to your idler hours (if any such you have) this little Amour, all that I shall say for it, is, that 'tis not Translation but an Original, that has more of realty than fiction, if I have not made it fuller of intreague, 'twas because I had a mind to keep close to the Truth.

I must own, Sir, the Obligations I have to you, deserves a greater testimony of my respect, than this little piece, too trivial to bear the honour of your Name, but my increasing Indisposition makes me fear I shall not have many opportunities of this Kind, and shou'd be loath to leave this ungrateful World, without acknowledging my Gratitude more signally than barely by word of Mouth, and without wishing you all the happiness your merit and admirable Vertues deserve and of assuring you how unfeignedly I am (and how Proud of being) Sir,

> Your most obliged and
> most humble servant
> A. Behn.

THE LUCKY MISTAKE:

A New Novel.

The River *Loyre* has on its delightful Banks abundance of handsome, beautiful and rich Towns and Villages, to which the noble Stream adds no small Graces and Advantages, blessing their Fields with Plenty, and their Eyes with a thousand Diversions. In one of these happily situated Towns, called *Orleans*, where abundance of People of the best Quality and Condition reside, there was a rich Nobleman, now retir'd from the busy Court, where in his Youth he had been bred, weary'd with the Toils of Ceremony and Noise, to enjoy that perfect Tranquillity of Life, which is no where to be found but in Retreat, a faithful Friend, and a good Library; and, as the admirable *Horace* says, in a little House and a large Garden. Count *Bellyaurd*, for so was this Nobleman call'd, was of this Opinion; and the rather, because he had one only Son, called *Rinaldo*, now grown to the Age of fifteen, who having all the excellent Qualities and Graces of Youth by Nature, he would bring him up in all Virtues and noble Sciences, which he believ'd the Gaiety and Lustre of the Court might divert: he therefore in his Retirement spar'd no Cost to those that could instruct and accomplish him; and he had the best Tutors and Masters that could be purchased at Court: *Bellyaurd* making far less Account of Riches than of fine Parts. He found his Son capable of all Impressions, having a Wit suitable to his delicate Person, so that he was the sole Joy of his Life, and the Darling of his Eyes.

In the very next House, which join'd close to that of *Bellyaurd's*, there lived another Count, who had in his Youth been banished the Court of *France* for some

Misunderstandings in some high Affairs wherein he was concern'd : his Name was *De Pais*, a Man of great Birth, but of no Fortune ; or at least one not suitable to the Grandeur of his Original. And as it is most natural for great Souls to be most proud (if I may call a handsome Disdain by that vulgar Name) when they are most depress'd ; so *De Pais* was more retir'd, more estrang'd from his Neighbours, and kept a greater Distance, than if he had enjoy'd all he had lost at Court ; and took more Solemnity and State upon him, because he would not be subject to the Reproaches of the World, by making himself familiar with it : So that he rarely visited ; and, contrary to the Custom of those in *France*, who are easy of Access, and free of Conversation, he kept his Family retir'd so close, that 'twas rare to see any of them ; and when they went abroad, which was but seldom, they wanted nothing as to outward Appearance, that was fit for his Quality, and what was much above his Condition.

This old Count had two only Daughters, of exceeding Beauty, who gave the generous Father ten thousand Torments, as often as he beheld them, when he consider'd their extreme Beauty, their fine Wit, their Innocence, Modesty, and above all their Birth ; and that he had not a Fortune to marry them according to their Quality ; and below it, he had rather see them laid in their silent Graves, than consent to it : for he scorn'd the World should see him forced by his Poverty to commit an Action below his Dignity.

There lived in a neighbouring Town, a certain Noble-man, Friend to *De Pais*, call'd Count *Vernole*, a Man of about forty years of Age, of low Stature, Complexion very black and swarthy, lean, lame, extreme proud and haughty; extracted of a Descent from the Blood-Royal ; not extremely brave, but very glorious : he had no very great Estate, but was in Election of a greater, and of an Addition of Honour from the King, his Father having done most

worthy Services against the *Hugonots*, and by the high
Favour of Cardinal *Mazarine*, was represented to his
Majesty, as a Man related to the Crown, of great Name,
but small Estate : so that there were now nothing but great
Expectations and Preparations in the Family of Count
Vernole to go to the Court, to which he daily hoped an
Invitation or Command.

Vernole's Fortune being hitherto something a-kin to that
of *De Pais*, there was a greater Correspondency between
these two Gentlemen, than they had with any other
Persons ; they accounting themselves above the rest of the
World, believed none so proper and fit for their Conversation, as that of each other: so that there was a very particular
Intimacy between them. Whenever they went abroad,
they clubb'd their Train, to make one great Show ; and
were always together, bemoaning each other's Fortune,
and that from so high a Descent, as one from Monarchs
by the Mother's side, and the other from Dukes of the
Father's Side, they were reduc'd by Fate to the Degree
of private Gentlemen. They would often consult how
to manage Affairs most to Advantage, and often *De Pais*
would ask Counsel of *Vernole*, how best he should dispose
of his Daughters, which now were about their ninth Year
the eldest, and eighth the youngest. *Vernole* had often seen
those two Buds of Beauty, and already saw opening in
Atlante's Face and Mind (for that was the Name of the
eldest, and *Charlot* the youngest) a Glory of Wit and
Beauty, which could not but one Day display it self,
with dazling Lustre, to the wondring World.

Vernole was a great Virtuoso, of a Humour nice, delicate,
critical and opinionative : he had nothing of the *French*
Mein in him, but all the Gravity of the Don. His ill-
favour'd Person, and his low Estate, put him out of Humour
with the World ; and because that should not upbraid or
reproach his Follies and Defects, he was sure to be beforehand with that, and to be always satirick upon it ; and

lov'd to live and act contrary to the Custom and Usage of all Mankind besides.

He was infinitely delighted to find a Man of his own Humour in *De Pais*, or at least a Man that would be persuaded to like his so well, to live up to it; and it was no little Joy and Satisfaction to him to find, that he kept his Daughters in that Severity, which was wholly agreeable to him, and so contrary to the Manner and Fashion of the *French* Quality; who allow all Freedoms, which to *Vernole's* rigid Nature, seem'd as so many Steps to Vice, and in his Opinion, the Ruiner of all Virtue and Honour in Womankind. *De Pais* was extremely glad his Conduct was so well interpreted, which was no other in him than a proud Frugality; who, because they could not appear in so much Gallantry as their Quality required, kept 'em retir'd, and unseen to all, but his particular Friends, of whom *Vernole* was the chief.

Vernole never appear'd before *Atlante* (which was seldom) but he assum'd a Gravity and Respect fit to have entertain'd a Maid of Twenty, or rather a Matron of much greater Years and Judgment. His Discourses were always of Matters of State or Philosophy; and sometimes when *De Pais* would (laughing) say, 'He might as well entertain *Atlante* with *Greek* and *Hebrew*,' he would reply gravely, 'You are mistaken, Sir, I finds the Seeds of great and profound Matter in the Soul of this young Maid, which ought to be nourish'd now while she is young, and they will grow up to very great Perfection: I find *Atlante* capable of the noble Virtues of the Mind, and am infinitely mistaken in my Observations, and Art of Physiognomy, if *Atlante* be not born for greater Things than her Fortune does now Promise: She will be very considerable in the World, (believe me) and this will arrive to her perfectly from the Force of her Charms.' *De Pais* was extremely overjoy'd to hear such Good prophesied of *Atlante*, and from that Time set a sort of an Esteem upon her, which he did not on *Charlot* his younger; whom, by the Persuasions of *Vernole*, he resolv'd to put in a Monastery, that what he had might descend to *Atlante*: not but he confess'd *Charlot* had Beauty extremely attractive, and a Wit that promised much, when it should be cultivated by Years and Experience; and would shew it self with great Advantage and Lustre in a Monastery. All this pleased *De Pais* very well, who was easily persuaded, since he had not a Fortune to marry her well in the World.

As yet *Vernole* had never spoke to *Atlante* of Love, nor did his Gravity think it Prudence to discover his Heart to so young a Maid; he waited her more sensible Years, when he could hope to have some Return. And all he expected from this her tender Age, was by his daily Converse with her, and the Presents he made her suitable to her Years, to ingratiate himself insensibly into her Friendship and Esteem, since she was not yet capable of Love; but even in that he mistook his Aim, for every day he grew more and more disagreeable to *Atlante*, and would have been her absolute Aversion, had she known she had every Day entertained a Lover; but as she grew in Years and Sense, he seemed the more despicable in her Eyes as to his Person; yet as she had respect to his Parts and Qualities, she paid him all the Complaisance she could, and which was due to him, and so must be confess'd. Tho' he had a stiff Formality in all he said and did, yet he had Wit and Learning, and was a great Philosopher. As much of his Learning as *Atlante* was capable of attaining to, he made her Mistress of, and that was no small Portion; for all his Discourse was fine and easily comprehended, his Notions of Philosophy fit for Ladies; and he took greater Pains with *Atlante*, than any Master would have done with a Scholar: So that it was most certain, he added very great Accomplishment to her natural Wit: and the more, because she took a great Delight in Philosophy; which very often made her impatient of his Coming, especially when she had many Questions to ask him concerning it, and she would often receive him with a Pleasure in her Face, which he did not fail to interpret to his own Advantage, being very apt to flatter himself. Her Sister *Charlot* would often ask her, 'How she could give whole Afternoons to so disagreeable a Man. What is it (said she) that charms you so? his tawny Leather-Face, his extraordinary high Nose, his wide Mouth and Eye-brows, that hang low'ring over his Eyes, his lean Carcase, and his lame and halting Hips?' But *Atlante* would discreetly reply, 'If I must grant all you say of Count *Vernole* to be true, yet he has a Wit and Learning that will atone sufficiently for all those Faults you mention : A fine Soul is infinitely to be preferr'd to a fine Body ; this decays, but that's eternal ; and Age that ruins one, refines the other.' Tho' possibly *Atlante* thought as ill of the Count as her Sister, yet in Respect to him, she would not own it.

Atlante was now arriv'd to her thirteenth Year, when her Beauty, which every Day increas'd, became the Discourse of the whole Town, which had already gain'd her as many Lovers as had beheld her ; for none saw her without languishing for her, or at least, but what were in very great Admiration of her. Every body talk'd of the young *Atlante*, and all the Noblemen, who had Sons (knowing the Smallness of her Fortune, and the Lustre of her Beauty) would send them, for fear of their being charm'd with her Beauty, either to some other part of the World, or exhorted them, by way of Precaution, to keep out of her Sight. Old *Bellyaurd* was one of those wise Parents ; and timely Prevention, as he thought, of *Rinaldo's* falling in Love with *Atlante*, perhaps was the Occasion of his being so : He had before heard of *Atlante*, and of her Beauty, yet it had made no Impressions on his Heart ; but his Father no sooner forbid him Loving, than he felt a new Desire tormenting him, of seeing this lovely and dangerous young

Person: he wonders at his unaccountable Pain, which daily sollicits him within, to go where he may behold this Beauty; of whom he frames a thousand Ideas, all such as were most agreeable to him; but then upbraids his Fancy for not forming her half so delicate as she was; and longs yet more to see her, to know how near she approaches to the Picture he has drawn of her in his Mind: and tho' he knew she liv'd the next House to him, yet he knew also she was kept within like a vow'd *Nun*, or with the Severity of a *Spaniard*. And tho' he had a Chamber, which had a jutting Window, that look'd just upon the Door of Monsieur *De Pais*, and that he would watch many Hours at a time, in hope to see them go out, yet he could never get a Glimpse of her; yet he heard she often frequented the Church of *our Lady*. Thither then young *Rinaldo* resolv'd to go, and did so two or three Mornings; in which time, to his unspeakable Grief, he saw no Beauty appear that charm'd him; and yet he fancy'd that *Atlante* was there, and that he had seen her; that some one of those young Ladies that he saw in the Church was she, tho' he had no body to enquire of, and that she was not so fair as the World reported; for which he would often sigh, as if he had lost some great Expectation. However, he ceased not to frequent this Church, and one day saw a young Beauty, who at first glimpse made his Heart leap to his Mouth, and fall a trembling again into its wonted Place; for it immediately told him, that that young Maid was *Atlante*: she was with her Sister *Charlot*, who was very handsome, but not comparable to *Atlante*. He fix'd his Eyes upon her as she kneel'd at the Altar; he never moved from that charming Face as long as she remain'd there; he forgot all Devotion, but what he paid to her; he ador'd her, he burnt and languish'd already for her, and found he must possess *Atlante* or die. Often as he gaz'd upon her, he saw her fair Eyes lifted up towards his, where they often met; which she perceiving, would cast hers down into her Bosom, or on her Book, and blush as if she had done a Fault. *Charlot* perceiv'd all the Motions of *Rinaldo*, how he folded his Arms, how he sigh'd and gaz'd on her Sister; she took notice of his Clothes, his Garniture, and every particular of his Dress, as young Girls use to do; and seeing him so very handsome, and so much better dress'd than all the young Cavaliers that were in the Church, she was very much pleas'd with him; and could not forbear saying, in a low Voice, to *Atlante*, 'Look, look my Sister, what a pretty Monsieur yonder is! see how fine his Face is, how delicate his Hair, how gallant his Dress! and do but look how he gazes on you!' This would make *Atlante* blush anew, who durst not raise her Eyes for fear she should encounter his. While he had the Pleasure to imagine they were talking of him, and he saw in the pretty Face of *Charlot*, that what she said was not to his Disadvantage, and by the Blushes of *Atlante*, that she was not displeas'd with what was spoken to her; he perceiv'd the young one importunate with her; and *Atlante* jogging her with her Elbow, as much as to say, Hold your Peace: all this he made a kind Interpretation of, and was transported with Joy at the good Omens. He was willing to flatter his new Flame, and to compliment his young Desire with a little Hope; but the divine Ceremony ceasing, *Atlante* left the Church, and it being very fair Weather, she walk'd home. *Rinaldo*, who saw her going, felt all the Agonies of a Lover, who parts with all that can make him happy; and seeing only *Atlante* attended with her Sister, and a Footman following with their Books, he was a thousand times about to speak to 'em; but he no sooner advanc'd a step or two towards 'em to that purpose (for he followed them) but his Heart fail'd, and a certain Awe and Reverence, or rather the Fears and Tremblings of a Lover, prevented him: but when he consider'd, that possibly he might never have so favourable an Opportunity again, he resolv'd a-new, and called up so much Courage to his Heart, as to speak to *Atlante ;* but before he did so, *Charlot* looking behind her, saw *Rinaldo* very near to 'em, and cry'd out with a Voice of Joy, 'Oh! Sister, Sister! look where the handsome *Monsieur* is, just behind us! sure he is some-body of Quality, for see he has two Footmen that follow him, in just such Liveries, and so rich as those of our Neighbour *Monsieur Bellyaurd*.' At this *Atlante* could not forbear, but before she was aware of it, turn'd her Head, and look'd on *Rinaldo ;* which encourag'd him to advance, and putting off his Hat, which he clapt under his Arm, with a low Bow, said, 'Ladies, you are slenderly attended, and so many Accidents arrive to the Fair in the rude Streets, that I humbly implore you will permit me, whose Duty it is as a Neighbour, to wait on you to your Door.' 'Sir, (said *Atlante* blushing) we fear no Insolence, and need no Protector; or if we did, we should not be so rude to take you out of your way, to serve us.' 'Madam, (said he) my way lies yours. I live at the next Door, and am Son to *Bellyaurd*, your Neighbour. But, Madam, (added he) if I were to go all my Life out of the way, to do you Service, I should take it for the greatest Happiness that could arrive to me; but, Madam, sure a Man can never be out of his Way, who has the Honour of so charming Company.' *Atlante* made no reply to this, but blush'd and bow'd: But *Charlot* said, 'Nay, Sir, if you are our Neighbour, we will give you leave to conduct us home; but pray, Sir, how came you to know we are your Neighbours? for we never saw you before, to our knowledge.' 'My pretty Miss, (reply'd *Rinaldo*) I knew it from that transcendent Beauty that appear'd in your Faces, and fine Shapes; for I have heard, there was no Beauty in the World like that of *Atlante's ;* and I no sooner saw her, but my Heart told me it was she.' 'Heart! (said *Charlot* laughing) why, do Hearts use to speak?' 'The most intelligible of any thing, (*Rinaldo* reply'd) when 'tis tenderly touch'd, when 'tis charm'd and transported.' At these Words he sigh'd, and *Atlante*, to his extreme Satisfaction, blush'd. 'Touch'd, charm'd, and transported, (said *Charlot*) what's that? And how do you do to have it be all these things? For I would give any thing in the World to have my Heart speak.' 'Oh! (said *Rinaldo*) your Heart is too young, it is not yet arrived to the Years of Speaking; about thirteen or fourteen, it may possibly be saying a thousand soft things to you; but it must be first inspir'd by some noble Object, whose Idea it must retain.' 'What (reply'd the pretty Prattler) I'll warrant I must be in Love?' 'Yes, (said *Rinaldo*) most passionately, or you will have but little Conversation with your Heart.' 'Oh! (reply'd she) I am afraid the Pleasure of such a Conversation, will not make me amends for the Pain that Love will give me.' 'That (said *Rinaldo*) is according as the Object is kind, and as you hope; if he love, and you hope, you will have double Pleasure: And in this, how great an Advantage have fair Ladies above us Men! 'Tis always impossible for you to love in vain, you have your Choice of a thousand Hearts, which you have subdu'd, and may not only chuse your Slaves, but be assur'd of 'em; without speaking, you are belov'd, it needs not cost you a Sigh or a Tear: But unhappy Man is often destin'd to give his Heart, where it is not regarded, to sigh, to weep, and languish, without any hope of Pity.' 'You speak so feelingly, Sir, (said *Charlot*) that I am afraid this is your Case.' 'Yes, Madam, (reply'd *Rinaldo*, sighing) I am that unhappy Man.' 'Indeed it is pity (said she.) Pray, how long have you been so?' 'Ever since I heard of the charming *Atlante*, (reply'd he, sighing again) I ador'd her Character; but now I have seen her, I die for her.' 'For me, Sir! (said *Atlante*, who had not yet spoke) this is the common Compliment of all the young Men, who pretend to be Lovers; and if one should pity all those Sighers, we should have but very little left for our selves.' 'I believe (said *Rinaldo*) there are none that tell you so, who do not

mean as they say : Yet among all those Adorers, and those
who say they will die for you, you will find none will
be so good as their Words but *Rinaldo*.' 'Perhaps (said
Atlante) of all those who tell me of Dying, there are none
that tell me of it with so little Reason as *Rinaldo*, if that
be your Name, Sir.' 'Madam, it is, (said he) and who am
transported with an unspeakable Joy, to hear those last
Words from your fair Mouth : and let me, Oh lovely
Atlante! assure you, that what I have said, are not Words
of course, but proceed from a Heart that has vow'd it self
eternally yours, even before I had the Happiness to behold
this divine Person; but now that my Eyes have made
good all my Heart before imagin'd, and did but hope, I
swear, I will die a thousand Deaths, rather than violate
what I have said to you; that I adore you; that my Soul
and all my Faculties, are charm'd with your Beauty and
Innocence, and that my Life and Fortune, not inconsid-
erable, shall be laid at your Feet.' This he spoke with a
Fervency of Passion, that left her no Doubt of what he
had said; yet she blush'd for Shame, and was a little angry
at her self, for suffering him to say so much to her, the
very first time she saw him, and accused her self for giving
him any Encouragement: And in this Confusion she
replied, 'Sir, you have said too much to be believ'd; and
I cannot imagine so short an Acquaintance can make so
considerable an Impression; of which Confession I accuse
my self much more than you, in that I did not only
hearken to what you said, without forbidding you to
entertain me at that rate, but for unheedily speaking something, that has encourag'd this Boldness; for so I must
call it, in a Man so great a Stranger to me.' 'Madam (said
he) if I have offended by the Suddenness of my presumptuous Discovery, I beseech you to consider my Reasons
for it, the few Opportunities I am like to have, and the
Impossibility of waiting on you, both from the Severity of
your Father and mine; who, ere I saw you, warn'd me

of my Fate, as if he foresaw I should fall in love, as soon
as I should chance to see you; and for that Reason has
kept me closer to my Studies, than hitherto I have been.
And from that time I began to feel a Flame, which was
kindled by Report alone, and the Description my Father
gave of your wondrous and dangerous Beauty : Therefore,
Madam, I have not suddenly told you of my Passion. I
have been long your Lover, and have long languish'd
without telling of my Pain; and you ought to pardon it
now, since it is done with all the Respect and religious
Awe, that 'tis possible for a Heart to deliver and unload
it self in; therefore, Madam, if you have by chance uttered
any thing, that I have taken Advantage or Hope from, I
assure you 'tis so small, that you have no reason to repent
it; but rather, if you would have me live, send me not
from you, without a Confirmation of that little Hope.
See, Madam, (said he, more earnestly and trembling) see
we are almost arriv'd at our Homes, send me not to mine
in a Despair that I cannot support with Life; but tell me,
I shall be bless'd with your Sight, sometimes in your
Balcony, which is very near to a jetting Window in our
House, from whence I have sent many a longing Look
towards yours, in hope to have seen my Soul's Tormentor.'
'I shall be very unwilling (said she) to enter into an
Intrigue of Love or Friendship with a Man, whose Parents
will be averse to my Happiness, and possibly mine as
refractory, tho' they cannot but know such an Alliance
would be very considerable, my Fortune not being suitable
to yours : I tell you this, that you may withdraw in time
from an Engagement, in which I find there will be a great
many Obstacles.' 'Oh! Madam, (reply'd *Rinaldo*, sighing)
if my Person be not disagreeable to you, you will have no
occasion to fear the rest; 'tis that I dread, and that which
is all my Fear.' He, sighing, beheld her with a languishing
Look, that told her, he expected her Answer; when she
reply'd, 'Sir, if that will be Satisfaction enough for you at

this time, I do assure you, I have no Aversion for your
Person, in which I find more to be valu'd, than in any I
have yet seen; and if what you say be real, and proceed
from a Heart truly affected, I find, in spite of me, you
will oblige me to give you Hope.'

They were come so near their own Houses, that he
had not time to return her any Answer; but with a low
Bow he acknowledg'd her Bounty, and express'd the Joy
her last Words had given him, by a Look that made her
understand he was charm'd and pleas'd: and she bowing
to him with an Air of Satisfaction in her Face, he was
well assur'd, there was nothing to be seen so lovely as she
then appear'd, and left her to go into her own House: but
till she was out of sight, he had not power to stir, and
then sighing, retired to his own Apartment, to think over
all that had past between them. He found nothing but
what gave him a thousand Joys, in all she had said; and
he blest this happy Day, and wondred how his Stars came
so kind, to make him in one hour at once see *Atlante*, and
have the happiness to know from her Mouth, that he was
not disagreeable to her: Yet with this Satisfaction, he had
a thousand Thoughts mix'd which were tormenting, and
those were the Fear of their Parents; he foresaw from
what his Father had said to him already, that it would be
difficult to draw him to a Consent of his Marriage with
Atlante. These Joys and Fears were his Companions all
the Night, in which he took but little Rest. Nor was
Atlante without her Inquietudes: She found *Rinaldo* more
in her Thoughts than she wish'd, and a sudden Change
of Humour, that made her know something was the matter
with her more than usual; she calls to mind *Rinaldo's*
speaking of the Conversation with his Heart, and found
hers would be tattling to her, if she would give way to
it; and yet the more she strove to avoid it, the more it
importun'd her, and in spight of all her Resistance, would
tell her, that *Rinaldo* had a thousand Charms: It tells her,

that he loves and adores her, and that she would be the
most cruel of her Sex, should she not be sensible of his
Passion. She finds a thousand Graces in his Person and
Conversation, and as many Advantages in his Fortune,
which was one of the most considerable in all those Parts;
for his Estate exceeded that of the most Noble Men in
Orleans, and she imagines she should be the most fortunate
of all Womankind in such a Match. With these Thoughts
she employ'd all the Hours of the Night; so that she lay
so long in Bed the next Day, that Count *Vernole*, who
had invited himself to Dinner, came before she had quitted
her Chamber, and she was forc'd to say, she had not been
well. He had brought her a very fine Book, newly come
out, of delicate Philosophy, fit for the Study of Ladies.
But he appear'd so disagreeable to that Heart, wholly taken
up with a new and fine Object, that she could now hardly
pay him that Civility she was wont to do; while on the
other side that little State and Pride *Atlante* assum'd, made
her appear the more charming to him : so that if *Atlante*
had no mind to begin a new Lesson of Philosophy, while
she fancied her Thoughts were much better employ'd,
the Count every moment expressing his Tenderness and
Passion, had as little an Inclination to instruct her, as she
had to be instructed : Love had taught her a new Lesson,
and he would fain teach her a new Lesson of Love, but
fears it will be a diminishing his Gravity and Grandeur,
to open the Secrets of his Heart to so young a Maid; he
therefore thinks it more agreeable to his Quality and
Years, being about Forty, to use her Father's Authority
in this Affair, and that it was sufficient for him to declare
himself to Monsieur *De Pais*, who he knew would be proud
of the Honour he did him. Some time past, before he could
be persuaded even to declare himself to her Father : he
fancies the little Coldness and Pride he saw in *Atlante's*
Face, which was not usual, proceeded from some Discovery
of Passion, which his Eyes had made, or now and then a

Sigh, that unawares broke forth; and accuses himself of a Levity below his Quality, and the Dignity of his Wit and Gravity; and therefore assumes a more rigid and formal Behaviour than he was wont, which rendred him yet more disagreeable than before; and 'twas with greater Pain than ever, she gave him that Respect which was due to his Quality.

Rinaldo, after a restless Night, was up very early in the Morning; and tho' he was not certain of seeing his adorable *Atlante*, he dress'd himself with all that Care, as if he had been to have waited on her, and got himself into the Window, that overlook'd Monsieur *De Pais's* Balcony, where he had not remain'd long, before he saw the pretty *Charlot* come into it, not with any design of seeing *Rinaldo*, but to look and gaze about her a little. *Rinaldo* saw her, and made her a very low Reverence, and found some disorder'd Joy on the sight of even *Charlot*, since she was Sister to *Atlante*. He call'd to her, (for the Window was so near her, he could easily be heard by her) and told her, 'He was infinitely indebted to her Bounty, for giving him an Opportunity yesterday of falling on that Discourse, which had made him the happiest Man in the World': He said, 'If she had not by her agreeable Conversation encourag'd him, and drawn him from one Word to another, he should never have had the Confidence to have told *Atlante*, how much he ador'd her.' 'I am very glad, (replyed *Charlot*) that I was the Occasion of the Beginning of an Amour, which was displeasing to neither one nor the other; for I assure you for your Comfort, my Sister nothing but thinks on you: We lie together, and you have taught her already to sigh so, that I could not sleep for her.' At this his Face was cover'd over with a rising Joy, which his Heart could not contain: And after some Discourse, in which this innocent Girl discovered more than *Atlante* wish'd she should, he besought her to become his Advocate; and since she had no Brother, to give him leave to assume that Honour, and call her Sister. Thus, by degrees, he flatter'd her into a Consent of carrying a Letter from him to *Atlante;* which she, who believ'd all as innocent as her self, and being not forbid to do so, immediately consented to; when he took his Pen and Ink, that stood in the Window, with Paper, and wrote *Atlante* this following Letter:

RINALDO to ATLANTE.

IF my Fate be so severe, as to deny me the Happiness of sighing out my Pain and Passion daily at your Feet, if there be any Faith in the Hope you were pleased to give me (as 'twere a Sin to doubt) Oh charming Atlante *! suffer me not to languish, both without beholding you, and without the Blessing of now and then a Billet, in answer to those that shall daily assure you of my eternal Faith and Vows; 'tis all I ask, till Fortune, and our Affairs, shall allow me the unspeakable Satisfaction of claiming you: yet if your Charity can sometimes afford me a sight of you, either from your Balcony in the Evening, or at a Church in the Morning, it would save me from that Despair and Torment, which must possess a Heart so unassur'd, as that of*

Your Eternal Adorer,

Rin. Bellyaurd.

He having writ and seal'd this, toss'd it into the Balcony to *Charlot,* having first look'd about to see if none perceiv'd them. She put it in her Bosom, and ran in to her Sister, whom by chance she found alone; *Vernole* having taken *De Pais* into the Garden, to discourse him concerning the sending *Charlot* to the Monastery, which Work he desir'd to see perform'd, before he declar'd his Intentions to *Atlante:* for among all his other good Qualities, he was very avaricious; and as fair as *Atlante* was, he thought she would be much fairer with the Addition of *Charlot's* Portion. This Affair of his with Monsieur *De Pais,* gave *Charlot* an opportunity of delivering her Letter to her Sister; who no sooner drew it from her Bosom, but *Atlante's* Face was covered over with Blushes: For she imagin'd from whence it came, and had a secret Joy in that Imagination, tho' she thought she must put on the Severity and Niceness of a Virgin, who would not be thought to have surrendered her Heart with so small an Assault, and the first too. So she demanded from whence *Charlot* had that Letter? Who replyed with Joy, 'From the fine young Gentleman, our Neighbour.' At which *Atlante* assum'd all the Gravity she could, to chide her Sister; who replied, 'Well, Sister, had you this day seen him, you would not have been angry to have receiv'd a Letter from him; he look'd so handsome, and was so richly dress'd, ten times finer than he was yesterday; and I promis'd him you should read it: therefore, pray let me keep my Word with him; and not only so, but carry him an Answer.' 'Well (said *Atlante*) to save your Credit with Monsieur *Rinaldo*, I will read it': Which she did, and finish'd with a Sigh. While she was reading, *Charlot* ran into the Garden, to see if they were not likely to be surpriz'd; and finding the Count and her Father set in an Arbour, in deep Discourse, she brought Pen, Ink, and Paper to her Sister, and told her, she might write without the Fear of being disturbed: and urged her so long to what was enough her Inclination, that she at last obtained this Answer:

ATLANTE to *RINALDO*.

CHARLOT, *your little importunate Advocate, has at last subdued me to a Consent of returning you This. She has put me on an Affair with which I am wholly unacquainted; and you ought to take this very kindly from me, since it is the very first time I ever writ to one of your Sex, tho' perhaps I might with less Danger have done it to any other Man. I tremble while I write, since I dread a Correspondence of this Nature, which may insensibly draw us into an Inconvenience, and engage*

*me beyond the Limits of that Nicety I ought to preserve: For
this Way we venture to say a thousand little kind Things,
which in Conversation we dare not do: for now none can see
us blush. I am sensible I shall this Way put my self too soon
into your Power; and tho' you have abundance of Merit, I
ought to be asham'd of confessing, I am but too sensible of it:
—But hold—I shall discover for your Repose (which I would
preserve) too much of the Heart of* Atlante.

She gave this Letter to *Charlot*; who immediately ran
into the Balcony with it, where she still found *Rinaldo* in
a melancholy Posture, leaning his Head on his Hand: She
shewed him the Letter, but was afraid to toss it to him,
for fear it might fall to the Ground; so he ran and fetched
a long Cane, which he cleft at one End, and held it while
she put the Letter into the Cleft, and staid not to hear
what he said to it. But never was Man so transported
with Joy, as he was at the reading of this Letter; it gives
him new Wounds; for to the Generous, nothing obliges
Love so much as Love: tho' it is now too much the
Nature of that inconstant Sex, to cease to love as soon as
they are sure of the Conquest. But it was far different with
our Cavalier; he was the more inflamed, by imagining he
had made some Impressions on the Heart of *Atlante*, and
kindled some Sparks there, that in time might increase to
something more; so that he now resolves to die hers: and
considering all the Obstacles that may possibly hinder his
Happiness, he found none but his Father's Obstinacy,
perhaps occasioned by the Meanness of *Atlante's* Fortune.
To this he urged again, that he was his only Son, and a
Son whom he loved equal to his own Life; and that certainly, as soon as he should behold him dying for *Atlante*,
which if he were forc'd to quit her he must be, he then
believed the Tenderness of so fond a Parent would break
forth into Pity, and plead within for his Consent. These
were the Thoughts that flatter'd this young Lover all

the Day; and whether he were riding the Great Horse, or at his Study of Philosophy, or Mathematicks, Singing, Dancing, or whatsoever other Exercise his Tutors ordered, his Thoughts were continually on *Atlante*. And now he profited no more, whatever he seem'd to do: every Day he fail'd not to write to her by the Hand of the kind *Charlot*; who, young as she was, had conceiv'd a great Friendship for *Rinaldo*, and fail'd not to fetch her Letters, and bring him Answers, such as he wish'd to receive. But all this did not satisfy our impatient Lover; Absence kill'd, and he was no longer able to support himself, without a sight of this adorable Maid; he therefore implores, she will give him that Satisfaction: And she at last grants it, with a better Will than he imagin'd. The next Day was the appointed Time, when she would, under Pretence of going to Church, give him an Assignation: And because all publick Places were dangerous, and might make a great Noise, and they had no private Place to trust to, *Rinaldo*, under Pretence of going up the River in his Pleasure-Boat, which he often did, sent to have it made ready by the next Day at Ten of the Clock. This was accordingly done, and he gave *Atlante* Notice of his Design of going an Hour or two on the River in his Boat, which lay near to such a Place, not far from the Church. She and *Charlot* came thither: and because they durst not come out without a Footman or two, they taking one, sent him with a *How-do-ye* to some young Ladies, and told him, he should find them at Church: So getting rid of their Spy, they hastened to the River-side, and found a Boat and *Rinaldo*, waiting to carry them on board his little Vessel, which was richly adorn'd, and a very handsome Collation ready for them, of cold Meats, Sallads and Sweetmeats.

As soon as they were come into the Pleasure-Boat, unseen of any, he kneel'd at the Feet of *Atlante*, and there utter'd so many passionate and tender Things to her, with a Voice so trembling and soft, with Eyes so languishing,

and a Fervency and a Fire so sincere, that her young
Heart, wholly uncapable of Artifice, could no longer resist
such Language, and such Looks of Love; she grows
tender, and he perceives it in her fine Eyes, who could not
dissemble; he reads her Heart in her Looks, and found it
yielding apace; and therefore assaults it anew, with fresh
Forces of Sighs and Tears: He implores she would assure
him of her Heart, which she could no other way do, than
by yielding to marry him: He would carry her to the next
Village, there consummate that Happiness, without which
he was able to live no longer; for he had a thousand Fears,
that some other Lover was, or would suddenly be provided
for her; and therefore he would make sure of her while
he had this Opportunity: and to that End, he answer'd
all the Objections she could make to the contrary. But
ever, when he named Marriage, she trembled, with fear
of doing something that she fancy'd she ought not to do
without the Consent of her Father. She was sensible of
the Advantage, but had been so us'd to a strict Obedience,
that she could not without Horror think of violating it;
and therefore besought him, as he valued her Repose, not
to urge her to that: And told him further, That if he
fear'd any Rival, she would give him what other Assurance
and Satisfaction he pleas'd, but that of Marriage; which
she could not consent to, till she knew such an Alliance
would not be fatal to him: for she fear'd, as passionately
as he lov'd her, when he should find she had occasion'd
him the Loss of his Fortune, or his Father's Affection, he
would grow to hate her. Tho' he answer'd to this all
that a fond Lover could urge, yet she was resolv'd, and
he forc'd to content himself with obliging her by his
Prayers and Protestations, his Sighs and Tears, to a Contract, which they solemnly made each other, vowing on
either Side, they would never marry any other. This being
solemnly concluded, he assum'd a Look more gay and
contented than before: He presented her a very rich Ring,

which she durst not put on her Finger, but hid it in her Bosom. And beholding each other now as Man and Wife, she suffer'd him all the decent Freedoms he could wish to take; so that the Hours of this Voyage seem'd the most soft and charming of his Life: and doubtless they were so; every Touch of *Atlante* transported him, every Look pierced his Soul, and he was all Raptures of Joy, when he consider'd this charming lovely Maid was his own.

Charlot all this while was gazing above-deck, admiring the Motion of the little Vessel, and how easily the Wind and Tide bore her up the River. She had never been in any thing of this kind before, and was very well pleas'd and entertain'd, when *Rinaldo* call'd her down to eat; where they enjoy'd themselves, as well as was possible: and *Charlot* was wondring to see such a Content in their Eyes.

But now they thought it was high time for them to return; they fancy the Footman missing them at Church, would go home and alarm their Father, and the Knight of the Ill-favour'd Countenance, as *Charlot* call'd Count *Vernole*, whose Severity put their Father on a greater Restriction of them, than naturally he would do of himself. At the Name of this Count, *Rinaldo* chang'd Colour, fearing he might be some Rival; and ask'd *Atlante*, if this *Vernole* was a-kin to her? She answer'd no; but was a very great Friend to her Father, and one who from their Infancy had had a particular Concern for their Breeding, and was her Master for Philosophy. 'Ah! (reply'd *Rinaldo*, sighing) this Man's Concern must proceed from something more than Friendship for her Father'; and therefore conjur'd her to tell him, whether he was not a Lover: 'A Lover! (reply'd *Atlante*) I assure you, he is a perfect Antidote against that Passion': And tho' she suffer'd his ugly Presence now, she should loathe and hate him, should he but name Love to her.

She said, she believed she need not fear any such Persecution, since he was a Man who was not at all amorous;

that he had too much of the Satire in his Humour, to harbour any Softness there: and Nature had form'd his Body to his Mind, wholly unfit for Love. And that he might set his Heart absolutely at rest, she asur'd him her Father had never yet propos'd any Marriage to her, tho' many advantageous ones were offer'd him every Day.

The Sails being turned to carry them back from whence they came; after having discoursed of a thousand Things, and all of Love, and Contrivance to carry on their mutual Design, they with Sighs parted; *Rinaldo* staying behind in the Pleasure-Boat, and they going a-shore in the Wherry that attended: after which he cast many an amorous and sad Look, and perhaps was answer'd by those of *Atlante*.

It was past Church-time two or three Hours, when they arrived at home, wholly unprepar'd with an Excuse, so absolutely was *Atlante's* Soul possest with softer Business. The first Person that they met was the Footman, who open'd the Door, and began to cry out how long he had waited in the Church, and how in vain; without giving them time to reply. *De Pais* came towards 'em, and with a frowning Look demanded where they had been? *Atlante*, who was not accustom'd to Excuses and Untruth, was a while at a stand; when *Charlot* with a Voice of Joy cry'd out, 'Oh Sir! we have been a-board of a fine little Ship': At this *Atlante* blush'd, fearing she would tell the Truth. But she proceeded on, and said, that they had not been above a Quarter of an Hour at Church, when the Lady —, with some other Ladies and Cavaliers, were going out of the Church, and that spying them, they would needs have 'em go with 'em: My Sister, Sir, continu'd she, was very loth to go, for fear you should be angry; but my Lady — was so importunate with her on one side, and I on the other, because I never saw a little Ship in my Life, that at last we prevail'd with her: therefore, good Sir, be not angry. He promised them he was not. And when they came in, they found Count *Vernole*, who had been inspiring *De Pais* with Severity, and counselled him to chide the young Ladies, for being too long absent, under Pretence of going to their Devotion. Nor was it enough for him to set the Father on, but himself with a Gravity, where Concern and Malice were both apparent, reproached *Atlante* with Levity; and told her, He believed she had some other Motive than the Invitation of a Lady, to go on Ship-board; and that she had too many Lovers, not to make them doubt that this was a design'd thing; and that she had heard Love from some one, for whom it was design'd. To this she made but a short Reply, That if it was so, she had no reason to conceal it, since she had Sense enough to look after herself; and if any body had made love to her, he might be assur'd, it was some one whose Quality and Merit deserved to be heard: and with a Look of Scorn, she passed on to another Room, and left him silently raging within with Jealousy: Which, if before she tormented him, this Declaration increas'd it to a pitch not to be conceal'd. And this Day he said so much to the Father, that he resolv'd forthwith to send *Charlot* to a Nunnery: and accordingly the next day he bid her prepare to go. *Charlot*, who was not yet arrived to the Years of Distinction, did not much regret it; and having no Trouble but leaving her Sister, she prepared to go to a Nunnery, not many Streets from that where she dwelt. The Lady Abbess was her Father's Kinswoman, and had treated her very well, as often as she came to visit her: so that with Satisfaction enough, she was condemned to a Monastick Life, and was now going for her Probation-Year. *Atlante* was troubled at her Departure, because she had no body to bring and to carry Letters between *Rinaldo* and she: however, she took her leave of her, and promis'd to come and see her as often as she should be permitted to go abroad; for she fear'd now some Constraint extraordinary would be put upon her: and so it happened.

Atlante's Chamber was that to which the Balcony

belong'd; and tho' she durst not appear there in the Day-time, she could in the Night, and that way give her Lover as many Hours of Conversation as she pleased, without being perceiv'd: But how to give *Rinaldo* notice of this, she could not tell; who not knowing *Charlot* was gone to a Monastery, waited many days at his Window to see her: at last, they neither of them knowing who to trust with any Message, one day, when he was, as usual upon his watch, he saw *Atlante* step into the Balcony, who having a Letter, in which she had put a piece of Lead, she tost it into his Window, whose Casement was open, and run in again unperceived by any but himself. The Paper contained only this:

My Chamber is that which looks into the Balcony; from whence, tho' I cannot converse with you in the Day, I can at Night, when I am retired to go to bed: therefore be at your Window. Farewel.

There needed no more to make him a diligent Watcher: and accordingly she was no sooner retired to her Chamber, but she would come into the Balcony, where she fail'd not to see him attending at his Window. This happy Contrivance was thus carry'd on for many Nights, where they entertain'd one another with all the Endearment that two Hearts could dictate, who were perfectly united and assur'd of each other; and this pleasing Conversation would often last till Day appear'd, and forced them to part.

But old *Bellyaurd* perceiving his Son frequent that Chamber more than usual, fancy'd something extraordinary must be the Cause of it; and one night asking for his Son, his Valet told him, he was gone into the great Chamber, so this was called: *Bellyaurd* asked the Valet what he did there; he told him he could not tell; for often he had lighted him thither, and that his Master would take the Candle from him at the Chamber-Door, and suffer him to go no farther. Tho' the old Gentleman could not imagine what Affairs he could have alone every Night in that Chamber, he had a Curiosity to see: and one unlucky Night, putting off his Shoes, he came to the Door of the Chamber, which was open; he enter'd softly, and saw the Candle set in the Chimney, and his Son at a great open Bay-Window: he stopt awhile to wait when he would turn, but finding him unmoveable, he advanced something farther, and at last heard the soft Dialogue of Love between him and *Atlante*, whom he knew to be she, by his often calling her by her Name in their Discourse. He heard enough to confirm him how Matters went; and unseen as he came, he returned, full of Indignation, and thought how to prevent so great an Evil, as this Passion of his Son might produce: at first he thought to round him severely in the Ear about it, and upbraid him for doing the only thing he had thought fit to forbid him; but then he thought that would but terrify him for awhile, and he would return again, where he had so great an Inclination, if he were near her; he therefore resolves to send him to *Paris*, that by Absence he might forget the young Beauty that had charm'd his Youth. Therefore, without letting *Rinaldo* know the Reason, and without taking Notice that he knew any thing of his Amour, he came to him one day, and told him, all the Masters he had for the improving him in noble Sciences were very dull, or very remiss: and that he resolved he should go for a Year or two to the Academy at *Paris*. To this the Son made a thousand Evasions; but the Father was positive, and not to be persuaded by all his Reasons: And finding he should absolutely displease him if he refus'd to go, and not daring to tell him the dear Cause of his Desire to remain at *Orleans*, he therefore, with a breaking Heart, consents to go, nay, resolves it, tho' it should be his Death. But alas! he considers that this Parting will not only prove the greatest Torment upon Earth to him, but that *Atlante* will share in his Misfortunes also: This Thought gives him a double Torment, and yet he finds no Way to evade it.

The Night that finished this fatal Day, he goes again to his wonted Station, the Window; where he had not sighed very long, but he saw *Atlante* enter the Balcony: He was not able a great while to speak to her, or to utter one Word. The Night was light enough to see him at the wonted Place; and she admires at his Silence, and demands the Reason in such obliging Terms as adds to his Grief; and he, with a deep Sigh, reply'd, 'Urge me not, my fair *Atlante*, to speak, lest by obeying you I give you more cause of Grief than my Silence is capable of doing': and then sighing again, he held his peace, and gave her leave to ask the Cause of these last Words. But when he made no Reply but by sighing, she imagin'd it much worse than indeed it was; and with a trembling and fainting Voice, she cried, 'Oh! *Rinaldo*, give me leave to divine that cruel News you are so unwilling to tell me: It is so,' added she, 'you are destin'd to some more fortunate Maid than *Atlante*.' At this Tears stopped her Speech, and she could utter no more. 'No, my dearest Charmer (reply'd *Rinaldo*, elevating his Voice) if that were all, you should see with what Fortitude I would die, rather than obey any such Commands. I am vow'd yours to the last Moment of my Life; and will be yours in spite of all the Opposition in the World: that Cruelty I could evade, but cannot this that threatens me.' 'Ah! (cried *Atlante*) let Fate do her worst, so she still continue *Rinaldo* mine, and keep that Faith he hath sworn to me entire: What can she do beside, that can afflict me?' 'She can separate me (cried he) for some time from *Atlante*.' 'Oh! (reply'd she) all Misfortunes fall so below that which I first imagin'd, that methinks I do not resent this, as I should otherwise have done: but I know, when I have a little more consider'd it, I shall even die with the Grief of it; Absence being so great an Enemy to Love, and making us soon forget the Object belov'd : This, tho' I never experienc'd, I have heard, and fear it may be my Fate.' He then convinc'd her Fears with a thousand new Vows, and a thousand Imprecations of Constancy. She then asked him, 'If their Loves were discover'd, that he was with such haste to depart?' He told her, 'Nothing of that was the Cause; and he could almost wish it were discover'd, since he could resolutely then refuse to go : but it was only to cultivate his Mind more effectually than he could do here; 'twas the Care of his Father to accomplish him the more; and therefore he could not contradict it. But (said he) I am not sent where Seas shall part us, nor vast Distances of Earth, but to *Paris*, from whence he might come in two Days to see her again; and that he would expect from that Balcony, that had given him so many happy Moments, many more when he should come to see her.' He besought her to send him away with all the Satisfaction she could, which she could no otherwise do, than by giving him new Assurances that she would never give away that Right he had in her to any other Lover : She vows this with innumerable Tears; and is almost angry with him for questioning her Faith. He tells her he has but one Night more to stay, and his Grief would be unspeakable, if he should not be able to take a better leave of her, than at a Window; and that, if she would give him leave, he would by a Rope or two, tied together, so as it may serve for Steps, ascend her Balcony; he not having time to provide a Ladder of Ropes. She tells him she has so great a Confidence in his Virtue and Love, that she will refuse him nothing, tho' it would be a very bold Venture for a Maid, to trust her self with a passionate young Man, in silence of Night : and tho' she did not extort a Vow from him to secure her, she expected he would have a care of her Honour. He swore to her, his Love was too religious for so base an Attempt. There needed not many Vows to confirm her Faith; and it was agreed on between them, that he should come the next Night into her Chamber.

It happen'd that Night, as it often did, that Count *Vernole* lay with Monsieur *De Pais*, which was in a Ground-Room, just under that of *Atlante's*. As soon as she knew all were in bed, she gave the word to *Rinaldo*, who was attending with the Impatience of a passionate Lover below, under the Window; and who no sooner heard the Balcony open, but he ascended with some difficulty, and enter'd the Chamber, where he found *Atlante* trembling with Joy and Fear: He throws himself at her Feet, as unable to speak as she; who nothing but blushed and bent down her Eyes, hardly daring to glance them towards the dear Object of her Desires, the Lord of all her Vows: She was asham'd to see a Man in her Chamber, where yet none had ever been alone, and by Night too. He saw her Fear, and felt her trembling; and after a thousand Sighs of Love had made way for Speech, he besought her to fear nothing from him, for his Flame was too sacred, and his Passion too holy to offer any thing but what Honour with Love might afford him. At last he brought her to some Courage, and the Roses of her fair Cheeks assum'd their wonted Colour, not blushing too red, nor languishing too pale. But when the Conversation began between them, it was the softest in the world: They said all that parting Lovers could say; all that Wit and Tenderness could express: They exchanged their Vows anew; and to confirm his, he tied a Bracelet of Diamonds about her Arm, and she returned him one of her Hair, which he had long begged, and she had on purpose made, which clasped together with Diamonds; this she put about his Arm, and he swore to carry it to his Grave. The Night was far spent in tender Vows, soft Sighs and Tears on both sides, and it was high time to part: but, as if Death had been to have arrived to them in that Minute, they both linger'd away the time, like

Lovers who had forgot themselves; and the Day was near approaching when he bid farewel, which he repeated very often: for still he was interrupted by some commanding Softness from *Atlante*, and then lost all his Power of going; till she, more courageous and careful of his Interest and her own Fame, forc'd him from her: and it was happy she did, for he was no sooner got over the Balcony, and she had flung him down his Rope, and shut the Door, but *Vernole*, whom Love and Contrivance kept waking, fancy'd several times he heard a Noise in *Atlante's* Chamber. And whether in passing over the Balcony, *Rinaldo* made any Noise or not, or whether it were still his jealous Fancy, he came up in his Night-Gown, with a Pistol in his Hand. *Atlante* was not so much lost in Grief, tho' she were all in Tears, but she heard a Man come up, and imagin'd it had been her Father, she not knowing of Count *Vernole's* lying in the House that Night; if she had, she possibly had taken more care to have been silent; but whoever it was, she could not get to bed soon enough, and therefore turn'd her self to her Dressing-Table, where a Candle stood, and where lay a Book open of the Story of *Ariadne* and *Theseus*. The Count turning the Latch, enter'd halting into her Chamber in his Night-Gown clapped close about him, which betray'd an ill-favour'd Shape, his Night-Cap on, without a Perriwig, which discover'd all his lean wither'd Jaws, his pale Face, and his Eyes staring: and made altogether so dreadful a Figure, that *Atlante*, who no more dreamt of him than of a Devil, had possibly have rather seen the last. She gave a great Shriek, which frighted *Vernole*; so both stood for a while staring on each other, till both were recollected: He told her the Care of her Honour had brought him thither; and then rolling his small Eyes round the Chamber, to see if he could discover any body, he proceeded, and cry'd, 'Madam, if I had no other Motive than your being up at this time of Night, or rather of Day, I could easily guess how you have been entertain'd.' 'What Insolence is this (said she, all in a rage) when to cover your Boldness of approaching my Chamber at this Hour, you would question how I have been entertain'd! Either explain your self, or quit my Chamber; for I do not use to see such terrible Objects here.' 'Possibly those you do see (said the Count) are indeed more agreeable, but I am afraid have not that Regard to your Honour as I have': And at that word he stepped to the Balcony, open'd it, and look'd out; but seeing no body, he shut it to again. This enraged *Atlante* beyond all Patience; and snatching the Pistol out of his Hand, she told him, He deserved to have it aimed at his Head, for having the Impudence to question her Honour, or her Conduct; and commanded him to avoid her Chamber as he lov'd his Life, which she believ'd he was fonder of than of her Honour. She speaking this in a Tone wholly transported with Rage, and at the same time holding the Pistol towards him, made him tremble with Fear; and he now found, whether she were guilty or not, it was his turn to beg Pardon: For you must know, however it came to pass that his Jealousy made him come up in that fierce Posture, at other times *Vernole* was the most tame and passive Man in the World, and one who was afraid of his own Shadow in the Night: He had a natural Aversion for Danger, and thought it below a Man of Wit, or common Sense, to be guilty of that brutal thing, called Courage or Fighting; His Philosophy told him, *It was safe sleeping in a whole Skin;* and possibly he apprehended as much Danger from this *Virago*, as ever he did from his own Sex. He therefore fell on his Knees, and besought her to hold her fair Hand, and not to suffer that, which was the greatest Mark of his Respect, to be the Cause of her Hate or Indignation. The pitiful Faces he made, and the Signs of Mortal Fear in him, had almost made her laugh, at least it allay'd her Anger; and she bid him rise and play the fool hereafter somewhere else, and not in her

Presence; yet for once she would deign to give him this Satisfaction, that she was got into a Book, which had many moving Stories very well writ; and that she found her self so well entertain'd, she had forgot how the Night passed. He most humbly thanked her for this Satisfaction, and retired, perhaps not so well satisfied as he pretended.

After this, he appear'd more submissive and respectful towards *Atlante;* and she carry'd herself more reserv'd and haughty towards him; which was one Reason, he would not yet discover his Passion.

Thus the Time run on at *Orleans,* while *Rinaldo* found himself daily languishing at *Paris.* He was indeed in the best Academy in the City, amongst a Number of brave and noble Youths, where all things that could accomplish them, were to be learn'd by those that had any Genius; but *Rinaldo* had other Thoughts, and other Business: his Time was wholly past in the most solitary Parts of the Garden, by the melancholy Fountains, and in the most gloomy Shades, where he could with most Liberty breathe out his Passion and his Griefs. He was past the Tutorage of a Boy; and his Masters could not upbraid him, but found he had some secret Cause of Grief, which made him not mind those Exercises, which were the Delight of the rest: so that nothing being able to divert his Melancholy, which daily increased upon him, he fear'd it would bring him into a Fever, if he did not give himself the Satisfaction of seeing *Atlante.* He had no sooner thought of this, but he was impatient to put it in execution; he resolved to go (having very good Horses) without acquainting any of his Servants with it. He got a very handsom and light Ladder of Ropes made, which he carry'd under his Coat, and away he rid for *Orleans,* stay'd at a little Village, till the Darkness of the Night might favour his Design: And then walking about *Atlante's* Lodgings, till he saw a Light in her Chamber, and then making that Noise on his Sword, as was agreed between them, he was heard by his adorable

Atlante, and suffer'd to mount her Chamber, where he would stay till almost break of Day, and then return to the Village, and take Horse, and away for *Paris* again. This, once in a Month, was his Exercise, without which he could not live; so that his whole Year was past in riding between *Orleans* and *Paris,* between Excess of Grief, and Excess of Joy by turns.

It was now that *Atlante,* arrived to her fifteenth Year, shone out with a Lustre of Beauty greater than ever; and in this Year, in the Absence of *Rinaldo,* had carry'd herself with that Severity of Life, without the youthful Desire of going abroad, or desiring any Diversion, but what she found in her own retired Thoughts, that *Vernole,* wholly unable longer to conceal his Passion, resolv'd to make a Publication of it, first to the Father, and then to the lovely Daughter, of whom he had some Hope, because she had carry'd her self very well towards him for this Year past; which she would never have done, if she had imagin'd he would ever have been her Lover: She had seen no Signs of any such Misfortune towards her in these many Years he had conversed with her, and she had no Cause to fear him. When one Day her Father taking her into the Garden, told her what Honour and Happiness was in store for her; and that now the Glory of his fall'n Family would rise again, since she had a Lover of an illustrious Blood, ally'd to Monarchs; and one whose Fortune was newly encreased to a very considerable Degree, answerable to his Birth. She changed Colour at this Discourse, imagining but too well who this illustrious Lover was; when *De Pais* proceeded and told her, 'Indeed his Person was not the most agreeable that ever was seen: but he marry'd her to Glory and Fortune, not the Man: And a Woman (says he) ought to look no further.'

She needed not any more to inform her who this intended Husband was; and therefore, bursting forth into Tears, she throws herself at his Feet, imploring him not

to use the Authority of a Father, to force her to a thing
so contrary to her Inclination: assuring him, she could
not consent to any such thing; and that she would rather
die than yield. She urged many Arguments for this her
Disobedience; but none would pass for current with the
old Gentleman, whose Pride had flatter'd him with Hopes
of so considerable a Son-in-law: He was very much
surpriz'd at *Atlante's* refusing what he believ'd she would
receive with Joy; and finding that no Arguments on his
Side could draw hers to an obedient Consent, he grew to
such a Rage, as very rarely possest him: vowing, if she
did not conform her Will to his, he would abandon her
to all the Cruelty of Contempt and Poverty: so that at
last she was forced to return him this Answer, 'That she
would strive all she could with her Heart; but she verily
believed she should never bring it to consent to a Marriage with Monsieur the Count.' The Father continued
threatning her, and gave her some Days to consider of
it: So leaving her in Tears, he returned to his Chamber,
to consider what Answer he should give Count *Vernole*,
who he knew would be impatient to learn what Success
he had, and what himself was to hope. *De Pais*, after
some Consideration, resolved to tell him, she receiv'd the
Offer very well, but that he must expect a little Maiden-
Nicety in the Case: and accordingly did tell him so; and
he was not at all doubtful of his good Fortune.

But *Atlante*, who resolved to die a thousand Deaths
rather than break her solemn Vows to *Rinaldo*, or to
marry the Count, cast about how she should avoid it with
the least Hazard of her Father's Rage. She found *Rinaldo*
the better and more advantageous Match of the two,
could they but get his Father's Consent: He was beautiful
and young; his Title was equal to that of *Vernole*, when
his Father should die; and his Estate exceeded his: yet
she dares not make a Discovery, for fear she should injure
her Lover; who at this Time, though she knew it not,

lay sick of a Fever, while she was wondering that he came not as he used to do. However she resolves to send him a Letter, and acquaint him with the Misfortune; which she did in these Terms:

ATLANTE to RINALDO.

MY Father's Authority would force me to violate my sacred Vows to you, and give them to the Count Vernole, *whom I mortally hate, yet could wish him the greatest Monarch in the World, that I might shew you I could even then despise him for your Sake. My Father is already too much enraged by my Denial, to hear Reason from me, if I should confess to him my Vows to you: So that I see nothing but a Prospect of Death before me; for assure your self, my* Rinaldo, *I will die rather than consent to marry any other: Therefore come my* Rinaldo, *and come quickly, to see my Funerals, instead of those Nuptials they vainly expect from*

Your Faithful

ATLANTE.

This Letter *Rinaldo* receiv'd; and there needed no more to make him fly to *Orleans*: This raised him soon from his Bed of Sickness, and getting immediately to horse, he arrived at his Father's House; who did not so much admire to see him, because he heard he was sick of a Fever, and gave him leave to return, if he pleas'd: He went directly to his Father's House, because he knew somewhat of the Business, he was resolv'd to make his Passion known, as soon as he had seen *Atlante*, from whom he was to take all his Measures: He therefore fail'd not, when all were in Bed, to rise and go from his Chamber into the Street; where finding a Light in *Atlante's* Chamber, for she every Night expected him, he made the usual Sign, and she went into the Balcony; and he having no Conveniency of mounting up into it, they discoursed, and said all they had to say. From thence she tells him of the Count's Passion, of her Father's Resolution, and that her own was rather to die his, than live any Body's else: And at last, as their Refuge, they resolv'd to discover the whole Matter; she to her Father, and he to his, to see what Accommodation they could make; if not, to die together. They parted at this Resolve, for she would permit him no longer to stay in the Street after such a Sickness; so he went home to bed, but not to sleep.

The next Day, at Dinner, Monsieur *Bellyaurd* believing his Son absolutely cur'd, by Absence, of his Passion; and speaking of all the News in the Town, among the rest, told him he was come in good time to dance at the Wedding of Count *Vernole* with *Atlante*, the Match being agreed on: 'No, Sir (reply'd *Rinaldo*) I shall never dance at the Marriage of Count *Vernole* with *Atlante*; and you will see in Monsieur *De Pais's* House a Funeral sooner than a Wedding.' And thereupon he told his Father all his Passion for that lovely Maid; and assur'd him, if he would not see him laid in his Grave, he must consent to this Match. *Bellyaurd* rose in a Fury, and told him, 'He had rather see him in his Grave, than in the Arms of *Atlante*: Not (continued he) so much for any Dislike I have to the young Lady, or the Smallness of her Fortune; but because I have so long warn'd you from such a Passion, and have with such Care endeavour'd by your Absence to prevent it.' He travers'd the Room very fast, still protesting against this Alliance: and was deaf to all *Rinaldo* could say. On the other side the Day being come, wherein *Atlante* was to give her final Answer to her Father concerning her Marriage with Count *Vernole*; she assum'd all the Courage and Resolution she could, to withstand the Storm that threatned a Denial. And her Father came to her, and demanding her Answer, she told him, 'She could not be the Wife of *Vernole*, since she was Wife to *Rinaldo*, only son to *Bellyaurd*.' If her Father storm'd before, he grew like a Man distracted at her Confession; and *Vernole* hearing them loud, ran to the Chamber to learn the Cause; where just as he enter'd he found *De Pais's* Sword drawn, and ready to kill his

Daughter, who lay all in Tears at his Feet. He with-held his Hand; and asking the Cause of his Rage, he was told all that *Atlante* had confess'd; which put *Vernole* quite beside all his Gravity, and made him discover the Infirmity of Anger, which he used to say ought to be dissembled by all wise Men: So that *De Pais* forgot his own to appease his, but 'twas in vain, for he went out of the House, vowing Revenge to *Rinaldo*: And to that end, being not very well assur'd of his own Courage, as I said before, and being of the Opinion, that no Man ought to expose his Life to him who has injur'd him; he hired *Swiss* and *Spanish* Soldiers to attend him in the nature of Footmen; and watch'd several Nights about *Bellyaurd's* Door, and that of *De Pais's*, believing he should some time or other see him under the Window of *Atlante*, or perhaps mounting into it: for now he no longer doubted, but this happy Lover was he, whom he fancy'd he heard go from the Balcony that Night he came up with his Pistol; and being more a *Spaniard* than a *Frenchman* in his Nature, he resolv'd to take him any way unguarded or unarm'd, if he came in his Way.

Atlante, who heard his Threatnings when he went from her in a Rage, fear'd his Cowardice might put him on some base Action, to deprive *Rinaldo* of his Life; and therefore thought it not safe to suffer him to come to her by Night, as he had before done; but sent him word in a Note, that he should forbear her Window, for *Vernole* had sworn his Death. This Note came, unseen by his Father, to his Hands: but this could not hinder him from coming to her Window, which he did as soon as it was dark: he came thither, only attended with his Valet, and two Footmen; for now he car'd not who knew the Secret. He had no sooner made the Sign, but he found himself incompass'd with *Vernole's* Bravoes; and himself standing at a distance cry'd out, 'That is he': With that they all drew on both sides, and *Rinaldo* receiv'd a Wound in his Arm. *Atlante* heard this, and ran crying out, 'That

Rinaldo, prest by Numbers, would be kill'd.' *De Pais*, who was reading in his Closet, took his Sword, and ran out; and, contrary to all Expectation, seeing *Rinaldo* fighting with his Back to the Door, pull'd him into the House, and fought himself with the Bravoes: who being very much wounded by *Rinaldo*, gave ground, and sheer'd off; and *De Pais*, putting up old *Bilbo* into the Scabbard, went into his House, where he found *Rinaldo* almost fainting with loss of Blood, and *Atlante*, with her Maids binding up his Wound; to whom *De Pais* said, 'This charity, *Atlante*, very well becomes you, and is what I can allow you; and I could wish you had no other Motive for this Action.' *Rinaldo* by degrees recover'd of his Fainting, and as well as his Weakness would permit him, he got up and made a low Reverence to *De Pais*, telling him, 'He had now a double Obligation to pay him all the Respect in the World; first, for his being the Father of *Atlante*; and secondly, for being the Preserver of his Life: two Tyes that should eternally oblige him to love and honour him, as his own Parent.' *De Pais* reply'd, 'He had done nothing but what common Humanity compell'd him to do : But if he would make good that Respect he profess'd towards him, it must be in quitting all Hopes of *Atlante*, whom he had destin'd to another, or an eternal Inclosure in a Monastery : He had another Daughter, whom if he would think worthy of his Regard, he should take his Alliance as a very great Honour; but his Word and Reputation, nay his Vows were past, to give *Atlante* to Count *Vernole*.' *Rinaldo*, who before he spoke took measure from *Atlante*'s Eyes, which told him her Heart was his, return'd this Answer to *De Pais*, 'That he was infinitely glad to find by the Generosity of his Offer, that he had no Aversion against his being his Son-in-law ; and that, next to *Atlante*, the greatest Happiness he could wish would be his receiving *Charlot* from his Hand; but that he could not think of quitting *Atlante*, how necessary soever it would be, for

Glory, and his—(the further) Repose.' *De Pais* would not
let him at this time argue the matter further, seeing he
was ill, and had need of looking after ; he therefore begg'd
he would for his Health's sake retire to his own House,
whither he himself conducted him, and left him to the Care
of his Men, who were escap'd the Fray ; and returning to
his own Chamber, he found *Atlante* retir'd, and so he went
to bed full of Thoughts. This Night had increas'd his
Esteem for *Rinaldo*, and lessen'd it for Count *Vernole ;* but
his Word and Honour being past, he could not break it,
neither with Safety nor Honour : for he knew the haughty
resenting Nature of the Count, and he fear'd some Danger
might arrive to the brave *Rinaldo*, which troubled him
very much. At last he resolv'd, that neither might take any
thing ill at his Hands, to lose *Atlante*, and send her to the
Monastery where her Sister was, and compel her to be a Nun.
This he thought would prevent Mischiefs on both sides; and
accordingly, the next Day, (having in the Morning sent
Word to the Lady Abbess what he would have done) he
carries *Atlante*, under pretence of visiting her Sister, (which
they often did) to the Monastery, where she was no sooner
come, but she was led into the Inclosure : Her Father had
rather sacrifice her, than she should be the Cause of the
Murder of two such noble Men as *Vernole* and *Rinaldo*.

The Noise of *Atlante's* being inclos'd, was soon spread
all over the busy Town, and *Rinaldo* was not the last to
whom the News arriv'd : He was for a few Days confin'd
to his Chamber ; where, when alone, he rav'd like a Man
distracted : But his Wounds had so incens'd his Father
against *Atlante*, that he swore he would see his Son die
of them, rather than suffer him to marry *Atlante ;* and
was extremely overjoy'd to find she was condemn'd, for
ever, to the Monastery. So that the Son thought it the
wisest Course, and most for the advantage of his Love,
to say nothing to contradict his Father ; but being almost
assur'd *Atlante* would never consent to be shut up in a

Cloyster, and abandon him, he flatter'd himself with hope, that he should steal her from thence, and marry her in spite of all Opposition. This he was impatient to put in practice: He believ'd, if he were not permitted to see *Atlante*, he had still a kind Advocate in *Charlot*, who was now arriv'd to her Thirteenth Year, and infinitely advanc'd in Wit and Beauty. *Rinaldo* therefore often goes to the Monastery, surrounding it, to see what Possibility there was of accomplishing his Design; if he could get her Consent, he finds it not impossible, and goes to visit *Charlot*; who had command not to see him, or speak to him. This was a Cruelty he look'd not for, and which gave him an unspeakable Trouble, and without her Aid it was wholly impossible to give *Atlante* any account of his Design. In this Perplexity he remain'd many Days, in which he languish'd almost to Death; he was distracted with Thought, and continually hovering about the Nunnery-Walls, in hope, at some time or other, to see or hear from that lovely Maid, who alone could make his Happiness. In these Traverses he often met *Vernole*, who had Liberty to see her when he pleas'd: If it happen'd that they chanc'd to meet in the Daytime, tho' *Vernole* was attended with an Equipage of Ruffians, and *Rinaldo* but only with a couple of Footmen, he could perceive *Vernole* shun him, grow pale, and almost tremble with Fear sometimes, and get to the other Side of the Street; and if he did not, *Rinaldo* having a mortal Hate to him, would often bear up so close to him, that he would jostle him against the Wall, which *Vernole* would patiently put up, and pass on; so that he could never be provok'd to fight by Day-light, how solitary soever the Place was where they met: but if they chanc'd to meet at Night, they were certain of a Skirmish, in which he would have no part himself; so that *Rinaldo* was often like to be assassinated, but still came off with some slight Wound. This continu'd so long, and made so great a Noise in the

Town, that the two old Gentlemen were mightily alarm'd by it; and Count *Bellyaurd* came to *De Pais*, one Day, to discourse with him of this Affair; and *Bellyaurd*, for the Preservation of his Son, was almost consenting, since there was no Remedy, that he should marry *Atlante*. *De Pais* confess'd the Honour he proffer'd him, and how troubled he was, that his Word was already past to his Friend, the Count *Vernole*, whom he said she should marry, or remain for ever a Nun; but if *Rinaldo* could displace his Love from *Atlante*, and place it on *Charlot*, he should gladly consent to the Match. *Bellyaurd*, who would now do anything for the Repose of his Son, tho' he believ'd this Exchange would not pass, yet resolv'd to propose it, since by marrying him he took him out of the Danger of *Vernole's* Assassinates, who would never leave him till they had dispatch'd him, should he marry *Atlante*.

While *Rinaldo* was contriving a thousand ways to come to speak to, or send Billets to *Atlante*, none of which could succeed without the Aid of *Charlot*, his Father came and propos'd this Agreement between *De Pais* and himself, to his Son. At first *Rinaldo* receiv'd it with a chang'd Countenance, and a breaking Heart; but swiftly turning from Thought to Thought, he conceiv'd this the only way to come at *Charlot*, and so consequently at *Atlante*: he therefore, after some dissembled Regret, consents, with a sad put-on Look: And *Charlot* had Notice given her to see and entertain *Rinaldo*. As yet they had not told her the Reason; which her Father would tell her, when he came to visit her, he said. *Rinaldo* over-joy'd at this Contrivance, and his own Dissimulation, goes to the Monastery, and visits *Charlot*; where he ought to have said something of this Proposition: but wholly bent upon other Thoughts, he sollicits her to convey some Letters, and Presents to *Atlante*; which she readily did, to the unspeakable Joy of the poor Distrest. Sometimes he would talk to *Charlot* of her own Affairs; asking her, if she resolv'd to become a Nun? To which she would sigh, and say, If she must, it would be extremely against her Inclinations; and, if it pleas'd her Father, she had rather begin the World with any tolerable Match.

Things past thus for some Days, in which our Lovers were happy, and *Vernole* assur'd he should have *Atlante*. But at last *De Pais* came to visit *Charlot*, who ask'd her, if she had seen *Rinaldo?* She answer'd, 'She had.' 'And how does he entertain you? (reply'd *De Pais*) Have you receiv'd him as a Husband? and has he behav'd himself like one?' At this a sudden Joy seiz'd the Heart of *Charlot;* and loth to confess what she had done for him to her Sister, she hung down her blushing Face to study for an Answer. *De Pais* continued, and told her the Agreement between *Bellyaurd* and him, for the saving of Bloodshed.

She, who blest the Cause, whatever it was, having always a great Friendship and Tenderness for *Rinaldo*, gave her Father a thousand Thanks for his Care; and assur'd him, since she was commanded by him, she would receive him as her Husband.

And the next Day, when *Rinaldo* came to visit her, as he us'd to do, and bringing a Letter with him, wherein he propos'd the flight of *Atlante;* he found a Coldness in *Charlot*, as soon as he told her his Design, and desir'd her to carry the Letter. He ask'd the Reason of this Change: She tells him she was inform'd of the Agreement between their two Fathers, and that she look'd upon herself as his Wife, and would act no more as a Confident; that she had ever a violent Inclination of Friendship for him, which she would soon improve into something more soft.

He could not deny the Agreement, nor his Promise; but it was in vain to tell her, he did it only to get a Correspondence with *Atlante:* She is obstinate, and he as pressing, with all the Tenderness of Persuasion: He vows he can never be any but *Atlante's*, and she may see him die, but never break his Vows. She urges her Claim in vain, so that at last she was overcome, and promised she would carry the Letter; which was to have her make her Escape that Night. He waits at the Gate for her Answer, and *Charlot* returns with one that pleased him very well; which was, that Night her Sister would make her Escape, and that he must stand in such a Place of the Nunnery-Wall, and she would come out to him.

After this she upbraids him with his false Promise to her, and of her Goodness to serve him after such a Disappointment. He receives her Reproaches with a thousand Sighs, and bemoans her Misfortune in not being capable of more than Friendship for her; and vows, that next *Atlante*, he esteems her of all Womankind. She seems to be obliged by this, and assured him, she would hasten the Flight of *Atlante*; and taking leave, he went home to order a Coach, and some Servants to assist him.

In the mean time Count *Vernole* came to visit *Atlante*; but she refused to be seen by him: And all he could do there that Afternoon, was entertaining *Charlot* at the Grate; to whom he spoke a great many fine Things, both of her improved Beauty and Wit; and how happy *Rinaldo* would be in so fair a Bride. She received this with all the Civility that was due to his Quality; and their Discourse being at an End, he took his Leave, being towards the Evening.

Rinaldo, wholly impatient, came betimes to the Corner of the dead Wall, where he was appointed to stand, having ordered his Footmen and Coach to come to him as soon it was dark. While he was there walking up and down, *Vernole* came by the End of the Wall to go home; and looking about, he saw, at the other End, *Rinaldo* walking, whose Back was towards him, but he knew him well; and tho' he feared and dreaded his Business there, he durst not encounter him, they being both attended but by one Footman a-piece. But *Vernole's* Jealousy and Indignation were so high, that he resolved to fetch his Bravoes to his Aid, and come and assault him: For he knew he waited there for some Message from *Atlante*.

In the mean Time it grew dark, and *Rinaldo's* Coach came with another Footman; which were hardly arrived, when *Vernole*, with his Assistants, came to the Corner of the Wall, and skreening themselves a little behind it, near to the Place where *Rinaldo* stood, who waited now close to a little Door, out of which the Gardeners used to throw the Weeds and Dirt, *Vernole* could perceive anon the Door to open, and a Woman come out of it, calling *Rinaldo* by his Name, who stept up to her, and caught her in his Arms with Signs of infinite Joy. *Vernole* being now all Rage, cry'd to his Assassinates, 'Fall on, and kill the Ravisher': And immediately they all fell on. *Rinaldo*, who had only his two Footmen on his Side, was forc'd to let go the Lady; who would have run into the Garden again, but the Door fell to and lock'd: so that while *Rinaldo* was fighting, and beaten back by the Bravoes, one of which he laid dead at his Feet, *Vernole* came to the frighted Lady, and taking her by the Hand, cry'd, 'Come, my fair Fugitive, you must go along with me.' She wholly scar'd out of her Senses, was willing to go any where out of the Terror she heard so near her, and without Reply, gave her self into his Hand, who carried her directly to her Father's House; where she was no sooner come, but he told her Father all that had past, and how she was running away with *Rinaldo*, but that his good Fortune brought him just in the lucky Minute. Her Father turning to reproach her, found by the Light of a Candle that this was *Charlot*, and not *Atlante*, whom *Vernole* had brought Home: At which *Vernole* was extremely astonish'd. Her Father demanded of her why she was running away with a Man, who was design'd her by Consent? 'Yes, (said *Charlot*) you had his Consent, Sir, and that of his Father; but I was far from getting it: I found he resolv'd to die rather than quit *Atlante*; and promising him my Assistance in his Amour, since he could never be mine, he got me to carry a Letter to

Atlante; which was, to desire her to fly away with him. Instead of carrying her this Letter, I told her, he was design'd for me, and had cancell'd all his Vows to her: She swoon'd at this News; and being recover'd a little, I left her in the Hands of the Nuns, to persuade her to live; which she resolves not to do without *Rinaldo.* Tho' they press'd me, yet I resolv'd to pursue my Design, which was to tell *Rinaldo* she would obey his kind Summons. He waited for her; but I put my self into his Hands in lieu of *Atlante;* and had not the Count receiv'd me, we had been marry'd by this time, by some false Light that could not have discover'd me: But I am satisfied, if I had, he would never have liv'd with me longer than the Cheat had been undiscover'd; for I find them both resolved to die, rather than change. And for my part, Sir, I was not so much in Love with *Rinaldo,* as I was out of love with the Nunnery; and took any Opportunity to quit a Life absolutely contrary to my Humour.' She spoke this with a Gaiety so brisk, and an Air so agreeable, that *Vernole* found it touch'd his Heart; and the rather because he found *Atlante* would never be his; or if she were, he should be still in Danger from the Resentment of *Rinaldo:* he therefore bowing to *Charlot,* and taking her by the Hand, cry'd, 'Madam, since Fortune has dispos'd you thus luckily for me, in my Possession, I humbly implore you would consent she should make me entirely happy, and give me the Prize for which I fought, and have conquer'd with my Sword.' 'My Lord, (reply'd *Charlot,* with a modest Air) I am superstitious enough to believe, since Fortune, so contrary to all our Designs, has given me into your Hands, that she from the beginning destin'd me to the Honour, which, with my Father's Consent, I shall receive as becomes me.' *De Pais* transported with Joy, to find all Things would be so well brought about, it being all one to him, whether *Charlot* or *Atlante* gave him Count *Vernole* for his Son-in-law, readily consented;

and immediately a Priest was sent for, and they were that Night marry'd. And it being now not above seven o'Clock, many of their Friends were invited, the Musick sent for, and as good a Supper as so short a Time would provide, was made ready.

All this was perform'd in as short a time as *Rinaldo* was fighting; and having kill'd one, and wounded the rest, they all fled before his conquering Sword, which was never drawn with so good a Will. When he came where his Coach stood, just against the Back-Garden-Door, he looked for his Mistress: But the Coachman told him, he was no sooner engaged, but a Man came, and with a thousand Reproaches on her Levity, bore her off.

This made our young Lover rave; and he is satisfied she is in the Hands of his Rival, and that he had been fighting, and shedding his Blood, only to secure her Flight with him. He lost all Patience, and it was with much ado his Servants persuaded him to return; telling him in their Opinion, she was more likely to get out of the Hands of his Rival, and come to him, than when she was in the Monastery.

He suffers himself to go into his Coach and be carry'd home; but he was no sooner alighted, than he heard Musick and Noise at *De Pais's* House. He saw Coaches surround his Door, and Pages and Footmen, with Flambeaux. The Sight and Noise of Joy made him ready to sink at the Door; and sending his Footmen to learn the Cause of this Triumph, the Pages that waited told him, That Count *Vernole* was this Night married to Monsieur *De Pais's* Daughter. He needed no more to deprive him of all Sense; and staggering against his Coach, he was caught by his Footmen and carried into his House, and to his Chamber, where they put him to Bed, all sensless as he was, and had much ado to recover him to Life. He ask'd for his Father, with a faint Voice, for he desir'd to see him before he died. It was told him he was gone to Count *Vernole's* Wedding, where there was a perfect

Peace agreed on between them, and all their Animosities laid aside. At this News *Rinaldo* fainted again; and his Servants call'd his Father home, and told him in what Condition they had brought home their Master, recounting to him all that was past. He hasten'd to *Rinaldo*, whom he found just recover'd of his Swooning; who, putting his Hand out to his Father, all cold and trembling, cry'd, 'Well, Sir, now you are satisfied, since you have seen *Atlante* married to Count *Vernole*. I hope now you will give your unfortunate Son leave to die; as you wish'd he should, rather than give him to the Arms of *Atlante*.' Here his Speech fail'd, and he fell again into a Fit of Swooning; His Father ready to die with fear of his Son's Death, kneel'd down by his Bed-side; and after having recover'd a little, he said, 'My dear Son, I have been indeed at the Wedding of Count *Vernole*, but 'tis not *Atlante* to whom he is married, but *Charlot*; who was the Person you were bearing from the Monastery, instead of *Atlante*, who is still reserv'd for you, and she is dying till she hear you are reserv'd for her; Therefore, as you regard her Life, make much of your own, and make your self fit to receive her; for her Father and I have agreed the Marriage already.' And without giving him leave to think, he call'd to one of his Gentlemen, and sent him to the Monastery, with this News to *Atlante*. *Rinaldo* bowed himself as low as he could in his Bed, and kiss'd the Hand of his Father, with Tears of Joy: But his Weakness continued all the next Day; and they were fain to bring *Atlante* to him, to confirm his Happiness.

It must only be guessed by Lovers, the perfect Joy these two receiv'd in the sight of each other. *Bellyaurd* received her as his Daughter; and the next Day made her so, with very great Solemnity, at which were *Vernole* and *Charlot*: Between *Rinaldo* and him was concluded a perfect Peace, and all thought themselves happy in this double Union.

THE UNFORTUNATE BRIDE;
OR, THE BLIND LADY A BEAUTY.

TO RICHARD NORTON, OF SOUTHWICK IN
HANTSHIRE, ESQUIRE.

Honour'd Sir,

Eminent Wit, Sir, no more than Eminent Beauty, can escape the Trouble and Presumption of Addresses; and that which can strike every body with Wonder, can never avoid the Praise which naturally flows from that Wonder: And Heaven is forc'd to hear the Addresses as well as praises of the Poor as Rich, of the Ignorant as Learned, and takes, nay rewards, the officious tho' perhaps impertinent Zeal of its least qualify'd Devotees. Wherefore, Sir, tho' your Merits meet with the Applause of the Learned and Witty, yet your Generosity will judge favourably of the untaught Zeal of an humbler Admirer, since what I do your eminent Vertues compel. The Beautiful will permit the most despicable of their Admirers to love them, tho' they never intend to make him happy, as unworthy their Love, but they will not be angry at the fatal Effect of their own Eyes.

But what I want in my self, Sir, to merit your Regard, I hope my Authoress will in some measure supply, so far at least to lessen my Presumption in prefixing your Name to a Posthumous Piece of hers, whom all the Men of Wit, that were her Contemporaries, look'd on as the Wonder of her Sex; and in none of her Performances has she shew'd so great a Mastery as in her Novels, where Nature always prevails; and if they are not true, they are so like it, that they do the business every jot as well.

This I hope, Sir, will induce you to pardon my Presumption in dedicating this Novel to you, and declaring my self, Sir,

Your most obedient

and most humble Servant,

S. Briscoe.

THE UNFORTUNATE BRIDE:
or, The Blind Lady a Beauty.

FRANKWIT and *Wildvill*, were two young Gentlemen of very considerable Fortunes, both born in *Staffordshire*, and, during their Minority, both educated together, by which Opportunity they contracted a very inviolable Friendship, a Friendship which grew up with them; and though it was remarkably known to every Body else, they knew it not themselves; they never made Profession of it in Words, but Actions; so true a Warmth their Fires could boast, as needed not the Effusion of their Breath to make it live. *Wildvill* was of the richest Family, but *Frankwit* of the noblest; *Wildvill* was admired for outward Qualifications, as Strength, and manly Proportions, *Frankwit* for a much softer Beauty, for his inward Endowments, Pleasing in his Conversation, of a free, and moving Air, humble in his Behaviour, and if he had any Pride, it was but just enough to shew that he did not affect Humility; his Mind bowed with a Motion as unconstrained as his Body, nor did he force this Vertue in the least, but he allowed it only. So aimable he was, that every Virgin that had Eyes, knew too she had a Heart, and knew as surely she should lose it. His *Cupid* could not be reputed blind, he never shot for him, but he was sure to wound. As every other Nymph admired him, so he was dear to all the Tuneful Sisters; the Muses were fired with him as much as their own radiant God *Apollo*; their loved Springs and Fountains were not so grateful to their Eyes as he, him they esteemed their *Helicon* and *Parnassus* too; in short, when ever he pleased, he could enjoy them all. Thus he enamour'd the whole Female Sex, but amongst all the sighing Captives of his Eyes, *Belvira* only boasted Charms to move him; her Parents lived near his, and even from their Childhood they felt mutual Love, as if their Eyes, at their first meeting, had struck out such Glances, as had kindled into amorous Flame. And now *Belvira* in her fourteenth Year, (when the fresh Spring of young Virginity began to cast more lively Bloomings in her Cheeks, and softer Longings in her Eyes) by her indulgent Father's Care was sent to *London* to a Friend, her Mother being lately dead: When, as if Fortune ordered it so, *Frankwit's* Father took a Journey to the other World, to let his Son the better enjoy the Pleasures and Delights of this: The young Lover now with all imaginable haste interred his Father, nor did he shed so many Tears for his Loss, as might in the least quench the Fire which he received from his *Belvira's* Eyes, but (Master of seventeen Hundred Pounds a Year, which his Father left him) with all the Wings of Love flies to *London*, and sollicits *Belvira* with such Fervency, that it might be thought he meant Death's Torch should kindle *Hymen's*; and now as soon as he arrives at his Journey's end, he goes to pay a Visit to the fair Mistress of his Soul, and assures her, That tho' he was absent from her, yet she was still with him; and that all the Road he travell'd, her beauteous Image danced before him, and like the ravished Prophet, he saw his Deity in every Bush; in short, he paid her constant Visits, the Sun ne'er rose or set, but still he saw it in her Company, and every Minute of the Day he counted by his Sighs. So incessantly he importuned her that she could no longer hold out, and was pleased in the surrender of her Heart, since it was he was Conqueror; and therefore felt a Triumph in her yielding. Their Flames now joyned, grew more and more, glowed in their Cheeks, and lightened in their Glances: Eager they looked, as if there were Pulses beating in their Eyes; and all endearing, at last she vowed, that *Frankwit* living she would ne'er be any other Man's. Thus they past on some time, while every Day rowl'd over fair; Heaven showed an Aspect all serene, and the Sun seemed to smile at what was done. He still caressed his Charmer, with an Innocence becoming his Sincerity; he lived upon her tender Breath, and basked in the bright Lustre of her Eyes, with Pride, and secret Joy.

He saw his Rivals languish for that Bliss, those Charms, those Raptures and extatick Transports, which he engrossed alone. But now some eighteen Months (some Ages in a Lover's Kalendar) winged with Delights, and fair *Belvira* now grown fit for riper Joys, knows hardly how she can deny her pressing Lover, and herself, to crown their Vows, and joyn their Hands as well as Hearts. All this while the young Gallant wash'd himself clean of that shining Dirt, his Gold; he fancied little of Heaven dwelt in his yellow Angels, but let them fly away, as it were on their own golden Wings; he only valued the smiling Babies in *Belvira's* Eyes. His Generosity was boundless, as his Love, for no Man ever truly loved, that was not generous. He thought his Estate, like his Passion, was a sort of a *Pontick* Ocean, it could never know an Ebb; But now he found it could be fathom'd, and that the Tide was turning, therefore he sollicits with more impatience the consummation of their Joys, that both might go like Martyrs from their Flames immediately to Heaven; and now at last it was agreed between them, that they should both be one, but not without some Reluctancy on the Female side; for 'tis the Humour of our Sex, to deny most eagerly those Grants to Lovers, for which most tenderly we sigh, so contradictory are we to our selves, as if the Deity had made us with a seeming Reluctancy to his own Designs; placing as much Discords in our Minds, as there is Harmony in our Faces. We are a sort of aiery Clouds, whose Lightning flash out one way, and the Thunder another. Our Words and Thoughts can ne'er agree. So this young charming Lady thought her Desires could live in their own longings, like Misers wealth-devouring Eyes; and e'er she consented to her Lover, prepared him first with speaking Looks, and then with a fore-running Sigh, applyed to the dear Charmer thus: '*Frankwit*, I am afraid to venture the Matrimonial Bondage, it may make you think your self too much confined, in being only free to one.' 'Ah! my dear *Belvira*,' he replied, 'That one, like *Manna*, has the Taste of all, why should I be displeased to be confined to Paradice, when it was the Curse of our Forefathers to be set at large, tho' they had the whole World to roam in: You have, my love, ubiquitary Charms, and you are all in all, in every Part.' 'Ay, but,' reply'd *Belvira*, 'we are all like Perfumes, and too continual Smelling makes us seem to have lost our Sweets, I'll be judged by my Cousin *Celesia* here, if it be not better to live still in mutual Love, without the last Enjoyment.' (I had forgot to tell my Reader that *Celesia* was an Heiress, the only Child of a rich *Turkey* Merchant, who, when he dyed, left her Fifty thousand Pound in Money, and some Estate in Land; but, poor Creature, she was Blind to all these Riches, having been born without the use of Sight, though in all other Respects charming to a wonder.) 'Indeed,' says *Celesia*, (for she saw clearly in her Mind) 'I admire you should ask my Judgment in such a Case, where I have never had the least Experience; but I believe it is but a sickly Soul which cannot nourish its Offspring of Desires without preying upon the Body.' 'Believe me,' reply'd *Frankwit*, 'I bewail your want of Sight, and I could almost wish you my own Eyes for a Moment, to view your charming Cousin, where you would see such Beauties as are too dazling to be long beheld; and if too daringly you gazed, you would feel the Misfortune of the loss of Sight, much greater than the want of it : And you would acknowledge, that in too presumptuously seeing, you would be blinder then, than now unhappily you are.'

'Ah! I must confess,' reply'd *Belvira*, 'my poor, dear Cousin is Blind, for I fancy she bears too great an Esteem for *Frankwit*, and only longs for Sight to look on him.' 'Indeed,' reply'd *Celesia*, 'I would be glad to see *Frankwit*, for I fancy he's as dazling, as he but now describ'd his Mistress, and if I fancy I see him, sure I do see him, for Sight is Fancy, is it not? or do you feel my Cousin with your Eyes?' 'This is indeed, a charming Blindness,' reply'd *Frankwit*, 'and the fancy of your Sight excels the certainty of ours. Strange! that there should be such Glances even in blindness? You, fair Maid, require not Eyes to conquer, if your Night has such Stars, what Sunshine would your Day of Sight have, if ever you should see?' 'I fear those Stars you talk of,' said *Belvira*, 'have some Influence on you, and by the Compass you sail by now, I guess you are steering to my Cousin. She is indeed charming enough to have been another Offspring of bright *Venus*, Blind like her Brother *Cupid*.' 'That *Cupid*,' reply'd *Celesia*, 'I am afraid has shot me, for methinks I would not have you marry *Frankwit*, but rather live as you do without the last Enjoyment, for methinks if he were marry'd, he would be more out of Sight than he already is.' 'Ah, Madam,' return'd *Frankwit*, 'Love is no Camelion, it cannot feed on Air alone.' 'No but,' rejoyn'd *Celesia*, 'you Lovers that are not Blind like Love it self, have am'rous Looks to feed on.' 'Ah! believe it,' said *Belvira*, ''tis better, *Frankwit*, not to lose Paradice by too much Knowledge; Marriage Enjoyments does but wake you from your sweet golden Dreams : Pleasure is but a Dream, dear *Frankwit*, but a Dream, and to be waken'd.' 'Ah! Dearest, but unkind *Belvira*,' answer'd *Frankwit*, 'sure there's no waking from Delight, in being lull'd on those soft Breasts of thine.' 'Alas! (reply'd the

Bride to be) it is that very lulling wakes you; Women enjoy'd, are like Romances read, or Raree-shows once seen, meer Tricks of the slight of Hand, which, when found out, you only wonder at your selves for wondering so before at them. 'Tis Expectation endears the Blessing; Heaven would not be Heaven, could we tell what 'tis. When the Plot's out you have done with the Play, and when the last Act's done, you see the Curtain drawn with great indifferency.' 'O my *Belvira*,' answered *Frankwit*, 'that Expectation were indeed a Monster which Enjoyment could not satisfy: I should take no pleasure,' he rejoin'd, 'running from Hill to Hill, like Children chasing that Sun, which I could never catch.' 'O thou shalt have it then, that Sun of Love,' reply'd *Belvira*, fir'd by this Complaint, and gently rush'd into Arms, (rejoyn'd) so *Phœbus* rushes radiant and unsullied, into a gilded Cloud. 'Well then, my dear *Belvira*,' answered *Frankwit*, 'be assured I shall be ever yours, as you are mine; fear not you shall never draw Bills of Love upon me so fast, as I shall wait in readiness to pay them; but now I talk of Bills, I must retire into *Cambridgeshire*, where I have a small Concern as yet unmortgaged, I will return thence with a Brace of thousand Pounds within a Week at furthest, with which our Nuptials, by their Celebration, shall be worthy of our Love. And then, my Life, my Soul, we shall be join'd, never to part again.' This tender Expression mov'd *Belvira* to shed some few Tears, and poor *Celesia* thought herself most unhappy that she had not Eyes to weep with too; but if she had, such was the greatness of her Grief, that sure she would have soon grown Blind with weeping. In short, after a great many soft Vows, and Promises of an inviolable Faith, they parted with a pompous sort of pleasing Woe; their Concern was of such a mixture of Joy and Sadness, as the Weather seems, when it both rains and shines. And now the last, the very last Adieu's was over, for the Farewels of Lovers hardly ever end, and *Frankwit* (the Time being Summer) reach'd *Cambridge* that Night, about Nine a Clock; (Strange! that he should have made such Haste to fly from what so much he lov'd!) and now, tir'd with the fatigue of his Journey, he thought fit to refresh himself by writing some few Lines to his belov'd *Belvira;* for a little Verse after the dull Prose Company of his Servant, was as great an Ease to him, (from whom it flow'd as naturally and unartificially, as his Love or his Breath) as a Pace or Hand-gallop, after a hard, uncouth, and rugged Trot. He therefore, finding his *Pegasus* was no way tir'd with his Land-travel, takes a short Journey thro' the Air, and writes as follows:

My dearest dear Belvira,

YOU knew my Soul, you knew it yours before,
I told it all, and now can tell no more;
Your Presents never wants fresh Charms to move, ⎫
But now more strange, and unknown Pow'r you prove, ⎬
For now your very Absence 'tis I love. ⎭
Something there is which strikes my wandring View,
And still before my Eyes I fancy you.
Charming you seem, all charming, heavenly fair, ⎫
Bright as a Goddess, does my Love appear, ⎬
You seem, *Belvira*, what indeed you are. ⎭
Like the Angelick Off-spring of the Skies,
With beatifick Glories in your Eyes:
Sparkling with radiant Lustre all Divine, ⎫
Angels, and Gods! oh Heavens! how bright they shine! ⎬
Are you *Belvira?* can I think you mine! ⎭
Beyond ev'n Thought, I do thy Beauties see,
Can such a Heaven of Heavens be kept for me!
Oh be assur'd, I shall be ever true,
I must——
For if I would, I can't be false to you.

Oh! how I wish I might no longer stay,
Tho' I resolve I will no Time delay,
One Tedious Week, and then I'll fleet away.

Tho' Love be blind, he shall conduct my Road,
Wing'd with almighty Love, to your Abode,
I'll fly, and grow Immortal as a God.

Short is my stay, yet my impatience strong,
Short tho' it is, alas! I think it long.

I'll come, my Life, new Blessings to pursue,
Love then shall fly a Flight he never flew,
I'll stretch his balmy Wings; I'm yours,—*Adieu.*

Frankwit.

This Letter *Belvira* receiv'd with unspeakable Joy,
and laid it up safely in her Bosom; laid it, where the
dear Author of it lay before, and wonderfully pleas'd with
his Humour of writing Verse, resolv'd not to be at all
behind-hand with him, and so writ as follows:

My dear Charmer,

YOU knew before what Power your Love could boast,
But now your constant Faith confirms me most.

Absent Sincerity the best assures,
Love may do much, but Faith much more allures,
For now your Constancy has bound me yours.

I find, methinks, in Verse some Pleasure too,
I cannot want a Muse, who write to you.
Ah! soon return, return, my charming Dear,
Heav'n knows how much we Mourn your Absence here:
My poor *Celesia* now would Charm your Soul,
Her Eyes, once Blind, do now Divinely rowl.
An aged Matron has by Charms unknown,
Given her clear Sight as perfect as thy own.
And yet, beyond her Eyes, she values thee,
'Tis for thy Sake alone she's glad to see.

She begg'd me, pray remember her to you,
That is a Task which now I gladly do.
Gladly, since so I only recommend
A dear Relation, and a dearer Friend,
Ne're shall my Love—but here my Note must end.

Your ever true Belvira.

When this Letter was written, it was strait shown to
Celesia, who look'd upon any Thing that belong'd to
Frankwit, with rejoycing Glances; so eagerly she perus'd
it, that her tender Eyes beginning to Water, she cry'd
out, (fancying she saw the Words dance before her View)
' Ah ! Cousin, Cousin, your Letter is running away, sure
it can't go itself to *Frankwit*.' A great Deal of other
pleasing innocent Things she said, but still her Eyes flow'd
more bright with lustrous Beams, as if they were to shine
out ; now all that glancing Radiancy which had been so
long kept secret, and, as if, as soon as the Cloud of Blindness once was broke, nothing but Lightnings were to flash
for ever after. Thus in mutual Discourse they spent their
Hours, while *Frankwit* was now ravished with the Receipt
of this charming Answer of *Belvira's*, and blest his own
Eyes which discovered to him the much welcome News of
fair *Celesia's*. Often he read the Letters o're and o're, but
there his Fate lay hid, for twas that very Fondness proved
his Ruin. He lodg'd at a Cousin's House of his, and there,
(it being a private Family) lodged likewise a Blackamoor
Lady, then a Widower ; a whimsical Knight had taken
a Fancy to enjoy her : *Enjoy her did I say? Enjoy the
Devil in the Flesh at once!* I know not how it was, but
he would fain have been a Bed with her, but she not consenting on unlawful Terms, *(but sure all Terms are with
her unlawful)* the Knight soon marry'd her, as if there
were not hell enough in Matrimony, but he must wed the
Devil too. The Knight a little after died, and left this
Lady of his (whom I shall *Moorea*) an Estate of six thousand

Pounds *per Ann.* Now this *Moorea* observed the joyous *Frankwit* with an eager Look, her Eyes seemed like Stars of the first Magnitude glaring in the Night; she greatly importuned him to discover the Occasion of his transport, but he denying it, (as 'tis the Humour of our Sex) made her the more Inquisitive; and being Jealous that it was from a Mistress, employ'd her Maid to steal it, and if she found it such, to bring it her: accordingly it succeeded, for *Frankwit* having drank hard with some of the Gentlemen of that Shire, found himself indisposed, and soon went to Bed, having put the Letter in his Pocket: The Maid therefore to *Moorea* contrived that all the other Servants should be out of the Way, that she might plausibly officiate in the Warming the Bed of the indisposed Lover, but likely, had it not been so, she had warmed it by his Intreaties in a more natural Manner; he being in Bed in an inner Room, she slips out the Letter from his Pocket, carries it to her Mistress to read, and so restores it whence she had it; in the Morning the poor Lover wakened in a violent Fever, burning with a Fire more hot than that of Love. In short, he continued Sick a considerable while, all which time the Lady *Moorea* constantly visited him, and he as unwillingly saw her (poor Gentleman) as he would have seen a Parson; for as the latter would have perswaded, so the former scared him to Repentance. In the mean while, during his sickness, several Letters were sent to him by his dear *Belvira*, and *Celesia* too, (then learning to write) had made a shift to give him a line or two in Postscript with her Cousin, but all was intercepted by the jealousy of the Black *Moorea*, black in her mind, and dark, as well as in her body. *Frankwit* too writ several Letters as he was able, complaining of her unkindness, those likewise were all stopt by the same Blackmoor Devil. At last, it happened that *Wildvill*, (who I told my Reader was *Frankwit's* friend) came to *London*, his Father likewise dead, and now Master of a very plentiful fortune, he resolves to marry, and paying a visit to *Belvira*, enquires of her concerning *Frankwit*, she all in mourning for the loss, told him his friend was dead. 'Ah! *Wildvill*, he is dead,' said she, 'and died not mine, a Blackmoor Lady had bewitched him from me; I received a Letter lately which informed me all; there was no name subscribed to it, but it intimated, that it was written at the request of dying *Frankwit*.' 'Oh! I am sorry at my Soul,' said *Wildvill*, 'for I loved him with the best, the dearest friendship; no doubt then,' rejoyned he, ''tis Witchcaft indeed that could make him false to you; what delight could he take in a Blackmoor Lady, tho' she had received him at once with a Soul as open as her longing arms, and with her Petticoat put off her modesty. Gods! How could he change a whole *Field Argent* into downright *Sables*.' ''Twas done,' returned *Celesia*, 'with no small blot, I fancy, to the Female 'Scutcheon.' In short, after some more discourse, but very sorrowful, *Wildvill* takes his leave, extreamly taken with the fair *Belvira*, more beauteous in her cloud of woe; he paid her afterwards frequent visits, and found her wonder for the odd inconstancy of *Frankwit*, greater than her sorrow, since he dy'd so unworthy of her. *Wildvill* attack'd her with all the force of vigorous love, and she (as she thought) fully convinc'd of *Frankwit's* death, urg'd by the fury and impatience of her new ardent Lover, soon surrender'd, and the day of their Nuptials now arriv'd, their hands were joyn'd. In the mean time *Frankwit* (for he still liv'd) knew nothing of the Injury the base *Moorea* practis'd, knew not that 'twas thro' her private order, that the fore-mention'd account of his falshood and his death was sent; but impatient to see his Dear *Belvira*, tho' yet extremely weak, rid post to *London*, and that very day arriv'd there, immediately after the Nuptials of his Mistress and his Friend were celebrated. I was at this time in *Cambridge*, and having some small acquaintance with this Blackmoor Lady, and sitting in her Room that evening, after *Frankwit's* departure thence, in *Moorea's* absence, saw inadvertently a bundle of Papers, which she had gathered up, as I suppose, to burn, since now they grew but useless, she having no farther Hopes of him: I fancy'd I knew the Hand, and thence my Curiosity only led me to see the Name, and finding *Belvira* sub-scrib'd, I began to guess there was some foul play in Hand. *Belvira* being my particularly intimate Acquaintance, I read one of them, and finding the Contents, convey'd them all secretly out with me, as I thought, in Point of Justice I was bound, and sent them to *Belvira* by that Night's Post; so that they came to her Hands soon after the Minute of her Marriage, with an Account how, and by what Means I came to light on them. No doubt but they exceedingly surpriz'd her: But Oh! Much more she grew amaz'd immediately after, to see the Poor, and now unhappy *Frankwit*, who privately had enquir'd for her below, being received as a Stranger, who said he had some urgent Business with her, in a back Chamber below Stairs. What Tongue, what Pen can express the mournful Sorrow of this Scene! At first they both stood Dumb, and almost Senseless; she took him for the Ghost of *Frankwit*; he looked so pale, new risen from his Sickness, he (for he had heard at his Entrance in the House, that his *Belvira* marry'd *Wildvill*) stood in Amaze, and like a Ghost indeed, wanted the Power to speak, till spoken to the first. At last, he draws his Sword, designing there to fall upon it in her Presence; she then imagining it his Ghost too sure, and come to kill her, shrieks out and Swoons; he ran immediately to her, and catch'd her in his Arms, and while he strove to revive and bring her to herself, tho' that he thought could never now be done, since she was marry'd. *Wildvill* missing his Bride, and hearing the loud Shriek, came running down, and entring the Room, sees his Bride lie clasp'd in *Frankwit's* Arms. 'Ha! Traytor!' He cries out, drawing his Sword with an impatient Fury, 'have you kept that Strumpet all this while, curst *Frankwit*, and now think fit to put your damn'd cast Mistress upon me: could not you forbear her neither ev'n on my Wedding Day? abominable Wretch!' Thus saying, he made a full Pass at *Frankwit*, and run him thro' the left Arm, and quite thro' the Body of the poor *Belvira*; that thrust immediately made her start, tho' *Frankwit's* Endeavours all before were useless. Strange! that her Death reviv'd her! For ah! she felt, that now she only liv'd to die! Striving thro' wild Amazement to run from such a Scene of Horror, as her Apprehensions shew'd her; down she dropt, and *Frankwit* seeing her fall, (all Friendship disannull'd by such a Chain of Injuries) Draws, fights with, and stabs his own lov'd *Wildvill*. Ah! Who can express the Horror and Distraction of this fatal Misunderstanding! The House was alarm'd, and in came poor *Celesia*, running in Confusion just as *Frankwit* was off'ring to kill himself, to die with a false Friend, and perjur'd Mistress, for he suppos'd them such. Poor *Celesia* now bemoan'd her unhappiness of sight, and wish'd she again were blind. *Wildvill* dy'd immediately, and *Belvira* only surviv'd him long enough to unfold all their most unhappy fate, desiring *Frankwit* with her dying breath, if ever he lov'd her, (and now she said that she deserv'd his love, since she had convinced him that she was not false) to marry her poor dear *Celesia*, and love her tenderly for her *Belvira's* sake; leaving her, being her nearest Relation, all her fortune, and he, much dearer than it all, to be added to her own; so joyning his and *Celesia's* Hands, she poured her last breath upon his Lips, and said, 'Dear *Frankwit, Frankwit*, I die yours.' With tears and wondrous sorrow he promis'd to obey her Will, and in some months after her interrment, he perform'd his promise.

THE DUMB VIRGIN; OR,
THE FORCE OF IMAGINATION.

INTRODUCTION.

CONSANGUINITY and love which are treated in this novel so romantically and with such tragic catastrophe had already been dealt with in happier mood by Mrs. Behn in *The Dutch Lover*. *Vide* Note on the Source of that play, Vol. I, p. 218.

In classic lore the Œdipus Saga enthralled the imagination of antiquity and inspired dramas amongst the world's masterpieces. Later forms of the tale may be found in Suidas and Cedrenus.

The Legend of St. Gregory, based on a similar theme, the hero of which, however, is innocent throughout, was widely diffused through mediæval Europe. It forms No. 81 of the *Gesta Romanorum*. There is an old English poem[1] on the subject, and it also received lyric treatment at the hands of the German meistersinger, Hartmann von Aue. An Italian story, *Il Figliuolo di germani*, the chronicle of St. Albinus, and the Servian romaunt of the Holy Foundling Simeon embody similar circumstances.

Matteo Bandello, Part II, has a famous[2] novel (35) with rubric, 'un gentiluomo navarrese sposa una, che era sua sorella e figliuola, non lo sapendo,' which is almost exactly the same as the thirtieth story of the *Heptameron*. As the good Bishop declares that it was related to him by a lady living in the district, it is probable that some current tradition furnished both him and the Queen of Navarre with these horrible incidents and that neither copied from the other.[3]

Bandello was imitated in Spanish by J. Perez de Montalvan, *Sucesos y Prodigios de Amor —La Mayor confusion ;* in Latin by D. Otho Melander ; and he also gave Desfontaines the subject of *L'Inceste Innocent ; Histoire Véritable* (Paris, 1644).. A similar tale is touched upon in *Amadis de Gaule*, and in a later century we find *Le Criminel sans le Savoir, Roman Historique et Poëtique* (Amsterdam and Paris, 1783). It is also found in Brevio's *Rime e Prose ;* Volgari, novella iv ; and in T. Grapulo (or Grappolino), *Il Convito Borghesiano* (Londra, 1800). A cognate legend is *Le Dit du Buef* and *Le Dit de la Bourjosee de Rome*. (ed. Jubinal, *Nouveau Recueil ;* and *Nouveau Recueil du Sénateur de Rome . . .* ed. Méon.) Again : the *Leggenda di Vergogna, etc. testi del buon secolo in prosa e in verso*, edited by A. D'Ancona (Bologna, 1869) repeats the same catastrophe. It is also related in Byshop's *Blossoms*.

---

[1] There are three MSS. *Vernon MS.*, Oxford, edited by Horstmann ; *MS. Cott, Cleop. D. ix*, British Museum ; *Auchinleck MS.*, Advocates' Library, Edinburgh, edited with glossary by F. Schultz, 1876.

[2] cf. Masuccio. *Il Novellino*, No. 23.

[3] Bandello's novels first appeared at Lucca, 4to, 1554. Marguerite of Angoulême died 21 December, 1549. The *Heptameron* was composed 1544–8 and published 1558.

In Luther's *Colloquia Mensalia,* under the article 'Auricular Confession', the occurrence is said to have taken place at Erfurt in Germany. Julio de Medrano, a Spanish writer of the sixteenth century, says that a similar story was related to him when he was in the Bourbonnois, where the inhabitants pointed out the house which had been the scene of these morbid passions. France, indeed, seems to have been the home of the tradition, and Le Roux de Lincy in the notes to his excellent edition of the *Heptameron* quotes from Millin, *Antiquités Nationales* (t. iii. f. xxviii. p. 6.) who, speaking of the Collegiate Church of Ecouis, says that in the midst of the nave there was a prominent white marbel tablet with this epitaph :—

> Cy-gist la fille, cy-gist le père,
> Cy-gist la soeur, cy-gist le frère ;
> Cy-gist la femme, et le mary,
> Et si n'y a que deux corps icy.

The tradition ran that a son of 'Madame d'Ecouis avait eu de sa mère sans la connaître et sans en être reconnu une fille nommée Cécile. Il épousa ensuite en Lorraine cette même Cécile qui était auprès de la Duchesse de Bar . . . Ils furent enterrés dans le même tombeau en 1512 à Ecouis.' An old sacristan used to supply curious visitors to the church with a leaflet detailing the narrative. The same story is attached to other parishes, and at Alincourt, a village between Amiens and Abbeville, the following lines are inscribed upon a grave :—

> Ci git le fils, ci git la mère,
> Ci git la fille avec le père,
> Ci git la soeur, ci git le frère,
> Ci git la femme et le mari,
> Et ne sont pas que trois corps ici.

When Walpole wrote his tragedy, *The Mysterious Mother* (1768), he states he had no knowledge of Bandello or the *Heptameron,* but he gives the following account of the origin of his theme. 'I had heard when very young, that a gentlewoman, under uncommon agonies of mind, had waited on Archbishop Tillotson and besought his counsel. A damsel that served her had, many years before, acquainted her that she was importuned by the gentlewoman's son to grant him a private meeting. The mother ordered the maiden to make the assignation, when she said she would discover herself and reprimand him for his criminal passion ; but, being hurried away by a much more criminal passion herself, she kept the assignation without discovering herself. The fruit of this horrid artifice was a daughter, whom the gentlewoman caused to be educated very privately in the country ; but proving very lovely and being accidentally met by her father-brother, who never had the slightest suspicion of the truth, he had fallen in love with and actually married her. The wretched guilty mother learning what had happened, and distracted with the consequence of her crime, had now resorted to the Archbishop to know in what manner she should act. The prelate charged her never to let her son and daughter know what had passed, as they were innocent of any criminal intention. For herself, he bad her almost despair.'

The same story occurs in the writings of the famous Calvinistic divine,

William Perkins (1558–1602), sometime Rector of St. Andrew's, Cambridge. Thence it was extracted for *The Spectator*.

In Mat Lewis' ghoulish romance, *The Monk* (1796) it will be remembered that Ambrosio, after having enjoyed Antonia, to whose bedchamber he has gained admittance by demoniacal aid, discovers that she is his sister, and heaping crime upon crime to sorcery and rape he has added incest.

There is a tragic little novel, '*The Illegal Lovers; a True Secret History. Being an Amour Between A Person of Condition and his Sister. Written by One who did reside in the Family.*' (8vo, 1728.)   After the death of his wife, Bellario falls in love with his sister Lindamira. Various sentimental letters pass between the two, and eventually Bellario in despair pistols himself.   The lady lives to wed another admirer.   The tale was obviously suggested by the *Love Letters between a Nobleman and his Sister*.

THE DUMB VIRGIN:
or, the Force of Imagination.

RINALDO, a Senator of the great City *Venice*, by a
plentiful Inheritance, and industrous Acquisitions, was
become Master of a very plentiful Estate; which, by the
Countenance of his Family, sprung from the best Houses
in *Italy*, had rendred him extreamly popular and honoured;
he had risen to the greatest Dignities of that State, all
which Offices he discharged with Wisdom and Conduct,
befitting the Importance of his Charge, and Character of
the Manager; but this great Person had some Accident in
his Children, sufficient to damp all the Pleasure of his more
smiling Fortunes; he married when young, a beautiful and
virtuous Lady, who had rendred him the happy Father
of a Son; but his Joys were soon disturbed by the following
Occasion.

There stands an Island in the *Adriatick* Sea, about
twenty Leagues from *Venice*, a Place wonderfully pleasant
in the Summer, where Art and Nature seem to out-rival
each other, or seem rather to combine in rendring it the
most pleasant of their products; being placed under the
most benign climate in the World, and situated exactly
between *Italy* and *Greece*, it appears an entire Epitome of
all the Pleasures in them both; the proper glories of the
Island were not a little augmented by the confluence of
Gentlemen and Ladies of the chiefest Rank in the City,
insomuch that this was a greater mark for Beauty and
Gallantry, than *Venice* for Trade. Among others *Rinaldo's*
Lady begged her Husband's permission to view this so
much celebrated place.

He was unwilling to trust his treasure to the treachery of the watry element; but repeating her request, he yielded to her desires, his love not permitting him the least shew of command, and so thro' its extent, conspiring its own destruction. His Lady with her young Son (whom she would not trust from her sight) and a splendid attendance in a Barge well fitted, sets out for the Island, *Rinaldo* being detained at home himself about some important affairs relating to the publick, committed the care of his dear Wife and Child to a faithful Servant call'd *Gaspar*; and for their greater security against Pyrates, had obtained his Brother, who commanded a *Venetian* Galley, to attend them as Convoy. In the evening they set out from *Venice*, with a prosperous gale, but a storm arising in the night, soon separated the Barge from her Convoy, and before morning drove her beyond the designed Port, when, instead of discovering the wish'd-for Island, they could see a *Turkish* Pyrate bearing towards them, with all her Sail; their late apprehensions of Shipwrack, were drowned in the greater danger of Captivity and lasting Slavery, their fears drove some into resolutions as extravagant as the terrors that caused them, but the confusion of all was so tumultuous, and the designs so various, that nothing could be put in execution for the publick safety; the greatest share of the passengers being Ladies, added strangely to the consternation; beauty always adds a pomp to woe, and by its splendid show, makes sorrow look greater and more moving. Some by their piteous plaints and wailings proclaimed their griefs aloud, whilst others bespoke their sorrows more emphatically by sitting mournfully silent; the fears of some animated them to extravagant actions, whilst the terrors of others were so mortifying, that they shewed no sign of Life, but by their trembling; some mourned the rigour of their proper fate, others conscious of the sorrows their Friends and Relations should sustain through their loss, made the griefs of them their own;

but the heaviest load of misfortunes lay on *Rinaldo's* Lady, besides the loss of her liberty, the danger of her honour, the separation from her dear Husband, the care for her tender Infant wrought rueful distractions; she caught her Child in her Arms, and with Tears extorted thro' Fear and Affection, she deplor'd the Misfortune of her Babe, the pretty Innocent smiling in the Embraces of its Mother, shew'd that Innocence cou'd deride the Persecution of Fortune; at length she delivered the Infant into the Hand of *Gasper*, begging him to use all Endeavours in its Preservation, by owning it for his, when they fell into the Hands of the Enemy.

But *Gasper*, who amidst the universal Consternation, had a peculiar Regard to his own Safety, and Master's Interest, undertook a Design desperately brave. Two long Planks, which lay lengthwise in the Barge, as Seats, he had ty'd together with Ropes, and taking the Infant from the Mother, whilst the whole Vessel was in a distracted Confusion, he fast'ned it to the Planks, and shoving both over-board before him, plung'd into the Sea after, dragging the Planks that bore the Infant with one Hand, and swimming with t'other, making the next Land; he had swam about two hundred Paces from the Barge before his Exploit was discover'd, but then the Griefs of *Rinaldo's* Lady were doubly augmented, seeing her Infant expos'd to the Fury of the merciless Winds and Waves, which she then judged more rigorous than the *Turks*; for to a weak Mind, that Danger works still the strongest, that's most in View; but when the Pirate, who by this time had fetch'd them within Shot, began to Fire, she seem'd pleas'd that her Infant was out of that Hazard, tho' exposed to a greater. Upon their Sign of yielding, the *Turk* launching out her Boat, brought them all on board her; but she had no time to examine her Booty, being saluted by a Broadside, vigorously discharg'd from a *Venetian* Galley, which bore down upon them, whilst they were taking aboard their

Spoil; this Galley was that commanded by *Rinaldo's* Brother, which cruising that Way in quest of the Barge, happily engag'd the *Turk*, before they had Leisure to offer any Violence to the Ladies, and plying her warmly the Space of two Hours, made her a Prize, to the inexpressible Joy of the poor Ladies, who all this time under Hatches, had sustain'd the Horrors of ten thousand Deaths by dreading one.

All the greater Dangers over, *Rinaldo's* Lady began to reflect on the strange Riddle of her Son's Fortune, who by shunning one Fate, had (in all Probability) fallen into a worse, for they were above ten Leagues from any Land, and the Sea still retain'd a Roughness, unsettled since the preceeding Storm; she therefore begg'd her Brother-in-Law to Sail with all Speed in Search of her Son and *Gasper;* but all in vain, for cruising that Day, and the succeeding Night along the Coasts, without making any Discovery of what they sought, he sent a Boat to be inform'd by the Peasants, of any such Landing upon their Coast; but they soon had a dismal Account, finding the Body of *Gasper* thrown dead on the Sand, and near to him the Planks, the unhappy Occasion of his Flight, and the Faithless Sustainers of the Infant. So thinking these mournful Objects Testimonies enough of the Infant's Loss, they return'd with the doleful Relation to their Captain and the Lady; her Grief at the recital of the Tragic Story, had almost transported her to Madness; what Account must she now make to the mournful Father, who esteem'd this Child the chief Treasure of his Life; she fear'd, that she might forfeit the Affection of a Husband, by being the unfortunate Cause of so great a Loss; but her Fears deceiv'd her, for altho' her Husband, receiv'd her with great Grief, 'twas nevertheless moderated by the Patience of a Christian, and the Joy for recovering his beloved Lady.

This Misfortune was soon lessen'd by the growing Hopes of another Off-spring, which made them divest their

Mourning, to make Preparations for the joyful Reception of this new Guest into the World; and upon its Appearance their Sorrows were redoubled, 'twas a Daughter, its Limbs were distorted, its Back bent, and tho' the face was the freest from Deformity, yet had it no Beauty to Recompence the Dis-symetry of the other Parts; Physicians being consulted in this Affair, derived the Cause from the Frights and dismal Apprehensions of the Mother, at her being taken by the Pyrates; about which time they found by Computation, the Conception of the Child to be; the Mother grew very Melancholy, rarely speaking, and not to be comforted by any Diversion. She conceiv'd again, but no hopes of better Fortune cou'd decrease her Grief, which growing with her Burden, eased her of both at once, for she died in Child-birth, and left the most beautiful Daughter to the World that ever adorn'd *Venice*, but naturally and unfortunately Dumb, which defect the learn'd attributed to the Silence and Melancholy of the Mother, as the Deformity of the other was to the Extravagance of her Frights.

Rinaldo, waving all Intentions of a second Marriage, directs his Thoughts to the Care of his Children, their Defects not lessening his Inclination, but stirring up his Endeavours in supplying the Defaults of Nature by the Industry of Art; he accordingly makes the greatest Provision for their Breeding and Education, which prov'd so effectual in a little Time, that their Progress was a greater Prodigy than themselves.

The Eldest, called *Belvideera*, was indefatigably addicted to Study, which she had improv'd so far, that by the sixteenth Year of her Age, she understood all the *European* Languages, and cou'd speak most of 'em, but was particularly pleas'd with the *English*, which gave me the Happiness of many Hours Conversation with her; and I may ingenuously declare, 'twas the most Pleasant I ever enjoy'd, for besides a piercing Wit, and depth of Understanding peculiar to herself, she delivered her Sentiments with that easiness and grace of Speech, that it charm'd all her Hearers.

The Beauties of the second Sister, nam'd *Maria*, grew with her Age, every twelve Months saluting her with a New-years Gift of some peculiar Charm; her Shapes were fine set off with a graceful and easy Carriage; the Majesty and Softness of her Face, at once wrought Love and Veneration; the Language of her Eyes sufficiently paid the Loss of her Tongue, and there was something so Commanding in her Look, that it struck every Beholder as dumb as herself; she was a great Proficient in Painting, which puts me in mind of a notable Story I can't omit; her Father had sent for the most Famous Painter in *Italy* to draw her Picture, she accordingly sat for it; he had drawn some of the Features of her Face; and coming to the Eye, desired her to give him as brisk and piercing a Glance as she cou'd; but the Vivacity of her Look so astonished the Painter, that thro' concern he let his Pencil drop and spoiled the Picture; he made a second Essay, but with no better Success, for rising in great Disorder, he swore it impossible to draw that which he cou'd not look upon; the Lady vexed at the Weakness of the Painter, took up his Pencils and the Picture, and sitting down to her Glass, finished it herself; she had improv'd her silent Conversation with her Sister so far, that she was understood by her, as if she had spoke, and I remember this Lady was the first I saw use the significative Way of Discourse by the Fingers; I dare not say 'twas she invented it (tho' it probably might have been an Invention of these ingenious Sisters) but I am positive none before her ever brought it to that Perfection.

In the seventeenth of *Belvideera*'s, and sixteenth Year of *Maria*'s Age, *Francisco*, Brother to *Rinaldo*, was made Admiral of the *Venetian* Fleet, and upon his first Entrance upon his Command, had obtained a signal Victory over the *Turks*; he returning to *Venice* with Triumph, applause and spoil, presented to the great Duke a young *English* Gentleman, who only as a Volunteer in the Action, had signalized himself very bravely in the Engagement, but particularly by first boarding the *Turkish* Admiral Galley, and killing her Commander hand to hand; the Fame of this Gentleman soon spread over all *Venice*, and the two Sisters sent presently for me, to give an Account of the Exploits of my Countryman, as their Unkle had recounted it to them; I was pleas'd to find so great an Example of *English* Bravery, so far from Home, and long'd extreamly to converse with him, vainly flattering myself, that he might have been of my Acquaintance. That very Night there was a grand Ball and Masquerade at the great Duke's Palace, for the most signal Joy of the late Success, thither *Belvideera* invited me to Accompany her and *Maria*, adding withal as a Motive, that we might there most probably meet, and Discourse with this young Hero; and equipping me with a Suit of Masquerade, they carried me in their Coach to the Ball, where we had pass'd half an Hour, when I saw enter a handsom Gentlemen in a rich *English* Dress; I show'd him to *Belvideera*, who moving towards him, with a gallant Air, slaps him on the Shoulder with her Fan, he turning about, and viewing her Person, the Defaults of which were not altogether hidden by her Disguise; 'Sir, (said he) if you are a Man, know that I am one, and will not bear Impertinence; but, if you are a Lady, Madam, as I hope in Heavens you are not, I must inform you, that I am under a Vow, not to converse with any Female to Night;' 'Know then, Sir, (answered *Belvideera* very smartly) that I am a Female, and you have broke your Vow already; but methinks, Sir, the Ladies are very little oblig'd to your Vow, which wou'd rob them of the Conversation of so fine a Gentleman.'

'Madam, (said the Gentleman) the Sweetness of your Voice bespeaks you a Lady, and I hope the breaking my Vow will be so far from Damning me, that I shall thereby merit Heaven, if I may be blest in your Divine Conversation.' *Belvideera* made such ingenious and smart Repartees to the Gentleman, who was himself a great Courtier, that he was entirely captivated with her Wit, insomuch, that he cou'd not refrain making Protestations of his Passion; he talked about half an Hour in such pure *Italian*, that I began to mistrust my *Englishman*, wherefore taking some Occasion to jest upon his Habit, I found 'twas only a Masquerade to cloak a down-right *Venetian;* in the mean Time, we perceiv'd a Gentleman Gallantly attir'd with no Disguise but a *Turkish* Turbant on, the richliest beset with Jewels I ever saw; he addressed *Maria* with all the Mien and Air of the finest Courtier; he had talked to her a good while before we heard him, but then *Belvideera,* knowing her poor Sister uncapable of any Defence, 'Sir, (said she to the *Venetian,*) yonder is a Lady of my Acquaintance, who lies under a Vow of Silence as you were, I must therefore beg your Pardon, and fly to her Relief': 'She can never be conquer'd, who has such a Champion,' (reply'd the Gentleman) upon which *Belvideera* turning from him, interpos'd between the Gentleman and her Sister, saying, 'This Lady, Sir, is under an Obligation of Silence, as a Penance imposed by her Father-Confessor.' 'Madam, (reply'd the Gentleman) whoever impos'd Silence on these fair Lips, is guilty of a greater Offence than any, such a fair Creature cou'd commit.' 'Why, Sir, (said *Belvideera*) have you seen the Lady's Beauty': 'Yes, Madam, (answer'd he) for urging her to talk, which I found she declin'd, I promis'd to disengage her from any farther Impertinence, upon a Sight of her Face; she agreed by paying the Price of her Liberty, which was ransom enough for any Thing under Heavens, but her fair Company'; he spoke in an Accent that easily shew'd him a Stranger; which *Belvideera* laying hold of, as an Occasion of Railery, 'Sir, (said she,) your Tongue pronounces you a great Stranger in this Part of the World, I hope you are not what that Turbant represents; perhaps, Sir, you think your self in the Seraglio'; 'Madam, (reply'd he,) this Turbant might have been in the *Turkish* Seraglio, but never in so fair a one as this; and this Turbant (taking it off) is now to be laid at the Foot of some Christian Lady, for whose safety, and by whose protecting Influence, I had the Happiness to win it from the Captain of the *Turkish* Admiral Galley.' We were all surpriz'd, knowing him then the young *English* Gentleman, we were so curious of seeing; *Belvideera* presently talk'd *English* to him, and made him some very pretty Complements upon his Victory, which so charm'd the young Soldier, that her Tongue claim'd an equal Share in his Heart with *Maria's* Eyes; 'Madam, (said he to her) if you have the Beauty of that Lady, or if she has your Wit, I am the most happy, or the most unfortunate Man alive.' 'Sir,' said the *Venetian* coming up, 'pray give me leave to share in your Misfortunes.' 'Sir, (said *Belvideera* very smartly) you must share in his good Fortunes, and learn to conquer Men, before you have the Honour of being subdu'd by Ladies, we scorn mean Prizes, Sir.' 'Madam, (said the *Venetian* in some Choler) perhaps I can subdue a Rival.' 'Pray, Sir, (said the Stranger) don't be angry with the Lady, she's not your Rival I hope, Sir.' Said the *Venetian*, 'I can't be angry at the Lady, because I love her; but my Anger must be levell'd at him, who after this Declaration dare own a Passion for her.' 'Madam, (said the *English* Gentleman turning from the *Venetian*) Honour now must extort a Confession from me, which the Awfulness of my Passion durst never have own'd : And I must declare,' added he in a louder Voice, 'to all the World, that I love you, lest this Gentleman shou'd think his Threats forc'd me to disown it.' 'O ! then (said *Belvideera*) you're his Rival in Honour, not in Love.' 'In honourable Love I am, Madam,' answer'd the Stranger. 'I'll try,' (said the *Venetian*, going off in

Choler,) he Whisper'd a little to a Gentleman, that stood at some Distance, and immediately went out; this was *Gonzago*, a Gentleman of good Reputation in *Venice*, his Principles were Honour and Gallantry, but the Former often sway'd by Passions, rais'd by the Latter. All this while, *Maria* and I were admiring the Stranger, whose Person was indeed wonderfully Amiable; his Motions were exact, yet free and unconstrain'd; the Tone of his Voice carried a sweet Air of Modesty in it, yet were all his Expressions manly; and to summ up all, he was as fine an *English* Gentleman, as I ever saw Step in the *Mall*.

Poor *Maria* never before envied her Sister the Advantage of Speech, or never deplor'd the Loss of her own with more Regret, she found something so Sweet in the Mien, Person, and Discourse of this Stranger, that her Eyes felt a dazling Pleasure in beholding him, and like flattering Mirrours represented every Action and Feature, with some heightning Advantage to her Imagination: *Belvideera* also had some secret Impulses of Spirit, which drew her insensibly into a great Esteem of the Gentleman; she ask'd him, by what good Genius, propitious to *Venice*, he was induced to Live so remote from his Country; he said, that he cou'd not imploy his Sword better than against the common Foe of Christianity; and besides, there was a peculiar Reason, which prompted him to serve there, which Time cou'd only make known. I made bold to ask him some peculiar Questions, about Affairs at Court, to most of which he gave Answers, that shew'd his Education liberal, and himself no Stranger to Quality; he call'd himself *Dangerfield*, which was a Name that so pleas'd me, that being since satisfied it was a Counterfeit, I us'd it in a Comedy of mine: We had talk'd 'till the greater Part of the Company being dispers'd, *Dangerfield* begg'd Leave to attend us to our Coach, and waiting us to the Door, the Gentleman, whom *Gonzago* whisper'd, advanc'd and offer'd his Service to hand *Maria*; she declin'd it, and upon his urging, she turn'd to the other Side of *Dangerfield*, who, by this Action of the Ladies finding himself intitled to her Protection, 'Sir, (said he) Favours from great Beauties, as from great Monarchs, must flow Voluntarily, not by Constraint, and whosoever wou'd extort from either, are liable to the great Severity of Punishment.' 'Oh! Sir, (reply'd the *Venetian* very arrogantly,) I understand not your Monarchy, we live here under a free State; besides, Sir, where there is no Punishment to be dreaded, the Law will prove of little Force; and so, Sir, by your Leave,' offering to push him aside, and lay hold on the Lady. *Dangerfield* returned the Justle so vigorously, that the *Venetian* fell down the Descent of some Stairs at the Door, and broke his Sword: *Dangerfield* leap'd down after him, to prosecute his Chastizement, but seeing his Sword broken, only whisper'd him, that if he wou'd meet him next Morning at Six, at the Back-part of St. *Mark's* Church, he wou'd satisfie him for the Loss of his Sword; upon which, the *Venetian* immediately went off, cursing his ill Fate, that prevented his quarrelling with *Dangerfield*, to whom he had born a grudging Envy ever since his Success in the late Engagement, and of whom, and his Lodgings, he had given *Gonzago* an Account, when he whisper'd him at the Ball. *Dangerfield* left us full of his Praises, and went home to his Lodgings, where he found a Note directed to him to this Effect:

SIR,

YOU declared Publickly at the Ball, you were my Rival in Love and Honour: If you dare prove it by Maintaining it, I shall be to morrow Morning at Six, at the Back-part of St. Mark's *Church, where I shall be ready to fall a Sacrifice to both.*
                                          Gonzago.

Dangerfield, on the Perusal of this Challenge, began to reflect on the Strangeness of that Evening's Adventure, which had engag'd him in a Passion for two Mistresses, and involv'd him in two Duels; and whether the Extravagance of his Passion, or the Oddness of his Fighting-Appointments, were most remarkable, he found hard to Determine; his Love was divided between the Beauty of one Lady, and Wit of another, either of which he loved passionately, yet nothing cou'd satisfy him, but the Possibility of enjoying both. He had appointed the Gentleman at the Ball to meet him at the same Time and Place, which *Gonzago's* Challenge to him imported; this Disturbance employed his Thought till Morning, when rising and dressing himself very richly, he walked to the appointed Place. *Erizo*, who was the Gentleman whose Sword he had broke, was in the Place before him; and *Gonzago* entered at the same Time with him. *Erizo*, was surprized to see *Gonzago*, as much as he was to find *Erizo* there. 'I don't remember, Friend (said *Gonzago*) that I desired your Company here this Morning.' 'As much as I expected yours,' answered *Erizo*. 'Come, Gentlemen, (said *Dangerfield*, interrupting them) I must fight you both, it seems: which shall I dispatch first?' 'Sir, (said *Erizo*) you challeng'd me, and therefore I claim your Promise.' 'Sir, (reply'd *Gonzago*) he must require the same of me first, as I challenged him.' Said *Erizo*, 'the Affront I received was unpardonable, and therefore I must fight him first, lest if he fall by your Hands, I be depriv'd of my Satisfaction.' 'Nay (reply'd *Gonzago*) my Love and Honour being laid at Stake, first claims his Blood; and therefore, Sir, (continued he to *Dangerfield*) defend yourself.' 'Hold (said *Erizo* interposing,) if you thrust home, you injure me, your Friend.' 'You have forfeited that title, (said *Gonzago* all in Choler,) and therefore if you stand not aside, I'll push at you.' 'Thrust home then, (said *Erizo*) and take what follows.' They immediately assaulted each other vigorously. 'Hold, Gentlemen, (said *Dangerfield* striking down their Swords) by righting your selves you injure me, robbing me of that Satisfaction, which you both owe me, and therefore, Gentlemen, you shall fight me, before any private Quarrel among your selves defraud me of my Revenge, and so one or both of you,' thrusting first at *Erizo*. 'I'm your Man,' (said *Gonzago*) parrying the Thrust made at *Erizo*. The Clashing of so many Swords alarm'd some Gentlemen at their *Mattins* in the Church, among whom was *Rinaldo*, who since the Death of his Wife, had constantly attended Morning-Service at the Church, wherein she was buried. He with Two or Three more, upon the Noise ran out, and parting the three Combatants, desired to know the Occasion of their Promiscuous Quarrel. *Gonzago* and *Erizo* knowing *Rinaldo*, gave him an Account of the Matter, as also who the Stranger was. *Rinaldo* was over-joy'd to find the brave *Britain*, whom he had received so great a Character of, from his Brother the Admiral, and accosting him very Courteously, 'Sir, (said he) I am sorry our Countrymen shou'd be so Ungrateful as to Injure any Person, who has been so Serviceable to the State; and pray, Gentlemen, (added he, addressing the other two) be intreated to suspend your Animosities, and come Dine with me at my House, where I hope to prevail with you to end your Resentments.' *Gonzago* and *Erizo* hearing him Compliment the Stranger at their Expence, told him in a Rage, they wou'd chuse some other Place than his House, to end their Resentments in, and walk'd off. *Dangerfield*, on *Rinaldo's* farther Request, accompanied him to his House.

Maria had newly risen, and with her Night-gown only thrown loose about her, had look'd out of the Window, just as her Father and *Dangerfield* were approaching the Gate, at the same Instant she cast her Eyes upon *Dangerfield*, and he accidentally look'd up to the Window where she stood, their Surprize was mutual, but that of *Dangerfield* the greater; he saw such an amazing Sight of Beauty, as made him doubt the Reality of the Object,

or distrust the Perfection of his Sight; he saw his dear
Lady, who had so captivated him the preceeding Day,
he saw her in all the heightning Circumstances of her
Charms, he saw her in all her native Beauties, free from
the Incumbrance of Dress, her Hair as black as Ebony,
hung flowing in careless Curls over her Shoulders, it
hung link'd in amorous Twinings, as if in Love with its
own Beauties; her Eyes not yet freed from the Dullness
of the late Sleep, cast a languishing Pleasure in their
Aspect, which heaviness of Sight added the greatest
Beauties to those Suns, because under the Shade of such
a Cloud, their Lustre cou'd only be view'd; the lambent
Drowsiness that play'd upon her Face, seem'd like a thin
Veil not to hide, but to heighten the Beauty which it
cover'd; her Night-gown hanging loose, discover'd her
charming Bosom, which cou'd bear no Name, but Transport, Wonder and Extasy, all which struck his Soul, as
soon as the Object hit his Eye; her Breasts with an easy
Heaving, show'd the Smoothness of her Soul and of her
Skin; their Motions were so languishingly soft, that they
cou'd not be said to rise and fall, but rather to swell up
towards Love, the Heat of which seem'd to melt them
down again; some scatter'd jetty Hairs, which hung
confus'dly over her Breasts, made her Bosom show like
Venus caught in *Vulcan's* Net, but 'twas the Spectator,
not she, was captivated. This *Dangerfield* saw, and all
this at once, and with Eyes that were adapted by a
preparatory Potion; what must then his Condition be?
He was stricken with such Amazement, that he was forced
to Support himself, by leaning on *Rinaldo's* Arm, who
started at his sudden Indisposition. 'I'm afraid, Sir, (said
he) you have received some Wound in the Duel.' 'Oh!
Sir, (said he) I am mortally wounded'; but recollecting
himself after a little Pause, 'now I am better.' *Rinaldo*
wou'd have sent for a Surgeon to have it searched. 'Your
pardon, Sir, (said *Dangerfield*) my Indisposition proceeds

from an inward Malady, not by a Sword, but like those made by *Achilles's* Spear, nothing can cure, but what gave the Wound.' *Rinaldo* guessing at the Distemper, but not the Cause of it, out of good Manners declined any further enquiry, but conducting him in, entertained him with all the Courtesy imaginable ; but in half a Hour, a Messenger came from the Senate, requiring his immediate Attendance; he lying under an indispensable Necessity of making his personal Appearance, begg'd *Dangerfield's* Pardon, intreating him to stay, and command his House till his return, and conducting him to a fine Library, said he might there find Entertainment, if he were addicted to Study ; adding withal, as a farther Engagement of his Patience, that he should meet the Admiral at the Senate, whom he wou'd bring home as an Addition to their Company at Dinner. *Dangerfield* needed none of these Motives to stay, being detained by a secret Inclination to the Place; walking therefore into the Library, *Rinaldo* went to the Senate. *Dangerfield* when alone, fell into deep Ruminating on his strange Condition, he knew himself in the House, with one of his dear Charmers, but durst not hope to see her, which added to his Torment; like *Tantalus* remov'd the farther from Happiness, by being nearer to it, contemplated so far on the Beauties of that dear Creature, that he concluded, if her Wit were like that of his t'other Mistress, he wou'd endeavour to confine his Passion wholly to that Object.

In the mean Time, *Maria* was no less confounded, she knew herself in Love with a Stranger, whose Residence was uncertain, she knew her own Modesty in concealing it ; and alas ! she knew her Dumbness uncapable of ever revealing it, at least, it must never expect any Return ; she had gather'd from her Sister's Discourse, that she was her Rival ; a Rival, who had the Precedency in Age, as the Advantage in Wit, and Intreague, which want of Speech render'd her uncapable of ; these Reflections, as they drew her farther from the dear Object, brought her nearer Despair; her Sister was gone that Morning with her Unkle, the Admiral, about two Miles from *Venice*, to drink some Mineral Waters, and *Maria* finding nothing to divert her, goes down to her Father's Library, to ease her Melancholy by reading. She was in the same loose Habit in which she appeared at the Window, her Distraction of Thought not permitting her any Care in dressing herself; she enter'd whilst *Dangerfield's* Thoughts were bent by a full Contemplation of her Idea, insomuch that his Surprize represented her as a Phantom only, created by the Strength of his Fancy; her depth of Thought had cast down her Eyes in a fix'd Posture so low, that she discover'd not *Dangerfield*, till she stood close where he sat, but then so sudden an Appearance of what she so lov'd, struck so violently on her Spirits, that she fell in a Swoon, and fell directly into *Dangerfield's* Arms; this soon wakened him from his Dream of Happiness, to a Reality of Bliss, he found his Phantom turn'd into the most charming Piece of Flesh and Blood that ever was, he found her, whom just now he despair'd of seeing; he found her with all her Beauties flowing loose in his Arms, the Greatness of the Pleasure rais'd by the two heightning Circumstances of Unexpectancy and Surprize, was too large for the Capacity of his Soul, he found himself beyond Expression happy, but could not digest the Surfeit; he had no sooner Leisure to consider on his Joy, but he must reflect on the Danger of her that caus'd it, which forced him to suspend his Happiness to administer some Relief to her expiring Senses: He had a Bottle of excellent Spirits in his Pocket, which holding to her Nose, soon recover'd her; she finding herself in the Arms of a Man, and in so loose a Dress, blush'd now more red, than she look'd lately pale; and disengaging herself in a Confusion, wou'd have flung from him; but he gently detaining her by a precarious Hold, threw himself on his Knees, and with the greatest Fervency of Passion cry'd out: 'For

Heavens sake, dearest Creature, be not offended at the accidental Blessing which Fortune, not Design, hath cast upon me; (She wou'd have rais'd him up,) No Madam, (continu'd he) never will I remove from this Posture, 'till you have pronounc'd my Pardon; I love you, Madam, to that Degree, that if you leave me in a distrust of your Anger, I cannot survive it; I beg, intreat, conjure you to speak, your Silence torments me worse than your Reproaches cou'd; am I so much disdain'd, that you will not afford me one Word?' The lamentable Plight of the wretched Lady every one may guess, but no Body can comprehend; she saw the dearest of Mankind prostrate at her Feet, and imploring what she wou'd as readily grant as he desire, yet herself under a Necessity of denying his Prayers, and her own easy Inclinations. The Motions of her Soul, wanting the freedom of Utterance, were like to tear her Heart asunder by so narrow a Confinement, like the force of Fire pent up, working more impetuously; 'till at last he redoubling his Importunity, her Thoughts wanting Conveyance by the Lips, burst out at her Eyes in a Flood of Tears; then moving towards a Writing-Desk, he following her still on his Knees, amidst her Sighs and Groans she took Pen and Paper, writ two Lines, which she gave him folded up, then flinging from him, ran up to her Chamber: He strangely surpriz'd at this odd manner of Proceeding, opening the Paper, read the following Words:

> *You can't my Pardon, nor my Anger move.*
> *For know, alas! I'm dumb, alas! I love.*

He was wonderfully Amaz'd reading these Words. 'Dumb, (cried he out) naturally Dumb? O ye niggard Powers, why was such a wond'rous Piece of Art left imperfect?' He had many other wild Reasonings upon the lamentable Subject, but falling from these to more calm Reflections, he examined her Note again, and finding by the last Words that she loved him, he might presently imagine, that if he found not some Means of declaring the Continuance of his Love, the innocent Lady might conjecture herself slighted, upon the Discovery of her Affection and Infirmity: Prompted, by which Thought, and animated by the Emotions of his Passion, he ventured to knock at her Door; she having by this Time dressed herself, ventured to let him in: *Dangerfield* ran towards her, and catching her with an eager Embrace, gave her a thousand Kisses; 'Madam, (said he) you find that pardoning Offences only prepares more, by emboldning the Offender; but, I hope, Madam,' shewing her the Note, 'this is a general Pardon for all Offences of this sort, by which I am so encouraged to Transgress, that I shall never cease Crimes of this Nature'; Kissing her again. His Happiness was interrupted by *Belvideera's* coming Home, who running up Stairs, called, 'Sister, Sister, I have News to tell you': Her Voice alarms *Maria*, who fearing the Jealousy of *Belvideera*, shou'd she find *Dangerfield* in her Bed-Chamber, made Signs that he shou'd run into the Closet, which she had just lock'd as *Belvideera* came in: 'Oh, Sister! (said *Belvideera*) in a lucky Hour went I abroad this Morning.' In a more lucky Hour stay'd I at home this Morning, thought *Maria*. 'I have, (continued she,) been Instrumental in parting two Gentlemen fighting this Morning, and what is more, my Father had parted them before, when engag'd with the fine *English* Gentleman we saw at the Ball yesterday; but the greatest News of all is, that this fine *English* Gentleman is now in the House, and must Dine here to Day; but you must not appear, Sister, because 'twere a Shame to let Strangers know that you are Dumb.' *Maria* perceived her Jealousy, pointed to her Limbs, intimating thereby, that it was as great a Shame for her to be seen by Strangers; but she made farther Signs, that since it was her Pleasure, she wou'd keep her Chamber all that Day, and not appear abroad. *Belvideera* was extreamly glad of her

Resolution, hoping that she shou'd enjoy *Dangerfield's* Conversation without any Interruption. The Consternation of the Spark in the Closet all this while was not little, he heard the Voice of the Charmer, that had so captivated him, he found that she was Sister to that Lady, whom he just now was making so many Protestations to, but he cou'd not imagine how she was Instrumental in parting the two Gentlemen, that shou'd have fought him; the Occasion was this:

Gonzago and *Erizo*, parting from *Rinaldo* and *Dangerfield*, had walk'd towards the *Rialto*, and both exasperated that they had missed their intended Revenge against *Dangerfield*, turned their Fury upon each other, first raising their Anger by incensed Expostulations, then drawing their Swords, engaged in a desperate Combat, when a Voice very loud calling, (*Erizo*, hold) stopt their Fury to see whence it proceeded ; when a Coach driving at full Flight stopt close by them, and *Francisco* the *Venetian* Admiral leaped out with his Sword drawn, saying, 'Gentlemen, pray let me be an Instrument of Pacification: As for your part, *Erizo*, this Proceeding suits not well with the Business I am to move in Favour of you in the Senate to Day ; the Post you sue for claims your Blood to be spilt against the common Foe, not in private Resentment, to the Destruction of a Citizen ; and therefore I intreat you as my Friend, or I command you as your Officer, to put up.' *Erizo*, unwilling to disoblige his Admiral, upon whose Favour his Advancement depended, told *Gonzago*, that he must find another time to talk with him. 'No, no, Gentlemen, (said the Admiral) you shall not part 'till I have reconciled you, and therefore let me know your Cause of Quarrel.' *Erizo* therefore related to him the whole Affair, and mentioning that *Dangerfield* was gone Home to Dine with *Rinaldo ;* 'With *Rinaldo* my Father?' said *Belvideera* from the Coach, overjoy'd with Hopes of seeing *Dangerfield* at Home. 'Yes, (reply'd *Gonzago* surpriz'd) if *Rinaldo* the Senator be your Father, Madam.' 'Yes, he is,' reply'd *Belvideera*. *Gonzago* then knew her to be the Lady he was enamour'd of, and for whom he wou'd have fought *Dangerfield*; and now cursed his ill Fate, that he had deny'd *Rinaldo's* Invitation, which lost him the Conversation of his Mistress, which his Rival wou'd be sure of. 'Come, come, Gentlemen, (said the Admiral) you shall accompany me to see this Stranger at *Rinaldo's* House, I bear a great Esteem for him, and so it behoves every loyal *Venetian*, for whose Service he hath been so signal.' *Erizo*, unwilling to deny the Admiral, and *Gonzago* glad of an Opportunity of his Mistress's Company, which he just now thought lost, consented to the Proposal, and mounting all into the Coach, the three Gentlemen were set down at the Senate, and the Lady drove Home as above-mentioned.

Rinaldo in the mean Time was not idle in the Senate, there being a Motion made for Election of a Captain to the *Rialto* Galleon, made void by the Death of its former Commander in the late Fight, and which was the Post designed by the Admiral for *Erizo*. *Rinaldo* catching an Opportunity of obliging *Dangerfield*, for whom he entertain'd a great Love and Respect, proposed him as a Candidate for the Command, urging his late brave Performance against the *Turks*, and how much it concerned the Interest of the State to encourage Foreigners. He being the Admiral's Brother, and being so fervent in the Affair, had by an unanimous Consent his Commission sign'd just as his Brother came into the Senate, who fearing how Things were carried, comforted *Erizo* by future Preferment; but *Erizo*, however he stifled his Resentment, was struck with Envy, that a Stranger, and his Enemy shou'd be preferred to him, and resolved Revenge on the first Opportunity. They all went home with *Rinaldo*, and arrived whilst *Belvideera* was talking above Stairs with her Sister. *Rinaldo*, impatient to communicate his Success to *Dangerfield*, ran into the Study, where he left him; but missing him there, went into the Garden, and searching all about, returned

to the Company, telling them he believ'd *Dangerfield* had
fallen asleep in some private Arbor in the Garden, where
he cou'd not find him, or else impatient of his long stay,
had departed ; but he was sure, if he had gone, he wou'd
soon return: However they went to Dinner, and *Belvideera*
came down, making an Apology for her Sister's Absence,
thro' an Indisposition that had seized her. *Gonzago* had
his wished for Opportunity of entertaining his Mistress,
whilst she always expecting some News of *Dangerfield*,
sat very uneasie in his Company ; whilst *Dangerfield* in the
Closet, was as impatient to see her. The short Discourse
she had with her Sister, gave him assurance that his Love
wou'd not be unacceptable. *Maria* durst not open the
Closet, afraid that her Sister shou'd come up every Minute,
besides, 'twas impossible to convey him out of the Chamber
undiscovered, untill 'twas dark, which made him Wonder
what occasioned his long Confinement ; and being tired
with sitting, got up to the Window, and softly opening
the Casement, looked out to take the Air ; his Footman
walking accidentally in the Court, and casting up his Eye
that way, spy'd him, which confirm'd his Patience in
attending for him at the Gate ; at length it grew Dark,
and *Maria* knowing that her Sister was engag'd in a
Match at Cards with her Father, *Gonzago* and *Erizo*, the
Admiral being gone, she came softly to the Closet, and
innocently took *Dangerfield* by the Hand, to lead him out,
he clapt the dear soft Hand to his Mouth, and kissing it
eagerly, it fired his Blood, and the unhappy Opportunity
adding to the Temptation, raised him to the highest Pitch
of Passion ; he found himself with the most beautiful
Creature in the World, one who loved him, he knew they
were alone in the Dark, in a Bed-chamber, he knew the
Lady young and melting, he knew besides she cou'd not
tell, and he was conscious of his Power in moving ; all
these wicked Thoughts concurring, establish'd him in the
Opinion, that this was the critical Minute of his Happiness,

resolving therefore not to lose it, he fell down on his
Knees, devouring her tender Hand, sighing out his Passion,
begging her to Crown it with her Love, making Ten
thousand Vows and Protestations of his Secrecy and
Constancy, urging all the Arguments that the Subtilty of
the Devil or Man could suggest. She held out against all
his Assaults above two Hours, and often endeavoured to
Struggle from him, but durst make no great Disturbance,
thro' fear of Alarming the Company below, at last he
redoubling his Passion with Sighs, Tears, and all the rest
of Love's Artillery, he at last gain'd the Fort, and the poor
conquered Lady, all panting, soft, and trembling every
Joynt, melted by his Embraces, he there fatally enjoy'd
the greatest Extasy of Bliss, heightned by the Circumstances of Stealth, and Difficulty in obtaining. The ruin'd
Lady now too late deplored the Loss of her Honour;
but he endeavour'd to Comfort her by making Vows of
Secrecy, and promising to salve her Reputation by a speedy
Marriage, which he certainly intended, had not the
unhappy *Crisis* of his Fate been so near. The Company
by this Time had gone off, and *Belvideera* had retir'd to
her Chamber, melancholy that she had missed her Hopes
of seeing *Dangerfield*. *Gonzago* and *Erizo* going out of the
Gate, saw *Dangerfield's* Footman, whom they knew, since
they saw him with his Master in the Morning. *Gonzago*
asked him why he waited there? 'For my Master, Sir,'
reply'd the Footman. 'Your Master is not here sure,'
said *Gonzago*. 'Yes, but he is, Sir,' said the Servant, 'for
I attended him hither this Morning with *Rinaldo*, and saw
him in the Afternoon look out of a Window above Stairs.'
'Ha!' said *Gonzago*, calling *Erizo* aside, 'by Heavens, he
lies here to Night then, and perhaps with my Mistress;
I perceiv'd she was not pressing for our Stay, but rather
urging our Departure. *Erizo*, *Erizo*, this Block must be
remov'd, he has stepped between you and a Command to
Day, and perhaps may lye between me and my Mistress

to Night.' 'By Hell (answered *Erizo*) thou hast raised a
Fury in me, that will not be lulled asleep, but by a Potion
of his Blood; let's dispatch this Blockhead first': And
running at the Footman, with one Thrust killed him.
Dangerfield by this time had been let out, and hearing the
Noise, ran to the Place; they presently assaulted him; he
defended himself very bravely the space of some Minutes,
having wounded *Gonzago* in the Breast; when *Rinaldo*
hearing the Noise, came out; but too late for *Dangerfield's*
Relief, and too soon for his own Fate; for *Gonzago*,
exasperated by his Wound, ran treacherously behind
Dangerfield, and thrust him quite thro' the Body. He
finding the mortal Wound, and wild with Rage, thrust
desperately forward at *Erizo*, when at the instant *Rinaldo*
striking in between to part them, received *Dangerfield's*
Sword in his Body, which pierced him quite thro'. He
no sooner fell, than *Dangerfield* perceived his fatal Error,
and the other Two fled. *Dangerfield* curs'd his Fate, and
begg'd with all the Prayers and Earnestness of a dying
Man, that *Rinaldo* wou'd forgive him. 'Oh!' said *Rinaldo*,
'you have ill rewarded me for my Care in your Concerns
in the Senate to Day.' The Servants coming out, took up
Rinaldo, and *Dangerfield* leaning upon his Sword, they led
him in. *Belvideera* first heard the Noise, and running down
first met the horrid Spectacle, her dear Father breathing
out his last, and her Lover, whom she had all that Day
flattered her self with Hopes of seeing, she now beheld in
Streams of his Blood; but what must poor *Maria's* Case
be? besides the Grief for her Father's Fate, she must view
that dear Man, lately Happy in her Embraces, now folded
in the Arms of Death, she finds herself bereft of a Parent,
her Love, her Honour, and the Defender of it, all at once;
and the greatest Torment is, that she must bear all this
Anguish, and cannot Ease her Soul by expressing it.
Belvideera sat wiping the Blood from her Father's Wound,
whilst mournful *Maria* sat by *Dangerfield*, administring

all the Help she cou'd to his fainting Spirits; whilst he viewed her with greater Excess of Grief, than he had heretofore with Pleasure; being sensible what was the Force of her silent Grief, and the Wrong he had done her, which now he cou'd never Redress: He had accidentally dropt his Wig in the Engagement, and inclining his Head over the Couch where he lay, *Rinaldo* casting his Eye upon him, perceiv'd the Mark of a bloody Dagger on his Neck, under his left Ear: 'Sir, (said *Rinaldo*, raising himself up) I conjure you answer me directly, were you born with the Mark of that Dagger, or have you received it since by Accident.' 'I was certainly born with it,' answer'd he. 'Just such a Mark had my Son *Cosmo*, who was lost in the *Adriatick*.' 'How! (reply'd *Dangerfield*, starting up with a wild Confusion) Lost! say'st thou in the *Adriatick?* Your Son lost in the *Adriatick?*' 'Yes, yes,' said *Rinaldo*, 'too surely lost in the *Adriatick*.' 'O ye impartial Powers (said *Dangerfield*) why did you not reveal this before? Or why not always conceal it? How happy had been the Discovery some few Hours ago, and how Tragical is it now? For know,' continued he, addressing himself to *Rinaldo*, 'know that my suppos'd Father, who was a *Turky* Merchant, upon his Death-bed call'd me to him, and told me 'twas time to undeceive me, I was not his Son, he found me in the *Adriatick* Sea, ty'd to two Planks in his Voyage from *Symrna* to *London*; having no Children, he educated me as his own, and finding me worth his Care, left me all his Inheritance with this dying Command, that I shou'd seek my Parents at *Venice*.' *Belvideera* hearkning all this while to the lamentable Story, then conjectured whence proceeded the natural Affection the whole Family bore him, and embracing him, cry'd out, 'Oh my unhappy Brother.' *Maria* all the while had strong and wild Convulsions of Sorrow within her, 'till the working Force of her Anguish racking at once all the Passages of her Breast, by a violent Impulse, broke the

Ligament that doubled in her Tongue, and she burst out with this Exclamation; 'Oh! Incest, Incest.' *Dangerfield* eccho'd that Outcry with this, 'O! Horror, Horror, I have enjoy'd my Sister, and murder'd my Father.' *Maria* running distracted about the Chamber, at last spy'd *Dangerfield's* Sword, by which he had supported himself into the House, and catching it up, reeking with the Blood of her Father, plung'd it into her Heart, and throwing herself into *Dangerfield's* Arms, calls out, 'O my Brother, O my Love,' and expir'd. All the Neighbourhood was soon alarm'd by the Out-cries of the Family. I lodged within three Doors of *Rinaldo's* House, and running presently thither, saw a more bloody Tragedy in Reality, than what the most moving Scene ever presented; the Father and Daughter were both dead, the unfortunate Son was gasping out his last, and the surviving Sister most miserable, because she must survive such Misfortunes, cry'd to me; 'O! behold the Fate of your wretched Country-man.' I cou'd make no Answer, being struck dumb by the Horror of such woeful Objects; but *Dangerfield* hearing her name his Country, turning towards me, with a languishing and weak Tone, 'Madam,' said he, 'I was your Country-man, and wou'd to Heavens I were so still; if you hear my Story mention'd, on your Return to *England*, pray give these strange Turns of my Fate not the Name of Crimes, but favour them with the Epithet of Misfortunes; my Name is not *Dangerfield;* but *Cla*—' His Voice there fail'd him, and he presently dy'd; Death seeming more favour-able than himself, concealing the fatal Author of so many Misfortunes, for I cou'd never since learn out his Name; but have done him the Justice, I hope, to make him be pity'd for his Misfortunes, not hated for his Crimes. *Francisco* being sent for, had *Gonzago* and *Erizo* apprehended, con-demn'd, and executed. *Belvideera* consign'd all her Father's Estate over to her Uncle, reserving only a Competency to maintain her a Recluse all the rest of her Life.

THE WANDERING BEAUTY.

THE WANDERING BEAUTY.

I was not above twelve Years old, as near as I can remember, when a Lady of my Acquaintance, who was particularly concern'd in many of the Passages, very pleasantly entertain'd me with the Relation of the young Lady *Arabella's* Adventures, who was eldest Daughter to Sir *Francis Fairname*, a Gentleman of a noble Family, and of a very large Estate in the West of *England*, a true Church-Man, a great Loyalist, and a most discreetly-indulgent Parent; nor was his Lady any Way inferiour to him in every Circumstance of Virtue. They had only two Children more, and those were of the soft, unhappy Sex too; all very beautiful, especially *Arabella*, and all very much alike; piously educated, and courtly too, of naturally-virtuous Principles and Inclinations.

'Twas about the sixteenth Year of her Age, that Sir *Robert Richland*, her Father's great Friend and inseparable Companion, but superiour to him in Estate as well as Years, felt the resistless Beauty of this young Lady raging and burning in his aged Veins, which had like to have been as fatal to him, as a Consumption, or his Climacterical Year of Sixty Three, in which he dy'd, as I am told, though he was then hardly Sixty. However, the Winter Medlar would fain have been inoculated in the Summer's Nacturine. His unseasonable Appetite grew so strong and inordinate, that he was oblig'd to discover it to Sir *Francis;* who, though he lov'd him very sincerely, had yet a Regard to his Daughter's Youth, and Satisfaction in the Choice of a Husband; especially, when he consider'd the great Disproportion in their Age, which he rightly imagin'd would be very disagreeable to *Arabella's* Inclinations:

This made him at first use all the most powerful and perswading Arguments in his Capacity, to convince Sir *Robert* of the Inequality of such a Match, but all to no Purpose; for his Passion increasing each Day more violently, the more assiduously, and with the greater Vehemence, he press'd his Friend to use his Interest and Authority with his Lady and Daughter, to consent to his almost unnatural Proposition; offering this as the most weighty and prevailing Argument, (which undoubtedly it was,) That since he was a Batchelor, he would settle his whole Estate upon her, if she surviv'd him, on the Day of Marriage, not desiring one Penny as a Portion with her. This Discourse wrought so powerfully with her Mother, that she promis'd the old Lover all the Assistance he could hope or expect from her: In order to which, the next Day she acquainted her fair Daughter with the Golden Advantage she was like to have, if she would but consent *to lye by the Parchment that convey'd them to her*. The dear, fair Creature, was so surpriz'd at this Overture made by her Mother, that her Roses turn'd all into Lillies, and she had like to have swoon'd away; but having a greater Command of her Passions than usually our Sex have, and chiefly Persons of her Age, she, after some little Disorder, which by no Means she could dissemble, she made as dutiful a Return to her Mother's Proposition, as her Aversion to it would permit; and, for that Time, got Liberty to retreat, and lament in private the Misfortune which she partly fore-saw was impending. But her Grief (alas) was no Cure of her Malady; for the next Day she was again doubly attack'd by her Father and Mother, with all the Reasons that Interest and Duty could urge, which she endeavour'd to obviate by all the Arguments that Nature and Inclination could offer; but she found them all in vain, since they continu'd their ungrateful Solicitations for several Days together, at the End of which, they both absolutely commanded her to prepare her self for her Nuptials with Sir *Robert;* so that finding her self under a Necessity of complying, or at least of seeming so, she made 'em hope, that her Duty had overcome her Aversion; upon which she had a whole Week's Liberty to walk where she would, unattended, or with what Company she pleas'd, and to make Visits to whom she had a Mind, either of her Relations or Acquaintance thereabouts; tho' for three or four Days before, she was strictly confin'd to her Chamber.

After Dinner, on the third Day of her Enlargement, being Summer Time, she propos'd to her Mother that she would take a Walk to a Cousin of hers, who liv'd about four Miles thence, to intreat her to be one of her Bride-Maids, being then in a careless plain Dress, and having before discours'd very pleasantly and freely of her Wedding-Day, of what Friends she would have invited to that Solemnity, and what Hospitality Sir *Robert* should keep when she was marry'd to him: All which was highly agreeable to her Parents, who then could not forbear thanking and kissing her for it, which she return'd to 'em both with a Shower of Tears. This did not a little surprize 'em at first, but asking her what could cause such Signs of Sorrow, after so chearful a Discourse on the late Subject? She answer'd, 'That the Thoughts of her going now suddenly to live from so dear and tender a Father and Mother, were the sole Occasion of such Expressions of Grief.' This affectionate Reply did amply satisfy their Doubts; and she presently took Leave of 'em, after having desir'd that they would not be uneasy if she should not return 'till a little before 'twas dark, or if her Cousin should oblige her to stay all Night with her; which they took for a discreet Caution in her, considering that young Maidens love dearly to talk of Marriage Affairs, especially when so near at Hand: And thus easily parted with her, when they had walk'd with her about a Mile, over a Field or two of their own.

Never before that Time was the dear Creature glad that her Father and Mother had left her, unless when they had press'd her to a Marriage with the old Knight. They were therefore no sooner got out of Sight, e're she took another Path, that led cross the Country, which she persu'd 'till past eight at Night, having walk'd ten Miles since two a Clock, when Sir *Francis* and her Mother left her: She was just now got to a little Cottage, the poor, but cleanly Habitation of a Husbandman and his Wife, who had one only Child, a Daughter, about the Lady *Arabella*'s Age and Stature. 'Twas happy for her she got thither before they were a Bed; for her soft and beautiful Limbs began now to be tir'd, and her tender Feet to be gall'd. To the good Woman of the House she applies her self, desiring Entertainment for that Night, offering her any reasonable Satisfaction. The good Wife, at first Sight of her, had Compassion of her, and immediately bid her walk in, telling her, that she might lye with her Daughter, if she pleas'd, who was very cleanly, tho' not very vine. The good Man of the House came in soon after, was very well pleas'd with his new Guest; so to Supper they went very seasonably; for the poor young Lady, who was e'en ready to faint with Thirst, and not overcharg'd with what she had eaten the Day before. After Supper they ask'd her whence she came, and how she durst venture to travel alone, and a Foot? To which she reply'd, That she came from a Relation who liv'd at *Exeter*, with whom she had stay'd 'till she found she was burthensome: That she was of *Welsh* Parents, and of a good Family; but her Father dying, left a cruel Mother-in-Law, with whom she could by no Means continue, especially since she would have forc'd her to marry an old Man, whom it was impossible she should love, tho' he was very rich: That she was now going to seek her Fortune in *London*, where she hop'd, at least, to get her a good Service. They all seem'd to pity her very heartily; and, in a little

Time after, they went to their two several Apartments, in one of which *Arabella* and the Damsel of the House went to Bed, where the young Lady slept soundly, notwithstanding the Hardness of her Lodging. In the Morning, about Four, according to her laudable Custom, the young hardy Maiden got up to her daily Employment; which waken'd *Arabella*, who presently bethought her self of an Expedient for her more secure and easy Escape from her Parents Pursuit and Knowledge, proposing to her Bedfellow an Exchange of their Wearing-Apparel. The Heiress and Hope of that little Family was extreamly fond of the Proposal, and ran immediately to acquaint her Mother with it, who was so well pleas'd, that she could hardly believe it, when the young Lady confirm'd it, and especially, when she understood the Exchange was to be made on even Hands. 'If you be in earnest, Forsooth, (said the Mother) you shall e'en have her Sunday-Cloaths.' 'Agreed (return'd *Arabella*) but we must change Shifts too; I have now a Couple about me, new and clean, I do assure you: For my Hoods and Head-dress you shall give me two Pinners, and her best Straw-Hat; and for my Shoes, which I have not worn above a Week, I will have her Holliday Shoes.' 'A Match, indeed, young Mistress,' cry'd the good Wife. So without more Ceremony, the young unhappy Lady was attir'd in her Bedfellow's Country Weeds, by Help of the Mother and Daughter. Then, after she had taken her Leave of the good old Man too, she put a broad round Shilling into his Wife's Hand, as a Reward for her Supper and Lodging, which she would fain have return'd, but t'other would not receive it. 'Nay, then, by the Mackins, (said her Hostess) you shall take a Breakfast e're you go, and a Dinner along with you, for Fear you should be sick by the Way.' *Arabella* stay'd to eat a Mess of warm Milk, and took some of their Yesterday's Provision with her in a little course Linnen Bag. Then asking for the direct Road to

London, and begging a few green Wall-nuts, she took her last Farewel of them.

Near Twelve at Noon she came to a pleasant Meadow, through which there ran a little Rivulet of clear Water, about nine miles from her last Lodging, but quite out of the Way to *London*. Here she sate down, and after drinking some of the Water out of the Hollow of her Hand, she open'd her Bag, and made as good a Meal as the Courseness of the Fare, and the Niceness of her Appetite would permit: After which, she bruis'd the outward green Shells of a Wall-nut or two, and smear'd her lovely Face, Hands, and Part of her Arms, with the Juice; then looking into the little purling Stream, that seem'd to murmur at the Injury she did to so much Beauty, she sigh'd and wept, to think to what base Extremities she was now likely to be reduc'd! That she should be forc'd to stain that Skin which Heaven had made so pure and white! 'But ah! (cry'd she to her self) if my Disobedience to my Parents had not stain'd my Conscience worse, this needed not to have been done.' Here she wept abundantly again; then, drying her Eyes, she wash'd her Feet to refresh 'em, and thence continu'd her Journey for ten Miles more, which she compass'd by seven a Clock; when she came to a Village, where she got Entertainment for that Night, paying for it, and the next Morning, before Six, as soon as she had fill'd her little Bag with what good Chear the Place afforded, she wander'd on 'till Twelve again, still crossing the Country, and taking her Course to the Northern Parts of *England*, which doubtless was the Reason her Father and his Servants miss'd of her in their Pursuit; for he imagin'd that for certain she had taken her nearest Way to *London*. After she had refresh'd her self for an Hour's Time by the Side of a Wood, she arose and wander'd again near twelve Miles by eight a Clock, and lodg'd at a good substantial Farmer's.

Thus she continu'd her Errantry for above a Fortnight,

having no more Money than just thirty Shillings, half of which brought her to Sir *Christian Kindly's* House in *Lancashire*. 'Twas near five a Clock in the Afternoon when she reach'd that happy Port, when, coming to the Hall Door, she enquir'd for the Lady of the House, who happily was just coming into the Hall with a little Miss in her Arms, of about four Years old, very much troubled with weak and sore Eyes: The fair Wanderer, addressing her self to the Lady with all the Humility and Modesty imaginable, begg'd to know if her Ladyship had any Place in her Family vacant, in which she might do her Service? To which the Lady return'd, (by Way of Question) Alas! poor Creature! what canst thou do? Any thing, may it please your Ladyship, (reply'd the disguis'd Beauty) any thing within my Strength and my Knowledge, I mean, Madam. Thou say'st well, (said the Lady) and I'm sorry I have not any vacant for thee. I beseech your Ladyship then (said *Arabella*) let me lodge in your Barn to-Night; for I am told it is a great Way hence to any Town, and I have but little Money. In my Barn, poor Girl! (cry'd the Lady, looking very earnestly on her) ay, God forbid else, unless we can find a better Lodging for thee. Art thou hungry or thirsty? Yes, Madam (reply'd the wandering Fair One) I could both eat and drink, if it please your Ladyship. The Lady commanded Victuals and Drink to be brought, and could not forbear staying in the Hall 'till she had done; when she ask'd her several Questions, as of what Country she was? To which she answer'd truly, of *Somersetshire*. What her Parents were, and if living? To which she return'd, They were good, honest, and religious People, and she hop'd they were alive, and in as good Health as when she left 'em. After the Lady had done catechising her, *Arabella*, looking on the little Child in her Ladyship's Arms, said, Pardon me, Madam, I beseech you, if I am too bold in asking your Ladyship how that pretty Creature's Eyes came to be so bad? By an extream Cold which she took, (reply'd the Lady.) I had not presum'd (return'd t'other) to have ask'd your Ladyship this Question, were I not assur'd that I have an infallible Cure for the Infirmity; and if, Madam, you will be pleas'd to let me apply it, I will tell your Ladyship the Remedy in private. The Lady was much surpriz'd to hear a young Creature, so meanly habited, talk so genteelly; and after surveying her very strictly, said the Lady, Have you ever experienc'd it before? Yes, Madam (reply'd the fair Physician) and never without happy Success: I dare engage, Madam, (added she) that I will make 'em as well as my own, by God's Blessing, or else I will be content to lose mine, which Heaven forbid. Amen, (cry'd the good Lady) for they are very fine ones, on my Word.—Stay, Child, I will desire Sir *Christian* to hear it with me; and if he approves it, you shall about it; and if it take good Effect, we will endeavour to requite the Care and Pains it shall cost you. Saying thus, she immediately left her, and return'd very speedily with Sir *Christian*, who having discours'd *Arabella* for some time, with great Satisfaction and Pleasure, took her into the Parlour with his Lady, where she communicated her Secret to 'em both; which they found so innocent and reasonable, that they desir'd her to prepare it as soon as possible, and to make her Application of it with all convenient Speed; which she could not do 'till the next Morning. In the mean Time she was order'd a Lodging with the House-Maid, who reported to her Lady, That she found her a very sweet and cleanly Bed-fellow; (adding) That she never saw nor felt so white, so smooth, and soft a Skin. *Arabella* continu'd her Remedy with such good Success, that in a Fortnight's Time little Miss's Eyes were as lively and strong as ever. This so endear'd her to the Knight and his Lady, that they created a new Office in their Family, purposely for her, which was, Attendant on their eldest Daughter *Eleanora*, a Lady much about her

Years and Stature; who was so charm'd with her Conversation, that she could not stir Abroad, nor eat, nor sleep, without *Peregrina Goodhouse* (for those were the Names she borrow'd :) Nor was her Modesty, Humility, and Sweetness of Temper, less engaging to her Fellow-Servants, who all strove which should best express their Love to her. On Festival-Days, and for the Entertainment of Strangers, she would lend her helping Hand to the Cook, and make the Sauce for every Dish, though her own Province was only to attend the young Lady, and prepare the Quidlings, and other Sweet-Meats, for the Reception of Sir *Christian's* Friends; all which she did to Admiration. In this State of easy Servitude she liv'd there for near three Years, very well contented at all Times, but when she bethought her self of her Father, Mother, and Sisters, courted by all the principal Men-Servants, whom she refus'd in so obliging a Manner, and with such sweet, obliging Words, that they could not think themselves injur'd, though they found their Addresses were in vain. Mr. *Prayfast*, the Chaplain himself, could not hold out against her Charms. For her Skin had long since recover'd its native Whiteness; nor did she need Ornaments of Cloaths to set her Beauty off, if any Thing could adorn her, since she was dress'd altogether as costly, though not so richly (perhaps) as *Eleanora*. *Prayfast* therefore found that the Spirit was too weak for the Flesh, and gave her very broad Signs of his Kindness in Sonnets, Anagrams, and Acrosticks, which she receiv'd very obligingly of him, taking a more convenient Time to laugh at 'em with her young Lady.

Her kind Reception of them encourag'd him to that Degree, that within a few Days after, supposing himself secure on her Side, he apply'd himself to the good old Knight, his Patron, for his Consent to a Marriage with her, who very readily comply'd with his Demands, esteeming it a very advantagious Match for *Peregrina*, and withal told him, That he would give him three hundred Pounds with her, besides the first Benefit that should fall in his Gift. But (said he) as I doubt not that you are sufficiently acquainted with her Virtues and other excellent Qualifications, 'tis necessary that you should know the worst that I can tell you of her, which is, that she came to us a meer Stranger, in a very mean, tho' cleanly Habit; and therefore, as she confesseth, we may conclude, of very humble, yet honest Parentage. A! (possibly) her Father might have been, or is, some Husbandman, or somewhat inferiour to that; for we took her up at the Door, begging one Night's Entertainment in the Barn. How, Sir! (cry'd *Prayfast*, starting) have you no better Knowledge of her Birth, than what you are pleas'd to discover now? No better, nor more (reply'd the Knight.) Alas! Sir, then (return'd the proud canonical Sort of a Farmer) she is no Wife for me; I shall dishonour my Family by marrying so basely. Were you never told any Thing of this before? (ask'd the Knight.) You know, Sir, (answer'd the Prelate that would be) that I have not had the Honour to officiate, as your Chaplain, much more than half a Year; in which Time, 'tis true, I have heard that she was receiv'd as a Stranger; but that she came in so low a Capacity I never learn'd 'till now. I find then, Parson, (said the Knight) that you do not like the Author of your Happiness, at least, who might be so, because she comes to you in such an humble Manner; I tell you the *Jews* are miserable for the same Reason. She cannot be such perfectly to me (return'd t'other) without the Advantage of good Birth. With that I'm sure she would not, return'd his Patron, and left him to go to *Peregrina*, whom he happily found alone. Child, (said he to her) have you any Obligation to Mr. *Prayfast?* As how, Sir? She ask'd. Do you love him? Have you made him any Promise of Marriage? Or has he any Way engag'd himself to you? Neither, Sir, (she answer'd.) 'Tis true, I love him as my Fellow-Servant, no otherwise. He has indeed been somewhat lavish of his Wit and Rhimes to me, which serv'd well enough to divert my young Lady and me. But of all Mankind, perhaps, he should be the last I would choose for a Husband. I thought (said the good-humour'd old Knight) that he had already obtain'd a Promise from you, since he came but just now to ask my Consent, which I freely gave him at first, upon that Thought; but he is doubtful of your Birth, and fears it may dishonour his Family, if he should marry you. On my Word, Sir, (return'd *Peregrina*, blushing with Disdain, no doubt) our Families are by no Means equal. What thy Family is, I know not; (said Sir *Christian*) but I am sure thou art infinitely superiour to him in all the natural Embelishments both of Body and Mind. Be just to thy self, and be not hasty to wed: Thou hast more Merit than Wealth alone can purchase. O! dear Sir, (she return'd) you ruin me with Obligations never to be re-paid, but in Acknowledgment, and that imperfectly too. Here they were interrupted by the young Lady, to whom she repeated the Conference betwixt Sir *Christian* and *Prayfast*, as soon as ever Sir *Christian* left the Room.

About a Week after, Sir *Lucius Lovewell*, (a young Gentleman, of a good Presence, Wit, and Learning enough, whose Father, dying near a Twelve-month before, had left him upwards of 3000*l.* a Year, which, too, was an excellent Accomplishment, tho' not the best; for he was admirably good-humour'd) came to visit Sir *Christian Kindly;* and, as some of the Family imagin'd, 'twas with Design to make his Addresses to the young Lady, Sir *Christian's* Daughter. Whatever his Thoughts were, his Treatment, there, was very generous and kind. He saw the Lady, and lik'd her very well; nay, doubtless, would have admitted a Passion for her, had not his Destiny at the same Time shewn him *Peregrina*. She was very beautiful, and he as sensible; and 'tis not to be doubted, but that he immediately took Fire. However, his Application and Courtship, free and unaffected, were chiefly directed to Sir *Christian's* Daughter : Some little Respects he paid to *Peregrina*, who could not choose but look on him as a very fine, good-humour'd, and well-accomplish'd Gentleman. When the Hour came that he thought fit to retreat, Sir *Christian* ask'd him, When he would make 'em happy again in his Conversation? To which he return'd, That since he was not above seven or eight Miles from him, and that there were Charms so attractive at Sir *Christian's*, he should take the Liberty to visit him sooner and oftener than he either expected or desir'd. T'other reply'd, That was impossible; and so, without much more Ceremony, he took his Leave of that delightful Company for two or three Days; at the End of which he return'd, with Thoughts much different from those at his first Coming thither, being strongly agitated by his Passion for *Peregrina*. He took and made all the Opportunities and Occasions that Chance and his own Fancy could offer and present to talk to her, both before, at, and after Dinner; and his Eyes were so constantly fix'd on her, that he seem'd to observe nothing else; which was so visible to Sir *Christian*, his Lady, and Daughter, that they were convinc'd of their Error, in believing, that he came to make his Court to the young Lady. This late Discovery of the young Knight's Inclinations, was no Way unpleasant to Sir *Christian* and his Lady; and to the young Lady it was most agreeable and obliging, since her Heart was already pre-engag'd elsewhere; and since she did equally desire the good Fortune of her beautiful Attendant with her own.

The Table was no sooner clear'd, and a loyal Health or two gone round, e're Sir *Christian* ask'd his young amorous Guest to take a Walk with him in the Gardens : To which Sir *Lucius* readily consented, designing to disclose that to him for a Secret, which was but too apparent to all that were present at Table : When therefore he thought he had sufficiently admir'd and commended the Neatness of the Walks and Beauty of the Flowers, he began, to this Effect:

Possibly, Sir *Christian*, I shall surprize you with the Discourse I'm going to make you; but 'tis certain no Man can avoid the Necessity of the Fate which he lies under; at least I have now found it so.—I came at first, Sir, with the Hopes of prevailing on you to honour and make me happy in a Marriage with Madam *Eleanora* your Daughter; but at the same Instant I was seiz'd with so irresistable a Passion for the charming *Peregrina*, that I find no Empire, Fame, nor Wit, can make me perfectly bless'd here below, without the Enjoyment of that beautiful Creature. Do not mistake me, Sir, (I beseech you, continu'd he) I mean an *honourable Enjoyment*.—I will make her my Wife, Sir, if you will be generously pleas'd to use your Interest with her on my Part.

To which the good old Knight reply'd, What you think (Sir) you have now imparted as a Secret, has been the general Observation of all my Family, e're since you gave us the Happiness of your Company to Day: Your Passion is too great to be disguis'd; and I am extremely pleas'd, that you can think any Thing in my House worthy the Honour you intend *Peregrina*. Indeed, had you made any particular and publick Address to my Daughter, I should have believ'd it want of Merit in her, or in us, her Parents, that you should, after that, quit your Pretensions to her, without any willing or known Offence committed on our Side. I therefore (Sir) approve your Choice, and promise you my utmost Assistance afar. She is really virtuous in all the Latitude of Virtue; her Beauty is too visible to be disputed ev'n by Envy it self: As for her Birth, she best can inform you of it; I must only let you know, that, as her Name imports, she was utterly a Stranger, and entertain'd by us in pure Charity. But the Antiquity and Honour of your Family can receive no Diminution by a Match with a beautiful and virtuous Creature, for whom, you say, and I believe, you have so true a Passion. I have now told you the worst (Sir) that I know of her; but your Wealth and Love may make you both eternally happy on Earth. And so they shall, *by her dear self*, (return'd the amorous Knight) if both of 'em may recommend me to her, with your Perswasions added, which still I beg. Say, rather you command; and with those three hundred Pounds which I promis'd her, if she marry'd with my Consent to Mr. *Prayfast*.

To this, the other smiling, reply'd, Her Person and Love is all I court or expect, Sir: But since you have thought her worthy of so great an Expression of your Favour and Kindness, I will receive it with all Humility as is from a Father, which I shall ever esteem you.—But see, Sir, (cry'd he in an Extasy) how she comes, led by Madam *Eleanora*, your Daughter. The young Lady coming to him, began thus: I know (Sir) 'tis my Father and Mother's Desire and Ambition to shew you the heartiest Welcome in their Power, which can by no Means be made appear so particularly and undisputably, as by presenting you with what you like best in the Family: In Assurance therefore that I shall merit their Favour by this Act, I have brought your dear *Peregrina* to you, not without Advice, and some Instructions of mine, that may concern her Happiness with you, if discreetly observ'd and persu'd by her. In short, (Sir) I have told her, that a Gentleman of so good a Figure, such excellent Parts, and generous Education, of so ancient and honourable a Family, together with so plentiful an Estate as you at present possess, is capable of bringing Happiness to any, the fairest Lady in this Country at least. O Madam! (return'd Sir *Lucius*) your Obligation is so great, that I want Sense to receive it as I ought; much more Words to return you any proportionable Acknowledgment of it. But give me Leave to say thus much, Madam; that my Thoughts of making my Court to your Ladiship, first invited me to give Sir *Christian*, your Father, the Trouble of a Visit, since the Death of mine. However, the over-ruling Powers have thought to divert my Purpose, and the offering of my Heart, which can never rest, but with this dear charming Creature.—Your Merits, Madam—are sufficient for the Gentleman on whom I entirely fix'd my Affections, before you did me the Honour and your self the Trouble of your first Visit (interrupted Sir *Christian's* Daughter.) And now, Sir, (added she to her Father) if you please, let us leave 'em to make an End of this Business between themselves. No, Madam, (cry'd Sir *Lucius*) your Father has promis'd me to make Use of his Interest with her for my Sake. This I now expect, Sir. Then (said the old Knight) thou dear beautiful and virtuous Stranger! if I have any Power to perswade thee, take my Advice, and this honourable Gentleman to thy loving Husband; I'm sure he'll prove so to thee. If I could command thee I would. Ah Sir! (said she, kneeling, with Tears falling from her charming Eyes) I know none living that has greater Right and Power.—But (alas Sir!) this honourable Person knows not the Meanness of my Birth, at least, he cannot think it any Way proportionable or suitable to his. O thou dear Creature, (cry'd her Lover, setting one Knee to the Ground, and taking her up) Sir *Christian* has already discours'd all thy Circumstances to me: Rise and bless me with thy Consent. I must ask my Lady's, Sir, (she reply'd.) See, here my Mother comes (said the young Lady) and entreated her good Word for Sir *Lucius*. The good ancient Lady began then to use all the Arguments to incline her to yield to her Happiness; and, in fine, she was prevail'd on to say, I do consent, and will endeavour to deserve the honourable Title of your dutiful Wife, Sir. 'Twas with no common Joy and Transport that he receiv'd her Hand, and kiss'd those dear Lips that gave him an Assurance of his Happiness; which he resolv'd

should begin about a Month or two afterwards; in which
Time he might send Orders to *London* for the making
their Wedding Cloaths. Into the House then they all
went, Sir *Lucius* leading *Peregrina*, and the first they met
of the Family was *Prayfast*, who was not a little surpriz'd
nor discompos'd at that Sight; and more especially when
Sir *Christian* told him, That tho' he did not think that
beautiful sweet Stranger worthy the Title of his Wife,
yet now he should be oblig'd to join her to that honourable
Person. The Slave bow'd, and look'd very pale.

All Things were at last got ready for the Consummation
of their Bliss, and *Prayfast* did their Business effectually,
tho' much against his Will; however he receiv'd the
Reward of twenty Broad Pieces. The Wedding was kept
for a Week at Sir *Christian's* House; after which they
adjourn'd to the Bridegroom's, where it lasted as long as
Sir *Christian*, his Lady, Daughter, and the rest of that
Family would stay. As they were leaving him, Sir *Lucius*
dispos'd of two hundred Pounds amongst Sir *Christian's*
Servants, and the rest of the three hundred he distributed
among the Poor of both Parishes.

When they were gone, the affectionate tender Bridegroom could by no Means be perswaded by any Gentlemen,
his Neighbours, to hunt with 'em, or to take any Divertise-
ment, tho' but for half a Day; esteeming it the highest
Unkindness imaginable to leave his Lady: Not that she
could be alone neither in his Absence; for she never
wanted the Visits of all the Ladies round about, and those
of the best Quality; who were equally charm'd with her
Sweetness of Temper, as the Men were with her outward Beauties. But in a Month's time, or thereabout,
observing that he was continually solicited and courted
to some Sport or Pastime with those Gentlemen of his
Neighbourhood, she was forc'd to do her self the Violence
to beg of him that he would divert himself with 'em, as
before their Marriage he us'd: And she had so good

Success, that he did allow himself two Days in the Week to hunt: In one of which, coming Home about five a Clock, and not finding his Lady below Stairs, he went directly up to her Chamber, where he saw her leaning her Head on her Hand, and her Handkerchief all bath'd in Tears. At this Sight he was strangely amaz'd and concern'd. Madam, (cry'd he in an unusual Tone) what means such Postures as these? Tell me! For I must know the Occasion. Surpriz'd, and trembling at this his unwonted Manner of saluting her, she started up, and then, falling on her Knees, she wept out, O thou dear Author and Lord of all my Joys on Earth! Look not, I beseech you, so wildly, nor speak terribly to me! Thou Center of all my Happiness below, (return'd he) rise, and make me acquainted with the dreadful Occasion of this afflicting and tormenting Sight! All you shall know, (she reply'd) dearest of human Blessings! But sit, and change your Looks; then I can speak. Speak then, my Life, (said he) but tell me all; all I must know. Is there a Thought about my Soul that you shall not partake? I'm sure there is not; (he reply'd) say on then. You know, Sir, (she return'd) that I have left my Parents now three Years, or thereabouts, and know not whether they are living or dead: I was reflecting, therefore, on the Troubles which my undutiful and long Absence may have caus'd them; for poor and mean as they may be, they well instructed me in all good Things; and I would once more, by your dear Permission, see them, and beg their Pardon for my Fault; for they are my Parents still, if living, Sir, though (unhappily) not worth your Regard. How! (cry'd he) can that Pair who gave my Dearest Birth, want my Regard, or ought I can do for them? No! thou shalt see them, and so will I: But tell me, *Peregrina*, is this the only Cause of your Discomposure? So may I still be bless'd in your dear Love, (she reply'd) as this is Truth, and all the Cause. When shall we see them, then? (he ask'd).

We see them, (cry'd she) O! your Goodness descends too much; and you confound me with your unmerited and unexpected Kindness. 'Tis I alone that have offended, and I alone am fit to see them. That must not be; (return'd her affectionate Husband) no, we'll both go together; and if they want, either provide for them there, or take them hither with us. Your Education shews their Principles, and 'tis no Shame to own virtuous Relations. Come, dry thy dear lamenting Eyes; the Beginning of the next Week we'll set forwards. Was ever Disobedience so rewarded with such a Husband? (said she) those Tears have wash'd that childish Guilt away; and there is no Reward above thy Virtue.

In a few Days, Monday began the Date of their Journey to the *West* of *England*; and in five or six Days more, by the Help of a Coach and Six, they got to *Cornwall*; where, in a little Town, of little Accommodation, they were oblig'd to take up their Lodgings the first Night. In the Morning (said his Lady to him) My Dear, about a Mile and a half hence lives one Sir *Francis Fairname* and his Lady, if yet they be living, who have a very fine House, and worth your seeing; I beg of you therefore, that you will be so kind to your self as to walk thither, and dine with the old Gentleman; for that you must, if you see him; whilst I stay here, and send to my Father and Mother, if to be found, and prepare them to receive you at your Return. I must not have no Denial; (added she) for if you refuse this Favour, all my Designs are lost. —Make Haste, my Life; 'tis now eleven a Clock; In your Absence I'll dress, to try if Change of Cloaths can hide me from them. This was so small a Request, that he did not stay to reply to't, but presently left her, and got thither in less than half an Hour, attended only by one Footman. He was very kindly and respectfully receiv'd by the old Gentleman, who had certainly been a very beautiful Person in his Youth; and Sir *Lucius*, fixing his Eyes upon his Face, could hardly remove 'em, being very pleasantly and surprisingly entertain'd with some Lines that he observ'd in it. But immediately recollecting himself, he told him, that having heard how fine a Seat that was, his Curiosity led him to beg the Favour that he might see it. The worthy old Knight return'd, that his House and all the Accommodations in it were at his Service: So inviting him in, he satisfy'd his pretended Curiosity; and after he had shewn all that was worthy the Sight of a Stranger, in the House, he led him into his Gardens, which furnish'd Sir *Lucius* with new Matter of Admiration; whence the old Knight brought him into the Parlour, telling him, that 'twas his Custom to suffer no Stranger to return, till he had either din'd or supp'd with him, according as the Hour of the Day or Night presented.

'Twas here the affectionate Husband was strangely surpriz'd at the Sight of a Picture, which so nearly counterfeited the Beauties of his dear-lov'd Lady, that he stood like an Image himself, gazing and varying; the Colours of his Face agitating by the Diversity of his Thoughts; which Sir *Francis* perceiving, ask'd him, What it was that so visibly concern'd him? To which he reply'd, That indeed he was concern'd, but with great Satisfaction and Pleasure, since he had never seen any Thing more beautiful than that Picture, unless it were a Lady for whom he had the most sincere Affection imaginable, and whom it did very nearly represent; and then enquir'd for whom that was drawn? Sir *Francis* answer'd him, 'Twas design'd for one who was, I dare not say who is, my Daughter; and the other two were drawn for her younger Sisters. And see, Sir, (persu'd he) here they come, following their Mother: At which Words Sir *Lucius* was oblig'd to divorce his Eyes from the charming Shadow, and make his Compliments to them; which were no sooner over than Dinner was serv'd in, where the young Knight eat as heartily as he could, considering he sate just opposite to it, and in

Sight of the two Ladies, who were now exactly like his own Wife, though not so very beautiful.

The Table being uncover'd, Sir *Lucius* desir'd to know why Sir *Francis* said, He doubted whether the Original of that Picture were yet his Daughter? To which the Mother return'd (big with Sorrow, which was seen in her Tears) That her Husband had spoken but too rightly: For (added she) 'tis now three Years since we have either seen her or heard from her. How, Madam! three Years, (cry'd Sir *Lucius*) I believe I can shew your Ladiship a dear Acquaintance of mine, so wonderfully like that Picture, that I am almost perswaded she is the very Original; only (pardon me, Madam) she tells me her Parents are of mean Birth and Fortune. Dear Sir, (cry'd the tender Mother) Is she in this Country? She is not two Miles hence, reply'd Sir *Lucius*. By all Things most dear to you, Sir, (said the Lady) let us be so happy as to see her, and that with all convenient Expedition! for it will be a Happiness to see any Creature, the only Like my dearest *Arabella*. *Arabella*, Madam! alas! No, Madam, her Name is *Peregrina*. No Matter for Names, Sir, (cry'd the Lady) I want the Sight of the dear Creature. Sir, (added the worthy old Knight) I can assure you it will be an eternal Obligation to us; or, if you please, we will wait on you to her. By no Means, Sir, (return'd Sir *Lucius*) I will repeat my Trouble to you with her, in an Hour at farthest. We shall desire the Continuance of such Trouble as long as we live, reply'd Sir *Francis*. So, without farther Ceremony, Sir *Lucius* left 'em and return'd to his Lady, whom he found ready dress'd, as he wish'd he might. Madam, (said he) where are your Father and Mother? I know not, yet, my Dear, she reply'd. Well, (return'd he) we will expect 'em, or send for 'em hither at Night; in the mean Time I have engag'd to bring you with me to Sir *Francis Fairname* and his Lady, with all imaginable Expedition. So immediately, as soon as Coach and Six and Equipage was ready, he hurry'd her away with him to Sir *Francis*, whom they found walking with his Lady and two Daughters in the outward Court, impatiently expecting their Coming. The Boot of the Coach (for that was the Fashion in those Days) was presently let down, and Sir *Lucius* led his Lady forwards to them; who coming within three or four Paces of the good old Knight, his Lady fell on her Knees, and begg'd their Pardon and Blessing. Her affectionate Father answer'd 'em with Tears from his Eyes; but the good ancient Lady was so overcome with Joy, that she fell into a Swoon, and had like to have been accompany'd by her Daughter, who fell upon her Knees by her, and with her Shrieks recall'd her, when she strait cry'd out, My Daughter, my Daughter's come again! my *Arabella* alive! Ay, my dear offended Mother! with all the Duty and Penitence that Humanity is capable of, return'd the Lady *Lovewell*. Her Sisters then express'd their Love in Tears, Embraces, and Kisses, while her dear Husband begg'd a Blessing of her Parents, who were very pleasantly surpriz'd, to know that their Daughter was so happily marry'd, and to a Gentleman of such an Estate and Quality as Sir *Lucius* seem'd to be: 'Twas late that Night e'er they went to Bed at Sir *Francis's*. The next Day, after they had all pretty well eas'd themselves of their Passions, Sir *Francis* told his Son-in-Law, that as he had three Daughters, so he had 3000*l*. a Year, and he would divide it equally among 'em; but for Joy of the Recovery of his eldest Daughter, and her fortunate Match with so worthy a Gentleman as Sir *Lucius*, who had given him an Account of his Estate and Quality, he promis'd him ten thousand Pounds in ready Money besides; whereas the other young Ladies were to have but five thousand a Piece, besides their Dividend of the Estate. And now, (said he) Daughter, the Cause of your Retreat from us, old Sir *Robert Richland*, has been dead these three Months, on such a Day. How, Sir, (cry'd she) on such a Day!

that was the very Day on which I was so happy as to be marry'd to my dear Sir *Lucius*.

She then gave her Father, and Mother, and Sisters, a Relation of all that had happen'd to her since her Absence from her dear Parents, who were extremely pleas'd with the Account of Sir *Christian* and his Lady's Hospitality and Kindness to her; and in less than a Fortnight after, they took a Journey to Sir *Lucius's*, carrying the two other young Ladies along with 'em; and, by the Way, they call'd at Sir *Christian's*, where they arriv'd Time enough to be present the next Day at Sir *Christian's* Daughter's Wedding, which they kept there for a whole Fortnight.

F I N I S .

THE UNHAPPY MISTAKE; OR,
THE IMPIOUS VOW PUNISH'D.

THE
UNHAPPY MISTAKE, &c.

THE Effects of Jealousy have ever been most fatal; and it is certainly one of the most tormenting Passions that an human Soul can be capable of, tho' it be created by the least Appearances of Reason: The Truth of which this following Story will evince.

Sir *Henry Hardyman* was a Gentleman of a very large Estate in *Somersetshire*, of a very generous Temper, hospitable almost to *Extravagancy; a plain down-right Dealer, wonderfully good-natur'd,* but very *passionate:* Whose Lady dying, left him only a Son and a Daughter; between whom there were about six Years Difference in their Age. *Miles Hardyman* (for so the Son was call'd) being the eldest; both of naturally virtuous Inclinations, which were carefully improv'd by a generous and pious Education. *Miles* was a very tall, large, and well-proportion'd Person at Two and Twenty; brave and active, and seem'd to be born for War, tho' he had a Heart as tender and capable of receiving the Impressions of Love as any of our Sex. He had been bred for some Years at the University; where, among other Things, he learn'd to fence; in which, however, he was mightily improv'd in a Twelvemonth's Time that he stay'd here in Town. *Lucretia*, his Sister, was beautiful enough, her Father designing to give ten thousand Pounds with her on Marriage; but (which is above all) she was incomparably good-humour'd.

At his Return to his Father in the Country, young *Hardyman* found Madam *Diana Constance*, a most beautiful Lady, with his Sister, at that Time about 16 Years old;

somewhat tall of her Age, of happy and virtuous Education. of an indifferent Fortune, not exceeding two thousand Pounds, which was no Way answerable to the Expectations he had after his Father's Death; but it was impossible he should not love her, she was so prodigiously charming both in her inward and outward Excellencies; especially since he had the Opportunity of conversing with her at his Father's for above a Month. 'Tis true, he had seen her before, but it was then five Years since. Love her he did then, and that most passionately; nor was she insensible or ungrateful. But our young Lovers had not Discretion enough to conceal the Symptoms of their Passion, which too visibly and frequently sally'd out at their Eyes before the old Gentleman; which made him prudently, as he thought, and timely enough, offer his Daughter *Lucretia* the Liberty of taking a small Journey with *Diana* to her House, which was not above 20 Miles thence, where that young Lady's Aunt govern'd in her Absence; for *Diana* had no other Relation, so near as she was, living in *England*, her only Brother *Lewis* having been in *Italy* and *France* ever since her Father dy'd, which was then near five Years past.

Lucretia, over-joy'd at her Father's pretended Kindness, propos'd it to the young Lady, her Friend, who was very fond of the Proposal, hoping that *Lucretia's* Brother might bear 'em Company there for some little Time; but old Sir *Henry* had quite different Thoughts of the Matter. The third Day, from the first Discourse of it, was assign'd for their Departure. In the mean Time young *Hardyman* knew not what to think of the Divorce he was going to suffer; for he began to have some Apprehensions that the old Knight was sensible, and displeas'd, that they lov'd each other: Not but that the Family of the *Constances* was as ancient and honourable as that of *Hardymans*, and was once endow'd with as plentiful an Estate, tho' now young *Lewis Constance* had not above 1200*l*. a Year. (O the unkind Distance that Money makes, even between Friends!)

Old 'Squire *Constance* was a very worthy Gentleman, and Sir *Henry* had a particular Friendship for him; but (perhaps) that dy'd with him, and only a neighbourly Kindness, or something more than an ordinary Respect, surviv'd to his Posterity. The Day came that was to carry 'em to the young Lady *Constance's*, and her Lover was preparing to attend 'em, when the old Gentleman ask'd him, What he meant by that Preparation? And whether he design'd to leave him alone? Or if he could think 'twere dutifully or decently done? To which the Son reply'd, That his Care of his Sister, and his Respect to a young Lady, in a Manner a Stranger to him, had misled his Thoughts from that Duty and Regard he ought to have pay'd to his Father, which he hop'd and begg'd he would pardon, tho' he design'd only just to have seen her safe there, and to have return'd at Night. With this the old Gentleman seem'd pacify'd for the present; and he bid him go take Leave of the Lady; which he did with a great deal of Concern, telling her, that he should be most miserable 'till he had the Happiness of seeing her again; however, he begg'd she would converse with him by Letters, which might (happily) a little palliate his Misfortune in her Absence: Adding, that he would be eternally hers, and none but hers. To which she made as kind a Return as he could wish; letting him know, that she desired to live no longer than she was assur'd that she was belov'd by him. Then taking as solemn a Farewel of her as if he had never been to see her more, after he had given his Sister a parting Kiss or two, he led 'em down to his Father, who saw 'em mounted, and attended by two of his Servants. After which he walked with 'em about a Mile from the House, where he and young *Hardyman* left 'em to persue their Journey.

In their Return to the House, said Sir *Henry*, I find, Son, I have hitherto mistaken your Inclinations: I thought they had altogether prompted you to great and manly Actions and Attempts; but, to my Sorrow, I now find my Error.

How, I beseech you, Sir? (ask'd the Son.) You are guilty of a foolish lazy Passion, (reply'd the Father) you are in Love, *Miles*; in Love with one who can no Way advance your Fortune, Family, nor Fame. 'Tis true, she has Beauty, and o'my Conscience she is virtuous too; but will Beauty and Virtue, with a small Portion of 2000*l.* answer to the Estate of near 4000*l.* a Year, which you must inherit if you survive me? Beauty and Virtue, Sir, (return'd young *Hardyman*) with the Addition of good Humour and Education, is a Dowry that may merit a Crown. Notion! Stuff! All Stuff (cry'd the old Knight) Money is Beauty, Virtue, good Humour, Education, Reputation, and high Birth. Thank Heaven, Sir, (said *Miles*) you don't live as if you believ'd your own Doctrine; you part with your Money very freely in your House-keeping, and I am happy to see it. 'Tis that I value it for; (reply'd the Father) I would therefore have thee, my Son, add to what in all Likelihood will be thine, so considerably, by Marriage, that thou mayst better deserve the Character of Hospitable *Hardyman* than thy Father Sir *Henry*.—Come, *Miles*, (return'd he) thou shalt think no more on her. I can't avoid it, Sir, (said t'other.) Well, well, think of her you may, (said Sir *Henry*) but not as for a Wife; no, if you mean to continue in your Father's Love, be not in Love with Madam *Diana*, nor with any of her Nymphs, tho' never so fair or so chast—unless they have got Store of Money, Store of Money, *Miles*. Come, come in, we'll take a Game at *Chess* before Dinner, if we can. I obey you, Sir, (return'd the Son) but if I win, I shall have the Liberty to love the Lady, I hope. I made no such Promise, (said the Knight) no, no Love without my Leave; but if you give me *Checque-Mate*, you shall have my Bay Gelding, and I would not take 50 Broad Pieces for him. I'll do my best, Sir, to deserve him, (said the young Gentleman.) 'Tis a mettl'd and fiery Beast (said Sir *Henry*.) They began their Game then, and had made about six Moves apiece before Dinner, which was serv'd up near four Hours after they sate down to play. It happen'd they had no Company din'd with 'em that Day; so they made a hasty Meal, and fell again to their former Dispute, which held 'em near six Hours longer; when, either the Knight's Inadvertency, or the young Gentleman's Skill and Application, gave him the Victory and Reward.

The next Day they hunted; the Day following, the House was fill'd with Friends, and Strangers; who came with 'em; all which were certain of a hearty Welcome e'er they return'd. Other Days other Company came in, as Neighbours; and none of all that made their Visits, could be dismiss'd under three or four Days at soonest.

Thus they past the Hours away for about six Weeks; in all which Time our Lover could get but one Opportunity of writing to his adorable, and that was by the Means of a Servant, who came with a Letter from his Sister *Lucretia* to Sir *Henry*, and another to him, that held one inclos'd to him from the beautiful *Diana*; the Words, as perfectly as I can remember 'em, were these, or to this Effect:

My Hardyman,

TOO Dear!—No,—too much lov'd!—That's impossible too. How have I enjoy'd my self with your Letters since my Absence from you! In the first, how movingly you lament the unkind Distances of Time and Place that thus divorces you from me! In another, in what tender and prevailing Words your Passion is express'd! In a Third, what invincible Arguments are urg'd to prove the Presence of your Soul to me in the Absence of your Body! A Fourth, how fill'd with just Complaints of a rigorous Father! What Assurances does the Fifth give me of your speedy Journey hither! And the Sixth, (for no less methought I should have receiv'd from you) confirms what you last said to me, That you will ever be mine, and none but mine.—O boundless Blessing!—*These (my Life) are the Dreams, which, for six several Nights, have mock'd the real Passion of*

Your forgotten Diana.

He read it, smil'd, and kiss'd it, and then proceeded to examine his Sisters, which held a great many Expressions of a tender Affection, and withal gave him Notice, that there was a mighty Spark lately come from Town into those Parts, that made his Court to the young Lady *Constance*; desiring him therefore to be as sudden in his Visit, if he intended any, as Possibility would permit. This startled and stung him: Wherefore, taking the Opportunity of his Father's Retirement, to write to the young Lady and his Sister; he dispatch'd a Letter to *Lucretia*, wherein he thank'd her for her Intelligence and Caution, and promis'd to be with her the next Night at farthest, if alive; and, at the same Time, writ to this Purpose to *Diana*:

Thou only Blessing for which I wish to live,

HOW delightfully do you punish my seeming Neglect! I acknowledge I have not sent to you 'till now, but it was because it was utterly impossible, my Father continually keeping so strict a Guard over me himself, that not even Mercury *could evade or illude his Vigilance. Alas! my Soul, he is now no Stranger to my Passion for you, which he pretends, at least, is highly offensive to him, for what Reasons I blush to think. But what signifies an Offence to him of so generous a Nature as my Love! I am assur'd I was born for you, or none other of your fair Sex, though attended with all the Advantages of Birth and Fortune. I will therefore proceed in this Affair, as if we were already united by the outward Ceremonies of the Church, and forsake him and all the World for you, my better Part! Be certain, therefore, that to-Morrow Night, e'er you sleep, you shall see (my Life, my Soul, my All)*

Your most sincere, and

Most passionate Lover,

Hardyman.

This, with the Letter to his Sister, he convey'd into the Servant's Hand that came from 'em, undiscover'd of his Father; who likewise dismiss'd the Messenger with his grave Epistle, full of musty Morals, to the two young gay Ladies. But he had an unlucky Thought, that he was overseen in giving his Son the Opportunity of retiring from him, whilst he was writing to his Daughter and t'other fair Creature, having a Jealousy that young *Hardyman* might have made Use of that very Article of Time to the same End. This made him very uneasy and restless. On t'other Side, the young Gentleman though he was extreamly satisfy'd with those endearing Expressions of Love which he found in *Diana's* Letter, yet he was all on Fire with the Apprehension of a Rival, and the Desire to see him, that he might dispute with him for the glorious Prize.

The next Day, at Four in the Afternoon, they went to Bowls about a Mile off; where, after several Ends, the Knight and his Party lay all nearest about the Jack for the Game, 'till young *Hardyman* put in a bold Cast, that beat all his Adversaries from the Block, and carry'd two of his Seconds close to it, his own Bowl lying partly upon it, which made them up. Ha! (cry'd a young Gentleman of his Side) bravely done, *Miles*, thou hast carry'd the Day, and kiss'd the Mistress. I hope I shall before 'tis dark yet, (return'd he.) Sir *Henry* overhearing him, said, (his Face all glowing red with Passion) How dare you, Sir, express your self so freely in my Hearing? There, (persu'd he, and struck him a Blow on the Ear) I first salute you thus: Do you know where you are, and who I am? Yes, you are my Father, Sir, (reply'd young *Hardyman*, bowing.) If you see her to Night, (said the passionate Father) resolve to see me no more. By Heaven, and all my Hopes, no more I will, after this Minute, (return'd the Son, being retreated some Distance from him, out of his Hearing.) So taking his Leave of the Company, with the usual Ceremony, he went directly Home, where immediately he order'd his Servant *Goodlad* to saddle their Horses, whilst he himself went up to his

Chamber, and took all the Rings and Jewels that his Mother had left him, and the Money that he had then in his Possession, which altogether amounted to near twelve hundred Pounds; and packing up some Linnen in his Portmanteau, he quickly mounted with his Servant, and made his Way towards the Lady *Constance's*.

'Twas near seven a Clock e'er they got within Sight of his Mistress's, when our Lover perceiv'd a Gentleman and his Servant mounted at some Distance on t'other Side of the House, as coming from *London :* This unfortunately happen'd to be *Lewis Constance*, just return'd from his Travels, whom young *Hardyman* had never seen before, and therefore could not know him at that Time: Observing therefore that they made to the same Place for which he was design'd, he halted a little, taking Covert under a large Elm-Tree, within a hundred Paces of the House, where he had the unlucky Opportunity to see his Mistress and Sister come out; whom *Lewis* perceiving at the same Time, alighted, and ran eagerly to embrace her, who receiv'd him with Arms expanded, crying, O my Dear, dearest Brother; but that last Word was stifled with Kisses. Do I once more hold thee in my Arms! O come in, and let me give my Joys a Loose! I am surpriz'd, and rave with extream Hapiness! O! thou art all to me that is valuable on Earth! (return'd he.) At these Words she, in a Manner, hal'd him in. This Sight was certainly the greatest Mortification to her Lover that ever Man surviv'd! He presently and positively concluded it could be none but that Rival, of whom his Sister had given him Advice in her Letter. What to do he could by no Means determine; sometimes he was for going in, and affronting him before his Mistress; a second Thought advis'd him to expect his coming out near that Place; upon another Consideration he was going to send him a Challenge, but by whom he knew not, for his Servant was as well known there as himself. At last he resolv'd to ride farther out of the Road, to see for some convenient Retreat that Night, where he might be undiscover'd: Such a Place he found about two Miles thence, at a good substantial Farmer's, who made him heartily welcome that Night, with the best Beer he had in his Cellar, so that he slept much better than he could have expected his Jealousy would have permitted: But the Morning renew'd and redoubled his Torture: But this jolly Landlord, hugely pleas'd with his good Company the Night past, visited him as he got out of his Bed, which was near two Hours after he wak'd; in which Time he had laid his Design how to proceed, in order to take Satisfaction of this Rival. He suffer'd himself, therefore, to be manag'd by the good Man of the House, who wou'd fain have made a Conquest of him; but he found that the young Gentleman could bear as much in his Head as he could on his Shoulders, which gave *Hardyman* the Opportunity of keeping a Stowage yet for a good Dinner: After which they fell to bumping it about, 'till the Farmer fell asleep; when young *Hardyman* retir'd into his Chamber, where, after a Turn or two, he writ as follows to his Mistress's Brother, whose Name he knew not; and therefore the Billet is not superscrib'd.

S I R,

YOU have done me an unpardonable Injury; and if you are a Gentleman, as you seem, you will give me Satisfaction within this Hour at the Place whither this Messenger shall lead you. Bring nothing with you but your Sword and your Servant, as I with mine, to take Care of him that falls.—'Till I see you, I am your Servant, &c.

An Hour before Supper, his kind Host wak'd, and they eat heartily together that Night, but did not drink so plentifully as they had since their first Meeting; young *Hardyman* telling him, that he was oblig'd to be mounted at the fore-mention'd Morning, in order to persue his Journey; and that, in the mean Time, he desir'd the

Favour of him to let one of his Servants carry a Letter from him, to one that was then at the young Lady *Constance's*: To which t'other readily agreed. The young Gentleman then made him a Present of a Tobacco-Box, with the Head of King *Charles* the First on the Lid, and his Arms on the Bottom in Silver; which was very acceptable to him, for he was a great Loyalist, tho' it was in the Height of *Oliver's Usurpation*. About four a-Clock in the Morning, as our jealous Lover had order'd him, one of the Servants came to him for the Letter; with which he receiv'd these Instructions, that he should deliver that Note into the Gentleman's own Hand, who came to the Lady *Constance's* the Night before the last. That he should shew that Gentleman to the Field where young *Hardyman*, should deliver the Note to the Servant, which was just a Mile from either House; or that he should bring an Answer to the Note from that Gentleman. The Fellow was a good Scholar, tho' he could neither read nor write. For he learn'd his Lesson perfectly well, and repeated it punctually to *Lewis Constance;* who was strangely surpriz'd at what he found in the Billet. He ask'd the Messenger if he knew his Name that sent it; or if he were a Gentleman? Nay (Mass, quoth the Fellow) I warrant he's a Gentleman; for he has given me nine good Shillings here, for coming but hither to you; but for his Name, you may e'en name it as well as I—He has got one to wait a top of him almost as fine as himself, zure. The surpriz'd Traveller jump'd out of his Bed, slipt on his Gown, and call'd up his Servant: Thence he went to his Sister's Chamber, with whom *Lucretia* lay: They both happen'd to be awake, and talking, as he came to the Door, which his Sister permitted him to unlock, and ask'd him the Reason of his so early Rising? Who reply'd, That since he could not sleep, he would take the Air a little. But first, Sister (continu'd he) I will refresh my self at your Lips: And now, Madam, (added he to *Lucretia*) I would beg a Cordial from you. For that (said his Sister) you shall be oblig'd to me this once; saying so, she gently turn'd *Lucretia's* Face towards him, and he had his Wish. Ten to one, but he had rather continu'd with *Lucretia*, than have gone to her Brother, had he known him; for he lov'd her truly and passionately: But being a Man of true Courage and Honour, he took his Leave of 'em, presently dress'd, and tripp'd away with the Messenger, who made more than ordinary Haste, because of his Success, which which was rewarded with another piece of Money; and he danc'd Home to the Sound of the Money in his Pocket.

No sooner was the Fellow out of Hearing, than *Lewis*, coming up to his Adversary, shew'd him the Billet, and said, Sent you this to me, Sir? I did, Sir, reply'd *Hardyman*: I never saw you 'till now, return'd *Lewis*; how then could I injure you? 'Tis enough that I know it, answer'd *Miles*. But to satisfy you, you shall know that I am sensible that you pretend to a fair Lady, to whom I have an elder Title. In short, you entrench on my Prerogative. I own no Subjection to you, (return'd *Constance*) and my Title is as good as your Prerogative, which I will maintain as I can hold this, (continu'd he, and drew his Sword) Hah! Nobly done! (cry'd *Hardyman* drawing) I could almost wish thou wert my Friend: You speak generously, return'd *Lewis*, I find I have to do with a Gentleman. Retire to a convenient Distance, said *Hardyman* to *Goodlad*. If you come near while we are disputing, my Sword shall thank you for't; and you, Sir, retire! said *Constance* to his Servant. And if you will keep your Life, keep your Distance! O my brave Enemy! (cry'd *Miles*) Give me thy Hand! Here they shook Hands, and gave one another the Compliment of the Hat, and then (said *Hardyman*) Come on, Sir! I am with you, Sir, (reply'd *Lewis* standing on his Guard) they were both equally knowing in the Use of their Swords; so that they fought for some few Minutes without any Wound receiv'd on either Side. But, at last, *Miles* being taller and much stronger than his Adversary, resolv'd to close with him; which he did, putting by a Pass that *Lewis* made at him with his left Hand, and at the same Time he run him quite thro' the Body, threw him, and disarm'd him. Rise if thou can'st! (cry'd *Hardyman*) thou art really brave. I will not put thee to the Shame of asking thy Life. Alas! I cannot rise, (reply'd *Lewis*, endeavouring to get up) so short a Life as mine were not worth the Breath of a Coward.—Make Haste! Fly hence! For thou are lost if thou stay'st. My Friends are many and great; they will murther thee by Law. Fly! Fly in Time! Heaven forgive us both! Amen! (Cry'd *Miles*) I hope thou may'st recover! 'Tis Pity so much Bravery and Honour should be lost so early. Farewel.—And now Adieu to the fair and faithless *Diana!* Ha! (Cry'd *Constance*) O bloody Mistake! But could speak no more for Loss of Blood. *Hardyman* heard not those last Words, being spoken with a fainting Voice, but in Haste mounted, and rode with all Speed for *London*, attended by *Goodlad*; whilst *Constance*'s Servant came up to him, and having all along travell'd with him, had two or three Times the Occasion of making Use of that Skill in Surgery which he had learn'd Abroad in *France* and *Italy*, which he now again practis'd on his Master, with such Success, that in less than half an Hour, he put his Master in a Capacity of leaning on him; and so walking Home with him, tho' very gently and slowly. By the Way, *Lewis* charg'd his Servant not to say which Way *Hardyman* took, unless he design'd to quit his Service for ever. But pardon me, Sir! (return'd t'other) your Wound is very dangerous, and I am not sure that it is not mortal: And if so, give me Leave to say, I shall persue him over all *England*, for Vengeance of your Death. 'Twas a Mistake on both Sides, I find; (said *Lewis*) therefore think not of Revenge: I was as hot and as much to blame as he. They were near an Hour getting to the House, after his Blood was stopp'd. As he was led in, designing to be carry'd to his Chamber, and to take his Bed as sick of an Ague, his Sister and *Lucretia* met him, and both swoon'd away at the Sight of him; but in a little Time they were recover'd, as if to torment him with their Tears, Sighs, and Lamentations. They ask'd him a thousand impertinent Questions, which he defer'd to answer, 'till he was laid in Bed; when he told his Sister, that the Gentleman who had thus treated him, bid her Adieu, by the Epithet of Fair and Faithless. For Heaven's Sake, (cry'd *Diana*) what Manner of Man was he? Very tall and well set, (reply'd her Brother) of an austere Aspect, but a well-favour'd Face, and prodigiously strong. Had he a Servant with him, Sir? (ask'd *Lucretia*) Yes, Madam (answer'd her Lover) and describ'd her Servant. Ah! my Prophetic Fears (cry'd she) It was my Brother, attended by *Goodlad*. Your Brother! Dearest and Fairest of your Sex, (said *Lewis*) Heaven send him safely out of *England* then! Nay, be he who he may, I wish the same; for he is truly brave. Alas, my dear, my cruel *Hardyman!* (cry'd *Diana*) Your *Hardyman*, Sister! (said *Lewis*) Ah! would he had been so! You might then have had Hopes of an affectionate Brother's Life; which yet I will endeavour to preserve, that by the Enjoyment of your dear and nearest Conversation, Madam, (persu'd he to *Lucretia*) I may be prepar'd to endure the only greater Joys of Heaven. But O! My Words prey on my Spirits. And all the World, like a huge Ship at Anchor, turn round with the ebbing Tide.—I can no more. At these Words both the Ladies shriek'd aloud, which made him sigh, and move his Hand as well as he could toward the Door; his Attendant perceiv'd it, and told 'em he sign'd to them to quit the Room; as indeed it was necessary they should, that he might repose a while if possible, at least that he might not be oblig'd to talk, nor look much about him. They obey'd the Necessity, but with some Reluctancy, and went into their own Chamber,

where they sigh'd, wept, and lamented their Misfortunes
for near two Hours together : When all on a suddain, the
Aunt, who had her Share of Sorrow too in this ugly Business, came running up to 'em, to let 'em know that old
Sir *Harry Hardyman* was below, and came to carry his
Daughter Madam *Lucretia* Home with him. This both
surpriz'd and troubled the young Ladies, who were yet
more disturb'd, when the Aunt told them, that he enquir'd
for his Son, and would not be convinc'd by any Argument
whatever ; no, nor Protestation in her Capacity, that young
Hardyman was not in the House, nor that he had not been
entertain'd there ever since he left his Father—But come,
Cousin and Madam, (said she to the young Ladies) go
down to him immediately, or I fear he'll come up to
you. *Lucretia* knew she must, and t'other would not be
there alone : So down they came to the Old testy Gentleman. Your Servant, Lady, (said he to *Diana*) *Lucretia* then
kneel'd for his Blessing. Very well, very well, (cry'd he
hastily) God bless you ! Where's your Brother ? Ha !
Where's your Brother ? I know not, Sir, (she answer'd)
I have not seen him since I have been here. No, (said he)
not since you have been in this Parlour last, you mean. I
mean, Sir, (she return'd) upon my Hopes of yours and
Heaven's Blessing, I have not seen him since I saw you, Sir,
within a Mile of our own House. Ha ! *Lucretia*, Ha ! (cry'd
the old Infidel) have a Care you pull not mine and Heaven's
Curse on your Head ! Believe me, Sir, (said *Diana*) to my
Knowledge, she has not. Why, Lady, (ask'd the passionate
Knight) are you so curious and fond of him your self, that
you will allow no Body else the Sight of him ? Not so much
as his own Sister ? I don't understand you, Sir, (she reply'd)
for, by my Hopes of Heaven, I have not seen him neither
since that Day I left you. Hey ! pass and repass, (cry'd
the old suspicious Father) *presto*, be gone !—This is all
Conjuration. 'Tis diabolical, dealing with the Devil ! In
Lies, I mean, on one Side or other ; for he told me to my

Teeth, at least, he said in my Hearing, on the Bowling-Green, but two Nights since, that he hop'd to see your Ladyship (for I suppose you are his Mistress) that Night e're 'twas dark: Upon which I gave him only a kind and fatherly Memorandum of his Duty, and he immediately left the Company and me, who have not set Eye on him, nor heard one Syllable of him since.—Now, judge you, Lady, if I have not Reason to conclude that he has been and is above still! No, (said the Aunt) you have no Reason to conclude so, when they both have told you solemnly the contrary; and when I can add, that I will take a formal Oath, if requir'd, that he has not been in this House since my Cousin *Lewis* went to travel, nor before, to the best of my Memory; and I am confident, neither my Cousin *Diana*, nor the Lady your Daughter, have seen him since they left him with you, Sir—I wish, indeed, my dear Cousin *Lewis* had not seen him since. How! What's that you say, good Lady? (ask'd the Knight) Is Mr. *Lewis Constance* then in *England?* And do you think that he has seen him so lately? for your Discourse seems to imply as much. Sir *Henry*, (reply'd the Aunt) you are very big with Questions, but I will endeavour to satisfy you in all of 'em.—My Cousin *Lewis Constance* is in *England;* nay, more, he is now in his Chamber a-Bed, and dangerously, if not mortally, wounded, by 'Squire *Miles Hardyman*, your Son. Heaven forbid, (cry'd the Father) sure 'tis impossible. All Things are so to the Incredulous. Look you, Sir, (continu'd she, seeing *Lewis's* Servant come in) do you remember his *French* Servant *Albert*, whom he took some Months before he left *England?*—There he is. Humh! (said the old Sceptic) I think verily 'tis the same. Ay, Sir, (said the Servant) I am the same, at your Service. How does your Master? (ask'd Sir *Henry*) Almost as bad as when the 'Squire your Son left him, (reply'd *Albert*) only I have stopp'd the Bleeding, and he is now dozing a little; to say the Truth, I have only Hopes of his Life because

I wish it. When was this done? (the Knight inquir'd)
Not three Hours since, (return'd t'other.) What was the
Occasion? (said Sir *Henry*) An ugly Mistake on both
Sides; your Son, as I understand, not knowing my Master,
took him for his Rival, and bad him quit his Pretensions
to the fair Lady, for whom he had a Passion : My Master
thought he meant the Lady *Lucretia*, your Daughter, Sir,
with whom I find he is passionately in Love,—and— Very
well—so—go on ! (interrupted the Knight with a Sigh)
—and was resolv'd to dispute his Title with him ; which
he did; but the 'Squire is as strong as the Horse he rides on !
—And ! 'tis a desperate Wound!—Which Way is he gone,
canst thou tell? (ask'd the Father) Yes, I can ; but I must
not, 'tis as much as my Place is worth. My Master would
not have him taken for all the World ; nay, I must needs
own he is a very brave Person. But you may let me know;
(said the Father) you may be confident I will not expose
him to the Law : Besides, if it please Heaven that your
Master recovers, there will be no Necessity of a Prosecution. —Prithee let me know ! You'll pardon me, Sir, (said
Lewis's trusty Servant) my Master, perhaps, may give you
that Satisfaction ; and I'll give you Notice, Sir—when you
may conveniently discourse him.—Your humble Servant,
Sir, (he added, bowing, and went out.) The old Gentleman was strangely mortify'd at this News of his Son ; and
his Absence perplex'd him more than any thing besides in
the Relation. He walk'd wildly up and down the Room,
sighing, foaming, and rolling his Eyes in a dreadful Manner;
and at the Noise of any Horse on the Road, out he would
start as nimbly as if he were as youthful as his Son, whom
he sought in vain among those Passengers. Then returning,
he cry'd out to her, O *Lucretia* ! Your Brother ! Where's
your Brother?—O my Son ! the Delight, Comfort, and
Pride of my Old Age ! Why dost thou fly me ? Then
answering as for young *Hardyman*, (said he) you struck
me publickly before much Company, in the Face of

my Companions.—Come, (reply'd he for himself) 'Twas Passion, *Miles*, 'twas Passion; Youth is guilty of many Errors, and shall not Age be allow'd their Infirmities? *Miles*, thou know'st I love thee.—Love thee above Riches or long Life.—O! Come to my Arms, dear Fugitive, and make Haste to preserve his, who gave thee thy Life!— Thus he went raving about the Room, whilst the sorrowful, compassionate Ladies express'd their Grief in Tears. After this loving Fit was over with him, he would start out in a contrary Madness, and threaten his Son with the greatest and the heaviest Punishment he could imagine; insomuch, that the young Ladies, who had Thoughts before of perswading *Lewis* to inform Sir *Harry* which Way his Son rode, were now afraid of proposing any such Thing to him. Dinner was at last serv'd in, to which *Diana* with much Difficulty prevail'd with him to sit. Indeed, neither he, nor any there present, had any great Appetite to eat; their Grief had more than satiated 'em. About five a-Clock, *Albert* signify'd to the Knight, that he might then most conveniently speak with his Master; but he begg'd that he would not disturb him beyond half a Quarter of an Hour: He went up therefore to him, follow'd by the young Lady and the Aunt: *Lewis* was the first that spoke, who, putting his Hand a little out of the Bed, said with a Sigh, Sir *Henry*, I hope you will pity a great Misfortune, and endeavour to pardon me, who was the greatest Occasion of it; which has doubly punish'd me in these Wounds, and in the Loss of that Gentleman's Conversation, whose only Friendship I would have courted. Heaven pardon you both the Injuries done to one another; (return'd the Knight) I grieve to see you thus, and the more, when I remember my self that 'twas done by my Son's unlucky Hand. Would he were here. —So would not I (said *Lewis*) 'till I am assur'd my Wound is not mortal, which I have some Reasons to believe it is not. Let me beg one Favour of you, Sir, (said Sir *Henry*) I beseech you do not deny me. It must be a very difficult Matter that you, Sir, shall not command of me, (reply'd *Constance.*) It can't be difficult to you to tell me, or to command your Servant to let me know what Road my Son took. He may be at *Bristol* long e're this, (return'd *Lewis.*) That was the Road they took (added the Servant.) I thank you, my worthy, my kind Friend! (said the afflicted Father) I will study to deserve this Kindness of you. How do you find your self now? that I may send him an Account by my Servant, if he is to be found in that City? Pretty hearty, (return'd *Lewis*) if the Wounds your adorable Daughter here has given me, do not prove more fatal than my Friend's your Son's. She blush'd, and he persu'd, My Servant has sent for the best Physician and Surgeon in all these Parts; I expect them every Minute, and then I shall be rightly inform'd in the State of my Body. I will defer my Messenger 'till then (said Sir *Henry.*) I will leave that to your Discretion, Sir, (return'd *Constance.*) As they were discoursing of 'em, in came the learned Sons of Art: The Surgeon prob'd his Wound afresh, which he found very large, but not mortal, his Loss of Blood being the most dangerous of all his Circumstances. The Country-*Æsculapius* approv'd of his first Intention, and of his Application; so dressing it once himself, he left the Cure of Health to the Physician, who prescrib'd some particular Remedy against Fevers, and a Cordial or two; took his Fee without any Scruples, as the Surgeon had done before, and then took both their Leaves. Sir *Henry* was as joyful as *Lewis's* Sister, or as his own Daughter *Lucretia*, who lov'd him perfectly, to hear the Wound was not mortal; and immediately dispatch'd a Man and Horse to *Bristol*, in Search of his Son: The Messenger return'd in a short Time with this Account only, that such a kind of a Gentleman and his Servant took Shipping the Day before, as 'twas suppos'd, for *London*. This put the old Gentleman into a perfect Frenzy. He ask'd the Fellow, Why the Devil he did not give

his Son the Letter he sent to him? Why he did not tell him,
that his poor old forsaken Father would receive him with
all the Tenderness of an indulgent Parent? And why he
did not assure his Son, from him, that on his Return, he
should be bless'd with the Lady *Diana?* And a thousand
other extravagant Questions, which no body could reply
to any better than the Messenger, who told him, trembling; First, That he could not deliver the Letter to his
Son, because he could not find him: And Secondly and
Lastly, being an Answer in full to all his Demands, That
he could not, nor durst tell the young Gentleman any
of those kind Things, since he had no Order to do so;
nor could he enter into his Worship's Heart, to know his
Thoughts: Which Return, tho' it was reasonable enough,
and might have been satisfactory to any other Man in
better Circumstances of Mind; so enrag'd Sir *Henry*, that
he had certainly kill'd the poor Slave, had not the Fellow
sav'd his Life by jumping down almost half the Stairs,
and continuing his Flight, Sir *Henry* still persuing him,
'till he came to the Stables, where finding the Door open,
Sir *Henry* ran in and saddl'd his Horse his own self, without
staying for any Attendant, or so much as taking his Leave
of the Wounded Gentleman, or Ladies, or giving Orders
to his Daughter when she should follow him Home,
whither he was posting alone; but the Servant who came
out with him, accidentally seeing him as he rode out at the
farthest Gate, so timely persu'd him, that he overtook him
about a Mile and half off the House. Home they got then
in less than three Hours Time, without one Word or
Syllable all the Way on either Side, unless now and then
a hearty Sigh or Groan from the afflicted Father, whose
Passion was so violent, and had so disorder'd him, that he
was constrain'd immediately to go to Bed, where he was
seiz'd with a dangerous Fever, which was attended with
a strange *Delirium*, or rather with an absolute Madness,
of which the Lady *Lucretia* had Advice that same Night,

tho' very late. This News so surpriz'd and afflicted her, as well for the Danger of her Lover as of her Father, that it threw her into a Swoon; out of which, when, with some Difficulty she was recover'd, with great Perplexity and Anguish of Mind she took a sad Farewel of the Lady *Diana*, but durst not be seen by her Brother on such an Occasion, as of taking Leave, lest it should retard his Recovery: To her Father's then she was convey'd with all convenient Expedition: The old Gentleman was so assiduously and lawfully attended by his fair affectionate Daughter, that in less than ten Days Time his Fever was much abated, and his *Delirium* had quite left him, and he knew every Body about him perfectly; only the Thoughts of his Son, by Fits, would choak and discompose him: However, he was very sensible of his Daughter's Piety in her Care of him, which was no little Comfort to him: Nor, indeed, could he be otherwise than sensible of it by her Looks, which were then pale and thin, by over-watching; which occasion'd her Sickness, as it caus'd her Father's Health: For no sooner could Sir *Henry* walk about the Room, than she was forc'd to keep her Bed; being afflicted with the same Distemper from which her Father was yet but hardly freed: Her Fever was high, but the *Delirium* was not so great: In which, yet, she should often discover her Passion for *Lewis Constance*, her wounded Lover; lamenting the great Danger his Life had been in, as if she had not receiv'd daily Letters of his Amendment. Then again, she would complain of her Brother's Absence, but more frequently of her Lover's; which her Father hearing, sent to invite him to come to her, with his Sister, as soon as young *Constance* was able to undertake the Journey; which he did the very next Day; and he and *Diana* gave the languishing Lady a Visit in her Chamber, just in the happy Time of an Interval, which, 'tis suppos'd, was the sole Cause of her Recovery; for the Sight of her Lover and Friend was better than the richest Cordial in her

Distemper. In a very short Time she left her Bed, when Sir *Henry*, to give her perfect Health, himself join'd the two Lovers Hands; and not many Weeks after, when her Beauty and Strength return'd in their wonted Vigour, he gave her 10000*l.* and his Blessing, which was a double Portion, on their Wedding-Day, which he celebrated with all the Cost and Mirth that his Estate and Sorrow would permit: Sorrow for the Loss of his Son, I mean, which still hung upon him, and still hover'd and croak'd over and about him, as Ravens, and other Birds of Prey, about Camps and dying People. His Melancholy, in few Months, increas'd to that Degree, that all Company and Conversation was odious to him, but that of Bats, Owls, Night-Ravens, *&c.* Nay, even his Daughter, his dear and only Child, as he imagin'd, was industriously avoided by him. In short, it got so intire a Mastery of him, that he would not nor did receive any Sustenance for many Days together; and at last it confin'd him to his Bed; where he lay wilfully speechless for two Days and Nights; his Son-in-Law, or his own Daughter, still attending a-Nights by Turns; when on the third Night, his *Lucretia* sitting close by him in Tears, he fetch'd a deep Sigh, which ended in a pitious Groan, and call'd faintly, *Lucretia! Lucretia!* The Lady being then almost as melancholy as her Father, did not hear him 'till the third Call; when falling on her Knees, and embracing his Hand, which he held out to her, she return'd with Tears then gushing out, Yes, Sir, it is I, your *Lucretia*, your dutiful, obedient, and affectionate *Lucretia*, and most sorrowfully-afflicted Daughter. Bless her, Heaven! (said the Father) I'm going now, (continu'd he weakly) O *Miles!* yet come and take thy last Farewel of thy dear Father! Art thou for ever gone from me? Wilt thou not come and take thy dying Father's Blessing? Then I will send it after thee. Bless him! O Heaven! Bless him! Sweet Heaven bless my Son! My *Miles!* Here he began to faulter in his Speech, when the Lady gave a

great Shriek, which wak'd and alarm'd her Husband, who
ran down to 'em in his Night-Gown, and, kneeling by the
Bed-side with his Lady, begg'd their departing Father's
Blessing on them. The Shriek had (it seems) recall'd the
dying Gentleman's fleeting Spirits, who moving his Hand
as well as he could, with Eyes lifted up, as it were, whisper'd,
Heaven bless you both! Bless me! Bless my—O *Miles!*
Then dy'd. His Death (no Doubt) was attended with the
Sighs, Tears, and unfeign'd Lamentations of the Lady and
her Husband; for, bating his sudden Passion, he was
certainly as good a Father, Friend, and Neighbour, as
England could boast. His Funeral was celebrated then
with all the Ceremonies due to his Quality and Estate:
And the young happy Couple felt their dying Parent's
Blessing in their mutual Love and uninterrupted Tran-
quillity: Whilst (alas) it yet far'd otherwise with their
Brother; of whose Fortune it is fit I should now give you
an Account.

From *Bristol* he arriv'd to *London* with his Servant
Goodlad; to whom he propos'd, either that he should
return to Sir *Henry,* or share in his Fortunes Abroad: The
faithful Servant told him, he would rather be unhappy in
his Service, than quit it for a large Estate. To which his
kind Master return'd, (embracing him) No more my
Servant now, but my Friend! No more *Goodlad,* but
Truelove! And I am—*Lostall!* 'Tis a very proper Name,
suitable to my wretched Circumstances. So after some
farther Discourse on their Design, they sold their Horses,
took Shipping, and went for *Germany,* where then was the
Seat of War.

Miles's Person and Address soon recommended him to the
chief Officers in the Army; and his Friend *Truelove* was
very well accepted with 'em. They both then mounted in
the same Regiment and Company, as Volunteers; and in
the first Battel behav'd themselves like brave *English*-men;
especially *Miles,* whom now we must call Mr. *Lostall,* who

signaliz'd himself that Day so much, that his Captain and
Lieutenant being kill'd, he succeeded to the former in the
Command of the Company, and *Truelove* was made his
Lieutenant. The next Field-Fight *Truelove* was kill'd, and
Lostall much wounded, after he had sufficiently reveng'd
his Friend's Death by the Slaughter of many of the Enemies.
Here it was that his Bravery was so particular, that he
was courted by the Lieutenant-General to accept of
the Command of a Troop of Horse; which gave him fresh
and continu'd Occasions of manifesting his Courage and
Conduct. All this while he liv'd too generously for his
Pay; so that in the three or four Years Time, the War
ceasing, he was oblig'd to make use of what Jewels and
Money he had left of his own, for his Pay was quite spent.
But at last his whole Fund being exhausted to about fifty
or threescore Pounds, he began to have Thoughts of
returning to his native Country, *England;* which in a
few Weeks he did, and appear'd at the *Tower* to some of
his Majesty's (King *Charles* the Second's) Officers, in a
very plain and coarse, but clean and decent Habit: To
one of these Officers he address'd himself, and desir'd to
mount his Guards under his Command, and in his Company; who very readily receiv'd him into Pay. (The Royal
Family had not then been restor'd much above a Twelve-
Month.) In this Post, his Behaviour was such, that he was
generally belov'd both by the Officers and private Soldiers,
most punctually and exactly doing his Duty; and when
he was off the Guard, he would employ himself in any
laborious Way whatsoever to get a little Money. And it
happen'd, that one Afternoon, as he was helping to clean
the *Tower* Ditch, (for he refus'd not to do the meanest
Office, in Hopes to expiate his Crime by such voluntary
Penances) a Gentleman, very richly dress'd, coming that
Way, saw him at Work; and taking particular Notice of
him, thought he should know that Face of his, though
some of the Lines had been struck out by a Scar or two:

And regarding him more earnestly, he was at last fully confirm'd, that he was the Man he thought him; which made him say to the Soldier, Prithee, Friend, What art thou doing there? The unhappy Gentleman return'd, in his Country Dialect, Why, Master, Cham helping to clear the *Tower* Ditch, zure, an't please you. 'Tis very hot, (said t'other) Art thou not a dry? Could'st thou not drink? Ay, Master, reply'd the Soldier, with all my Heart. Well, (said the Gentleman) I'll give thee a Flaggon or two; Where is the best Drink? At yonder House, Master, (answer'd the Soldier) where you see yon Soldier at the Door, there be the best Drink and the best Measure, zure: Chil woit a top o your Worship az Zoon as you be got thare. I'll take thy Word, said t'other, and went directly to the Place; where he had hardly sate down, and call'd for some Drink, e'er the Soldier came in, to whom the Gentleman gave one Pot, and drank to him out of another. *Lostall*, that was the Soldier, whipp'd off his Flaggon, and said, bowing, Well, Master, God bless your Worship! Ich can but love and thank you, and was going; but the Gentleman, who had farther Business with him, with some Difficulty prevail'd on him to sit down, for a Minute or two, after the Soldier had urg'd that he must mind his Business, for he had yet half a Day's Work almost to complete, and he would not wrong any Body of a Quarter of an Hour's Labour for all the World. Th'art a very honest Fellow, I believe, said his Friend; but prithee what does thy whole Day's Work come to? Eighteen-pence, reply'd *Lostall*: Look, there 'tis for thee, said the Gentleman. Ay; but an't like your Worship, who must make an End of my Day's Business? (the Soldier ask'd.) Get any Body else to do it for thee, and I'll pay him. Can'st prevail with one of thy Fellow-Soldiers to be so kind? Yes, Master, thank God, cham not so ill belov'd nother. Here's honest *Frank* will do so much vor me, Zure: Wilt not, *Frank?* (withal my Heart, *Tom*, reply'd his Comrade.) Here, Friend, (said *Lostall's*

new Acquaintance) here's Eighteen-pence for thee too. I
thank your Honour, return'd the Soldier, but should have
but Nine-pence. No Matter what thou should'st have,
I'll give thee no less, said the strange Gentleman. Heavens
bless your Honour! (cry'd the Soldier) and after he had
swigg'd off a Pot of good Drink, took *Lostall's* Pick-ax and
Spade, and went about his Business. Now (said the Stranger)
let us go and take a Glass of Wine, if there be any that is
good hereabouts, for I fancy thou'rt a mighty honest Fellow;
and I like thy Company mainly. Cham very much bound
to behold you, Master, (return'd *Lostall*) and chave a Fancy
that you be and a *West*-Country-Man, zure; (added he)
you do a take zo like en; vor *Mainly* be our Country Word,
zure. We'll talk more of that by and by, said t'other:
Mean while I'll discharge the House, and walk whither
thou wilt lead me. That shan't be var, zure; (return'd
Lostall) vor the *Gun* upon the Hill there, has the best
Report for Wine and Zeck Ale hereabouts. There they
arriv'd then in a little Time, got a Room to themselves,
and had better Wine than the Gentleman expected. After
a Glass or two a-piece, his unknown Friend ask'd *Lostall*
what Country-Man he was? To whom the Soldier reply'd,
That he was a *Zomerzetshire* Man, zure. Did'st thou never
hear then of one Sir *Henry Hardyman*? (the Stranger ask'd.)
Hier of'n! (cry'd t'other) yes, zure; chave a zeen'en often.
Ah! Zure my Mother and I have had many a zwindging
Pitcher of good Drink, and many a good Piece of Meat at
his House. Humh! (cry'd the Gentleman) It seems your
Mother and you knew him, then? Ay, zure, mainly well;
ich mean, by zight, mainly well, by zight. They had a
great deal of farther Discourse, which lasted near two Hours;
in which Time the Gentleman had the Opportunity to be
fully assur'd, that this was *Miles Hardyman*, for whom he
took him at first. At that first Conference, *Miles* told him
his Name was honest *Tom Lostall*; and that he had been a
Souldier about five Years; having first obtain'd the Dignity

of a Serjeant, and afterward had the Honour to be a Trooper, which was the greatest Post of Honour that he could boast of. At last, his new Friend ask'd *Miles*, if he should see him there at Three in the Afternoon the next Day? *Miles* return'd, That he should be at his Post upon Duty then; and that without Leave from his Lieutenant, who then would command the Guards at the *Tower*, he could not stir a Foot with him. His Friend return'd, That he would endeavour to get Leave for him for an Hour or two: After which they drank off their Wine; the Gentleman pay'd the Reckoning, and gave *Miles* a Broad piece to drink more Wine 'till he came, if he pleas'd, and then parted 'till the next Day. When his Friend was gone, *Miles* had the Opportunity of reflecting on that Day's Adventure. He thought he had seen the Gentleman's Face, and heard his Voice, but where, and upon what Occasion, he could not imagine; but he was in Hopes, that on a second Interview, he might recollect himself where it was he had seen him. 'Twas exactly Three a-Clock the next Afternoon, when his Friend came in his own Mourning-Coach, accompany'd by another, who look'd like a Gentleman, though he wore no Sword. His Friend was attended by two of his own Foot-men in black Liveries. *Miles* was at his Post, when his Friend ask'd where the Officer of the Guard was? The Soldier reply'd, That he was at the *Gun*. The Gentleman went directly to the Lieutenant, and desir'd the Liberty of an Hour or two for *Miles*, then *Tom Lostall*, to take a Glass of Wine with him: The Lieutenant return'd, That he might keep him a Week or two, if he pleas'd, and he would excuse him; for (added he) there is not a more obedient nor better Soldier than *Tom* was in the whole Regiment; and that he believ'd he was as brave as obedient. The Gentleman reply'd, That he was very happy to hear so good a Character of him; and having obtain'd Leave for his Friend, made his Compliment, and return'd, to take *Miles* along with him: When he came to the trusty

Centinel, he commanded the Boot to be let down, and desir'd *Miles* to come into the Coach, telling him, That the Officer had given him Leave. Ah! Sir, (return'd *Miles*) altho' he has, I cannot, nor will quit my Post, 'till I am reliev'd by a Corporal; on which, without any more Words, the Gentleman once more went to the Lieutenant, and told him what the Soldier's Answer was. The Officer smil'd, and reply'd, That he had forgot to send a Corporal with him, e'er he was got out o' Sight, and begg'd the Gentleman's Pardon that he had given him a second Trouble. Then immediately calling for a Corporal, he dispatch'd him with the Gentleman to relieve *Miles*, who then, with some little Difficulty, was prevail'd on to step into the Coach, which carry'd 'em into some Tavern or other in *Leadenhall-street*; where, after a Bottle or two, his Friend told *Miles*, that the Gentleman who came with him in the Coach, had some Business with him in another Room. *Miles* was surpriz'd at that, and look'd earnestly on his Friend's Companion; and seeing he had no Sword, pull'd off his own, and walk'd with him into the next Room; where he ask'd the Stranger, What Business he had with him? To which the other reply'd, That he must take Measure of him. How! (cry'd *Miles*) take Measure of me? That need not be; for I can tell how tall I am. I am (continu'd he) six Foot and two Inches high. I believe as much (said t'other.) But, Sir, I am a Taylor, and must take Measure of you to make a Suit of Cloaths or two for you; or half a Dozen, if you please. Pray, good Mr. Taylor (said *Miles*) don't mock me; for tho' cham a poor Fellow, yet cham no Vool zure. I don't, indeed, Sir, reply'd t'other. Why, who shall pay for 'em? Your Friend, the Gentleman in the next Room: I'll take his Word for a thousand Pounds, and more; and he has already promis'd to be my Pay-Master for as many Suits as you shall bespeak, and of what Price you please. Ah! mary, (cry'd *Miles*) he is a Right Worshipful Gentleman; and ich caunt but love 'n and thank 'n. The Taylor then took Measure of him, and they return'd to the Gentleman; who, after a Bottle or two a-piece, ask'd *Miles* when he should mount the Guard next? *Miles* told him four Days thence, and he should be posted in the same Place, and that his Captain would then command the Guard, who was a very noble Captain, and a good Officer. His Friend, who then had no farther Business with *Miles* at that Time, once more parted with him, 'till Three a-Clock the next Saturday; when he return'd, and ask'd if the Captain were at the *Gun*, or no? *Miles* assur'd him he was. His Friend then went down directly to the Tavern, where he found the Captain, the Lieutenant, and Ensign; upon his Address the Captain most readily gave his Consent that *Miles* might stay with him a Month, if he would; and added many Things in Praise of his trusty and dutiful Soldier. The Gentleman then farther entreated, that he might have the Liberty to give him and the other Officers a Supper that Night; and that they would permit their poor Soldier, *Tom Lostall*, the Honour to eat with 'em there. To the first, the Captain and the rest seem'd something averse; but to the last they all readily agreed; and at length the Gentleman's Importunity prevail'd on 'em to accept his Kindness, he urging that it was in Acknowledgment of all those Favours they had plac'd on his Friend *Tom*. With his pleasing Success he came to *Miles*, not forgetting then to take a Corporal with him. At this second Invitation into the Coach, *Miles* did not use much Ceremony, but stepp'd in, and would have sate over against the Gentleman, by the Gentleman-Taylor; but his Friend oblig'd him to sit on the same Seat with him. They came then again to their old Tavern in *Leadenhall-street*, and were shew'd into a large Room; where they had not been above six Minutes, e'er the Gentleman's Servants, and another, who belong'd to Monsieur Taylor, brought two or three large Bags; out of one they took Shirts, half Shirts, Bands, and

Stockings; out of another, a Mourning-Suit; out of a third, a Mourning Cloak, Hat, and a large Hatband, with black Cloth-Shoes; and one of the Gentleman's Servants laid down a Mourning Sword and Belt on the Table: *Miles* was amaz'd at the Sight of all these Things, and kept his Eyes fix'd on 'em, 'till his Friend cry'd, Come, *Tom!* Put on your Linnen first! Here! (continu'd he to his Servant) Bid 'em light some Faggots here! For, tho' 'tis Summer, the Linnen may want Airing, and there may be some ugly cold Vapours about the Room, which a good Fire will draw away. *Miles* was still in a Maze! But the Fire being well kindled, the Gentleman himself took a Shirt, and air'd it; commanding one of his Servants to help *Tom* to undress. *Miles* was strangely out o' Countenance at this, and told his Friend, that he was of Age and Ability to pull off his own Cloaths; that he never us'd to have any *Valets de Chambre;* (as they call'd 'em) and for his Part, he was asham'd, and sorry that so worshipful a Gentleman should take the Trouble to warm a Shirt for him. Besides (added he) chave Heat enough (zure) to warm my Shirt. In short, he put on his Shirt, half Shirt, his Cloaths and all Appurtenances, as modishly as the best *Valet de Chambre* in *Paris* could. When *Miles* was dress'd, his Friend told him, That he believ'd he look'd then more like himself than ever he had done since his Return to *England.* Ah! Noble Sir! said *Miles, Vine Feathers make vine Birds.* But pray, Sir, Why must I wear Mourning? Because there is a particular Friend of mine dead, for whose Loss I can never sufficiently mourn my self; and therefore I desire that all whom I love should mourn with me for him, return'd the Gentleman; not but that there are three other Suits in Hand for you at this Time. *Miles* began then to suspect something of his Father's Death, which had like to have made him betray his Grief at his Eyes; which his Friend perceiving, took him by the Hand, and said, Here, my dear Friend! To the Memory of my departed Friend!

You are so very like what he was, considering your Difference in Years, that I can't choose but love you next to my Wife and my own Sister. Ah! Sir! (said he, and lapping his Handkerchief to his Eyes) How can I deserve this of you? I have told you (reply'd t'other.) But—Come! Take your Glass, and about with it! He did so; and they were indifferently pleasant, the Subject of Discourse being chang'd, 'till about a quarter after Five; when the Gentleman call'd to pay, and took Coach with *Miles* only, for the *Gun-Tavern;* where he order'd a very noble Supper to be got ready with all Expedition; mean while they entertain'd one another, in a Room as distant from the Officers as the House would permit: *Miles* relating to his new Friend all his Misfortunes Abroad, but still disguising the true Occasion of his leaving *England*. Something more than an Hour after, one of the Drawers came to let 'em know, that Supper was just going to be serv'd up. They went then directly to the Officers, whom they found all together, with two or three Gentlemen more of their Acquaintance: They all saluted the Gentleman who had invited 'em first, and then complimented *Miles*, whom they mistook for another Friend of the Gentleman's that gave 'em the Invitation; not in the least imagining that it was *Tom Lostall*. When they were all sat, the Captain ask'd, Where is our trusty and well-beloved Friend Mr. *Thomas Lostall?* Most honoured Captain! (reply'd *Miles*) I am here, most humbly at your Honour's Service, and all my other noble Officers. Ha! *Tom!* (cry'd the Lieutenant) I thought indeed when thou first cam'st in, that I should have seen that hardy Face of thine before. Face, Hands, Body, and Heart and all, are at your, all your Honours Service, as long as I live. We doubt it not, dear *Tom!* (return'd his Officers, unanimously.) Come, noble Gentlemen! (interrupted *Miles's* Friend) Supper is here, let us fall to: I doubt not that after Supper I shall surprise you farther. They then fell to eating heartily; and after the Table was clear'd they drank merrily : At last, after the King's, Queen's, Duke's, and all the Royal Family's, and the Officers Healths, his Friend begg'd that he might begin a Health to *Tom Lostall;* which was carry'd about very heartily; every one had a good Word for him, one commending his Bravery, another, his ready Obedience; and a third, his Knowledge in material Discipline, *&c.* 'till at length it grew late, their Stomachs grew heavy, and their Heads light; when the Gentleman, *Miles's* Friend, calling for a Bill, he found it amounted to seven Pounds ten Shillings, odd Pence, which he whisper'd *Tom Lostall* to pay ; who was in a Manner Thunder-struck at so strange a Sound ; but, recollecting himself, he return'd, That if his Friend pleas'd, he would leave his Cloak, and any Thing else, 'till the House were farther satisfy'd : T'other said, He was sure *Miles* had Money enough about him to discharge two such Bills : To which *Miles* reply'd, That if he had any Money about him, 'twas none of his own, and that 'twas certainly conjur'd into his Pockets. No Matter how it came there (said t'other ;) but you have above twenty Pounds about you of your own Money : Pray feel. *Miles* then felt, and pull'd out as much Silver as he could grasp, and laid it down on the Table. Hang this white Pelf; (cry'd his Friend) pay it in Gold, like your self, Come, apply your Hand to another Pocket : He did so, and brought out as many Broad-Pieces as Hand could hold. Now (continu'd his Friend) give the Waiter eight of 'em, and let him take the Overplus for his Attendance. *Miles* readily obey'd, and they were *Very Welcome, Gentlemen.*

Now, honoured Captain, (said his Friend) and you, Gentlemen, his other worthy Officers, he pleas'd to receive your Soldier, as Sir *Miles Hardyman*, Bar., Son to the late Sir *Henry Hardyman* of *Somersetshire*, my dear and honoured Brother-in-Law : Who is certainly—the most unhappy Wretch crawling on Earth ! (interrupted *Miles*) O just Heaven ! (persu'd he) How have I been rack'd in my Soul

ever since the Impious Vow I made, that I never would
see my dearest Father more! This is neither a Time nor
Place to vent your Sorrows, my dearest Brother! (said
his Friend, tenderly embracing him.) I have something
now more material than your Expressions of Grief can
be here, since your honoured Father has been dead these five
Years almost:—Which is to let you know, that you are
now Master of four thousand Pounds a Year; and if you
will forgive me two Years Revenue, I will refund the
rest, and put you into immediate and quiet Possession;
which I promise before all this worthy and honourable
Company. To which *Miles* return'd, That he did not
deserve to inherit one Foot of his Father's Lands, tho'
they were entail'd on him, since he had been so strangely
undutiful; and that he rather thought his Friend ought
to enjoy it all in Right of his Sister, who never offended
his Father in the whole Course of her Life: —But, I
beseech you, Sir, (continu'd he to his Friend) how long
is it since I have been so happy in so good and generous
a Brother-in-Law? Some Months before Sir *Henry* our
Father dy'd, who gave us his latest Blessing, except that
which his last Breath bequeath'd and sigh'd after you.
O undutiful and ungrateful Villain that I am, to so kind,
and so indulgent, and so merciful a Father: (cry'd *Miles*)
But Heaven, I fear, has farther Punishments in Store for
so profligate a Wretch and so disobedient a Son. —But
your Name, Sir, if you please? (persu'd he to his Brother)
I am *Lewis Constance*, whom once you unhappily mistook
for your Rival. Unhappily, indeed: (return'd *Miles*) I
thought I had seen you before. Ay, Sir, (return'd *Constance*) but you could never think to have seen me again,
when you wounded and left me for dead, within a Mile
of my House. O! thou art brave, (cry'd his Brother,
embracing him affectionately) 'tis too much Happiness,
for such a Reprobate to find so true a Friend and so just
a Brother. This, this does in some Measure compensate

for the Loss of so dear a Father.—Take, take all, my
Brother! (persu'd he, kissing *Lewis's* Cheek) Take all
thou hast receiv'd of what is call'd mine, and share my
whole Estate with me: But pardon me, I beseech you
my most honour'd Officers, and all you Gentlemen here
present, (continu'd he to the whole Company, who sate
silent and gazing at one another, on the Occasion of so
unusual an Adventure) pardon the Effects of Grief and
Joy in a distracted Creature! O, Sir *Miles*, (cry'd his
Captain) we grieve for your Misfortune, and rejoice at
your Happiness in so noble a Friend and so just a Brother.
Miles then went on, and gave the Company a full but
short Account of the Occasion of all his Troubles, and
of all his Accidents he met with both Abroad and at
Home, to the first Day that *Constance* saw him digging
in the *Tower*-Ditch. About one that Morning, which
preceded that Afternoon (persu'd he) whereon I saw my
dear Brother here, then a Stranger to me, I dream'd I
saw my Father at a Distance, and heard him calling to
me to quit my honourable Employment in his Majesty's
Service: This (my Thought) he repeated seven or nine
Times, I know not which; but I was so disturb'd at it, that
I began to wake, and with my Eyes but half open was
preparing to rise; when I fancy'd I felt a cold Hand take
me by the Hand, and force me on my hard Bolster again,
with these Words, take thy Rest, *Miles!* This I confess
did somewhat surprize me; but I concluded, 'twas the
Effect of my Melancholy, which, indeed, has held me
ever since I last left *England*: I therefore resolutely started
up, and jump'd out of Bed, designing to leave you, and
sit up with my Fellow-Soldiers on the Guard; but just
then I heard the Watchman cry, *Past one a Clock and a
Star-light Morning;* when, considering that I was to be
at Work in the Ditch by four a Clock, I went to Bed
again, and slumber'd, doz'd, and dream'd, 'til Four; ever
when I turn'd me, still hearing, as I foolishly imagin'd,

my Father crying to me, *Miles!* Sleep, my *Miles!* Go
not to that nasty Place, nor do such servile Offices! tho'
thou dost, I'll have thee out this Day, nay, I will pull
thee out: And then I foolishly imagin'd, that the same
cold Hand pull'd me out of the Ditch; and being in less
than a Minute's Time perfectly awake, I found my self
on my Feet in the Middle of the Room; I soon put on
my Cloaths then, and went to my Labour. Were you
thus disturb'd when you were Abroad? (the Captain ask'd)
O worse, Sir, (answer'd *Miles*) especially on a Tuesday
Night, a little after One, being the Twelth of *November*,
New Style, I was wak'd by a Voice, which (methought)
cry'd, *Miles, Miles, Miles!* Get hence, go Home, go to
England! I was startled at it, but regarded it only as proceeding from my going to Sleep with a full Stomach, and
so endeavour'd to sleep again, which I did, till a second
Time it rouz'd me, with *Miles* twice repeated,—hazard
not thy Life here in a foreign Service! Home! to *England!*
to *England!* to *England!* This disturb'd me much more
than at first; but, after I had lay'n awake near half an
Hour, and heard nothing of it all that Time, I assur'd
my self 'twas nothing but a Dream, and so once more
address'd my self to Sleep, which I enjoy'd without
Interruption for above two Hours; when I was the third
Time alarm'd, and that with a louder Voice, which cry'd,
as twice before, *Miles! Miles! Miles! Miles!* Go Home!
Go to *England!* Hazard not thy Soul here! At which
I started up, and with a faultering Speech, and Eyes half
sear'd together, I cry'd, In the Name of Heaven, who
calls? Thy Father, *Miles:* Go Home! Go Home! Go
Home! (it said.) O then I knew, I mean, I thought I
knew it was my Father's Voice; and turning to the Bed-
Side, from whence the Sound proceeded, I saw, these
Eyes then open, these very Eyes, at least, my Soul saw
my Father, my own dear Father, lifting up his joined
Hands, as if he begg'd me to return to *England*. I saw

him beg it of me.—O Heaven! The Father begs it of the Son! O obstinate, rebellious, cruel, unnatural, barbarous, inhuman Son! Why did not I go Home then! Why did I not from that Moment begin my Journey to *England*? But I hope, e'er long, I shall begin a better. Here his o'ercharg'd Heart found some little Relief at his Eyes, and they confess'd his Mother: But he soon resum'd the Man, and then *Constance* said, Did you ne'er dream of your Sister, Sir? Yes, often, Brother, (return'd *Miles*) but then most particularly, before e'er I heard the first Call of the Voice; when (my Thought) I saw her in Tears by my Bed Side, kneeling with a Gentleman, whom I thought I had once seen; but knew him not then, tho', now I recal my Dream, the Face was exactly yours. 'Twas I, indeed, Sir, (return'd *Lewis*) who bore her Company, with Tears, at your Father's Bed-Side; and at twelve a Clock at Night your Father dy'd. But come, Sir, (persu'd he) 'tis now near twelve a Clock, and there is Company waits for you at Home, at my House here in Town; I humbly beg the Captain's Leave, that I may rob 'em of so dutiful a Soldier for a Week or two. Sir, (return'd the Captain) Sir *Miles* knows how to command himself, and may command us when he pleases. Captain, Lieutenant, and Ensign, (reply'd Sir *Miles*) I am, and ever will continue, during Life, your most dutiful Soldier, and your most obedient and humble Servant. Thus they parted.

As soon as *Constance* was got within Doors, his Lady and Sir *Miles*'s Sister, who both did expect him that Night, came running into the Hall to welcome him? his Sister embrac'd and kiss'd him twenty and twenty Times again, dropping Tears of Joy and Grief, whilst his Mistress stood a little Distance, weeping sincerely for Joy to see her Love return'd: But long he did not suffer her in that Posture; for, breaking from his Sister's tender Embraces, with a seasonable Compliment he ran to his Mistress, and kneeling, kiss'd her Hand, when she was going to kneel to him; which he perceiving, started up and took her in his Arms, and there, it may be presum'd, they kiss'd and talk'd prettily; 'till her Brother perswaded 'em to retire into the Parlour, where he propos'd to 'em that they should marry on the very next morning; and accordingly they were, after *Lewis* had deliver'd all Sir *Henry's* Estate to Sir *Miles*, and given him Bills on his Banker for the Payment of ten thousand Pounds, being the Moiety of Sir *Miles's* Revenue for five Years. Before they went to Church, Sir *Miles*, who then had on a rich bridal Suit, borrow'd his Brother's best Coach, and both he and *Lewis* went and fetch'd the Captain, Lieutenant, and Ensign, to be Witnesses of their Marriage. The Captain gave the Bride, and afterwards they feasted and laugh'd heartily, 'till Twelve at Night, when the Bride was put to Bed; and there was not a Officer of 'em all, who would not have been glad to have gone to Bed to her; but Sir *Miles* better supply'd their Places.

APPENDIX.

APPENDIX.

APPENDIX.

ORONOOKO: EPISTLE DEDICATORY.

TO THE RIGHT HONOURABLE
THE LORD MAITLAND.

My Lord,

Since the World is grown so Nice and Critical upon Dedications, and will Needs be Judging the Book by the Wit of the Patron; we ought, with a great deal of Circumspection to chuse a Person against whom there can be no Exception; and whose Wit and Worth truly Merits all that one is capable of saying upon that Occasion.

The most part of Dedications are charg'd with Flattery; and if the World knows a Man has some Vices, they will not allow one to speak of his Virtues. This, My Lord, is for want of thinking Rightly; if Men wou'd consider with Reason, they wou'd have another sort of Opinion, and Esteem of Dedications; and wou'd believe almost every Great Man has enough to make him Worthy of all that can be said of him there. My Lord, a Picture-drawer, when he intends to make a good Picture, essays the Face many Ways, and in many Lights, before he begins; that he may chuse from the several turns of it, which is most Agreeable and gives it the best Grace; and if there be a Scar, an ungrateful Mole, or any little Defect, they leave it out; and yet make the Picture extreamly like: But he who has the good Fortune to draw a Face that is exactly Charming in all its Parts and Features, what Colours or Agreements can be added to make it Finer? All that he can give is but its due; and Glories in a Piece whose Original alone gives it its Perfection. An ill Hand may diminish, but a good Hand cannot augment its Beauty. A Poet is a Painter in his way; he draws to the Life, but in another kind; we draw the Nobler part, the Soul and Mind; the Pictures of the Pen shall out-last those of the Pencil, and even Worlds themselves. 'Tis a short Chronicle of those Lives that possibly wou'd be forgotten by other Historians, or lye neglected there, however deserving an immortal Fame; for Men of eminent Parts are as Exemplary as even Monarchs themselves; and Virtue is a noble Lesson to be learn'd, and 'tis by Comparison we can Judge and Chuse. 'Tis by such illustrious Presidents as your Lordship the World can be Better'd and

Refin'd; when a great part of the lazy Nobility shall, with Shame, behold the admirable Accomplishments of a Man so Great, and so Young.

Your Lordship has Read innumerable Volumes of Men and Books, not Vainly for the gust of Novelty, but Knowledge, excellent Knowledge : Like the industrious Bee, from every Flower you return Laden with the precious Dew, which you are sure to turn to the Publick Good. You hoard no one Reflection, but lay it all out in the Glorious Service of your Religion and Country; to both which you are a useful and necessary Honour : They both want such Supporters; and 'tis only Men of so elevated Parts, and fine Knowledge ; such noble Principles of Loyalty and Religion this Nation Sighs for. Where shall we find a Man so Young, like St. Augustine, in the midst of all his Youth and Gaiety, Teaching the World Divine Precepts, true Notions of Faith, and Excellent Morality, and, at the same time be also a perfect Pattern of all that accomplish a Great Man? You have, My Lord, all that refin'd Wit that Charms, and the Affability that Obliges; a Generosity that gives a Lustre to your Nobility; that Hospitality, and Greatness of Mind that ingages the World; and that admirable Conduct, that so well Instructs it. Our Nation ought to regret and bemoan their Misfortunes, for not being able to claim the Honour of the Birth of a Man who is so fit to serve his Majesty, and his Kingdoms in all Great and Publick Affairs ; And to the Glory of your Nation, be it spoken, it produces more considerable Men, for all fine Sence, Wit, Wisdom, Breeding and Generosity (for the generality of the Nobility) than all other Nations can Boast; and the Fruitfulness of your Virtues sufficiently make amends for the Barrenness of your Soil : Which however cannot be incommode to your Lordship ; since your Quality and the Veneration that the Commonalty naturally pay their Lords creates a flowing Plenty there . . . that makes you Happy. And to compleat your Happiness, my Lord, Heaven has blest you with a Lady, to whom it has given all the Graces, Beauties, and Virtues of her Sex ; all the Youth, Sweetness of Nature, of a most illustrious Family ; and who is a most rare Example to all Wives of Quality, for her eminent Piety, Easiness, and Condescention ; and as absolutely merits Respect from all the World as she does that Passion and Resignation she receives from your Lordship ; and which is, on her part, with so much Tenderness return'd. Methinks your tranquil Lives are an Image of the new Made and Beautiful Pair in Paradise : And 'tis the Prayers and Wishes of all, who have the Honour to know you, that it may Eternally so continue with Additions of all the Blessings this World can give you.

My Lord, the Obligations I have to some of the Great Men of your Nation, particularly to your Lordship, gives me an Ambition of making my Acknowledgements by all the Opportunities I can ; and such humble Fruits as my Industry produces I lay at your Lordship's Feet. This is a true Story, of a Man Gallant enough to merit your Protection, and, had he always been so Fortunate, he had not made so Inglorious an end : The Royal Slave I had the Honour to know in my Travels to the other World ; and though I had none above me in that Country yet I wanted power to preserve this Great Man. If there be anything that seems Romantick I beseech your Lordship to consider these Countries do, in all things, so far differ from ours that they produce unconceivable Wonders, at least, so they appear to us, because New and Strange. What I have mentioned I have taken care shou'd be Truth, let the Critical Reader judge as he pleases. 'Twill be no Commendation to the Book to assure your Lordship I writ it in a few Hours, though it may serve to Excuse some of its Faults of Connexion, for I never rested my Pen a Moment for Thought : 'Tis purely the Merit of my Slave that must render it worthy of the Honour it begs ; and the Author of that of Subscribing herself,

> My Lord
> Your Lordship's most oblig'd
> and obedient Servant
> A. Behn.

Notes : Critical and Explanatory.

The Black Lady.

p. 3 *Bridges-Street.* Brydges Street lies between Russell Street and Catherine Street. Drury Lane Theatre is at its N.E. corner. It early acquired no very enviable repute. e.g. In the Epilogue to Crowne's *Sir Courtly Nice* (1685) we have: 'Our Bridges Street is grown a strumpet fair'; and Dryden, in the Epilogue to *King Arthur* (1691), gave Mrs. Brace-girdle, who entered, her hands full of billets-doux, the following lines to speak :—

> Here one desires my ladyship to meet   [*Pulls out one.*
> At the kind couch above in Bridges-Street.
> Oh sharping knave ! that would have—you know what,
> For a poor sneaking treat of chocolate.

p. 8 *Star-Inn on Fish-street-Hill.* Fish Street Hill, or, New Fish Street, runs from Eastcheap to Lower Thames Street, and was the main thorough-fare to old London Bridge. cf. 2 *Henry VI*, iv, viii : 'Cade. Up Fish Street ! down St. Magnus' corner ! kill and knock down ! throw them into the Thames.'

p. 9 *the Exchange.* The New Exchange, a kind of bazaar on the South side of the Strand. It was an immensely popular resort, and continued so until the latter years of the reign of Queen Anne. There are innumerable references to its shops, its sempstresses and haberdashers. Thomas Duffet was a milliner here before he took to writing farces, prologues and poems.

p. 17 *last new Plays, being then in the Year* 1683. The new plays acted at the Theatre Royal in 1682 were : Southerne's *The Loyal Brother ; or, The Persian Prince ;* Tate's *Ingratitude of a Commonwealth ; or, The Fall of Caius Marius Coriolanus ;* Settle's *The Heir of Morocco, with the Death of Gayland ;* Banks' *The Unhappy Favourite ; or, the Earl of Essex ;* D'Urfey's *The Injur'd Princess ; or, The Fatal Wager.* There were also an unusual number of revivals of the older plays at this house. At Dorset Garden the following were produced : Otway's *Venice Preserv'd ; or, A Plot Discovered ;* Mrs. Behn's *The City Heiress ; or, Sir Timothy Treatall ;* D'Urfey's *The Royalist ;* Mrs. Behn's *The False Count ; or, A New Way to Play an Old Game ;* Banks' *Virtue Betray'd ; or, Anna Bullen ;* Mrs. Behn's *The Roundheads ; or, The Good Old Cause ;* Ravenscroft's *The London Cuckolds ;* and *Romulus and Hersilia ; or, The Sabine War,* an anonymous tragedy. There were also notable revivals of Randolph's *The Jealous Lovers,* and Fletcher's *The Maid in the Mill.* The two Companies amalgamated in the autumn, opening at the Theatre Royal, 16 November, for which occasion a special Prologue and Epilogue were written by Dryden. 4 December, Dryden and Lee's famous tragedy, *The Duke of Guise*, had a triumphant first night. It will be remembered that Mrs. Behn is writing of incidents which took place on 6 January, 1683, Twelfth Night, so 'the last new plays' must refer to the productions of 1682. Of course, fresh songs, and probably musical entertainments, would be inserted at the different revivals of the older plays which were so frequent during that year.

p. 20 *Statira, . . . Roxana.* In allusion to the two rival princesses for Alexander's love as they appear in Nat Lee's famous tragedy, *The Rival Queens; or, Alexander the Great,* produced at Drury Lane, 1677. It held the stage over a century and a half, longest of his plays, and is indeed an excellent piece. Originally, Hart played Alexander; Mrs. Marshall, the glowing Roxana; and Mrs. Boutell, Statira. Genest chronicles a performance at Drury Lane, 23 June, 1823, with Kean as Alexander; Mrs. W. West, Statira; Mrs. Glover, Roxana.

p. 24 *forty the Lurch.* 'Lurch' is a very common old term (now rare) 'used in various games to denote a certain concluding state of the game in which one player is enormously ahead of the other; often a "maiden set" or love-game.'—*N. E. D.* cf. Urquhart's *Rabelais* (1653), II, xii: 'By two of my table-men in the corner point I have gained the lurch.' Gouldman's *Latin Dictionary* (1674), gives: 'A lurch; *duplex palma, facilis victoria.*'

p. 26 *to Locket's, where they din'd.* This fashionable Ordinary stood on the site of Drummond's Bank, Charing Cross. It was named from Adam Locket, the landlord, who died in 1688. In 1702, however, we find an Edward Locket, probably a son, as proprietor. The reputation of the house was on the wane during the latter years of Anne, and in the reign of George I its vogue entirely ceased. There are very frequent references. In *The Country Wife* (1675), Horner tells Pinchwife: 'Thou art as shy of my kindness as a Lombard-street alderman of a courtier's civility at Locket's' (iv, iii). In Shadwell's *The Scowerers* (1691), old Tope, replying to a health, cries: 'I'll answer you in a couple of Brimmers of Claret at Locket's at Dinner' (i, 1). In Vanbrugh's *The Relapse* (1696), Lord Foppington, when asked if he dines at home, surmises: ''tis passible I may dine with some of aur House at Lacket's,' which shows that it was then the very rendezvous of fashion and quality.

p. 27 *A King and no King.* Langbaine testifies to the popularity of Beaumont and Fletcher's play both before and after the Restoration. Pepys saw it 14 March, 1661, and again, 26 September the same year. The 1676 quarto 'as it is now acted at the Theatre Royal by his Majestie's Servants' gives a full cast with Hart as Arbaces; Kynaston, Tigranes; Mohun, Mardonius; Lacy, Bessus; Mrs. Betty Cox, Panthea; Mrs. Marshall, Spaconia. In the earlier production Nell Gwynne had acted Panthea. The two Companies amalgamated in 1682, opening 16 November. Hart 'never Acted more' after this date. Mrs. Marshall had retired in 1677; and in 1683 Betterton was playing Arbaces with quite a new allotment of the other rôles.

p. 27 *The Rose.* There are repeated references to this celebrated tavern which stood in Russell Street, Covent Garden. *vide The Younger*

Brother, i, II (Vol. IV), Motteux' Song: 'Thence to the Rose where he takes his three Flasks,' and the note on that passage.

p. 29 *The London-Cuckolds*. Ravenscroft's rollicking comedy, which had been produced with great success at the Duke's House in 1682 (4to, 1682), long kept the boards with undiminished favour, being very frequently given each season. Genest has the following true and pertinent remark: 'If it be the province of Comedy not to retail morality to a yawning pit but to make the audience laugh and to keep them in good humour this play must be allowed to be one of the best Comedies in the English language.' 29 October (the old Lord Mayor's Day), 1751, Garrick substituted *Eastward Hoe* at Drury Lane for the annual performance of *The London Cuckolds*, a change not approved by the audience, who promptly damned their new fare. Ravenscroft's comedy was given that evening at Covent Garden, and on 9 November, the following year. It was also performed there in 1753. 9 November, 1754, George II ordered *The Provoked Husband*. It has often been stated (e.g. by Professor A. W. Ward—'Ravenscroft'—*Dictionary of National Biography*) that this royal command gave *The London Cuckolds* its final *congé*, but such was neither the intent nor the case. The play is billed at Covent Garden, 10 November, 1755; in 1757; and 9 November, 1758. Shuter excelled as Dashwell. A two act version was played at Covent Garden, 10 April, 1782, and repeated on the 12th. This was for the benefit of Quick, who acted Doodle.

p. 30 *Your Honour . . . must be set down at Long's*. Long's was a famous Ordinary in the Haymarket. It was here that in 1678 Lord Pembroke killed Mr. Coney with his fist. He was tried by his Peers and acquitted. There was at the same period a second tavern in Covent Garden kept by Ben Long, Long's brother. In Dryden's *Mr. Limberham* (1678), Brainsick cries: 'I have won a wager to be spent luxuriously at Long's.' In Etheredge's *The Man of Mode* (1676), the following conversation occurs:—

Bellair. Where do you dine?
Dorimant. At Long's or Locket's.
Medley. At Long's let it be.

THE KING OF BANTAM.

p. 30 *the King's Box*. The seats in the boxes of the Restoration Theatre were let out severally to separate persons, and although the King had, of course, his own private box when he saw a play, yet when he was not present even the royal box was apportioned to individuals as the rest. There are many allusions to this which prove, moreover, that the front row of the King's box was the most conspicuous and highly coveted position in the house. In Etheredge's *The Man of Mode* (1676), Dorimant, hearing of a young gentlewoman lately come to town and being taken with his own handsome face, wagers that she must be 'some awkward, ill-fashioned, country toad, who, not having above four dozen of black hairs on her head, has adorned her baldness with a large white fruz, that she may look sparkishly in the forefront of the

King's box at an old play.' In Tom Brown's *Letters from the Dead to the Living*[1] we have one from Julian, 'late Secretary to the Muses,' to Will. Pierre of Lincoln's Inn Fields Playhouse, wherein, recalling how in his lampoons whilst he lived characters about town were shown in no very enviable light, he particularizes that 'the antiquated Coquet was told of her age and ugliness, tho' her vanity plac'd her in the first row in the King's box at the playhouse.'

p. 31 *Jermain-Street.* Jermyn Street runs parallel with Piccadilly from the Haymarket to St. James. It was built *circa* 1667, and derives its name from Henry Jermyn, Earl of St. Albans. Shadwell spells it Germin Street, and it was in a house here that old Snarl was wont to receive amorous castigation at the hands of Mrs. Figgup.—*The Virtuoso* (1676), iii, 11. It was a fashionable quarter. From 1675 to 1681 the Duke of Marlborough, then Colonel Churchill, lived here. La Belle Stuart, Duchess of Richmond, had a house near Eagle Passage, 1681–3, and was succeeded therein by the Countess of Northumberland. Next door dwelt Henry Saville, Rochester's friend, 1681–3. Three doors from the Duchess again was living in 1683 Simon Verelest, the painter. In 1684 Sir William Soames followed him. In after years also there have been a large number of famous residents connected with this favourite street.

p. 34 *after having . . . thrown their Majesties own Shoes and Stockings.* For this old bridal custom see *ante*, Vol. III (p. 223), *The Lucky Chance*, ii, 11: 'we'll toss the Stocking'; and the note on that passage.

THE UNFORTUNATE HAPPY LADY.

p. 43 *Ros Solis.* A potent and well-liked tipple.

> We abandon all ale
> And beer that is stale
> Rosa-solis and damnable hum,
> But we will rack
> In the praise of sack
> 'Gainst Omne quod exit in um.
> —*Witts Recreation* (1654).

The Accomplished Female Instructor gives the following recipe: 'Rossa Solis; Take of clean spirits, not too strong, two quarts and a quart of spring-water; let them seethe gently over a soft fire till about a pint is evaporated; then put in four spoonfuls of orange-flower-water, and as much of very good cinnamon-water; crush 3 eggs in pieces, and throw them in shell and all; stir it well, and when it boiles up a little take it off.' This drink was so great a favourite with Louis XIV that a particular sort was named Rossolis du Roi.

---

[1] This actual letter was written by Boyer, together with the reply which is dated 5 November, 1701. Julian was a well-known journalistic scribbler and ribald ballader of the time. William Peer [Pierre], a young actor of little account, is only cast for such walk-on rôles as Jasper, a valet, in Shadwell's *The Scowerers* (1691); the Parson in D'Urfey's *Love for Money* (1696).

p. 51 *The Cheats, Mother, the Cheats.* John Wilson's excellent comedy, *The Cheats*, which was written and produced in 1662, attained great popularity. It ran into four editions ('imprimatur, 5 November, 1663'); 4to, 1664; 1671; 1684; 1693. Caustically satirizing the Puritans, it became a stock piece, and was acted as late as May, 1721, when Griffin, Harper, Diggs, and Mrs. Gifford sustained the parts which had been created by Lacy, Mohun, Hart, and Mrs. Corey.

THE FAIR JILT.

p. 70 *To Henry Pain, Esq.* Henry Neville Payne, politician and author, was a thorough Tory and an ardent partisan of James II. Downes ascribes to him three plays: *The Fatal Jealousy*, produced at Dorset Garden in the winter of 1672, a good, if somewhat vehement, tragedy (4to, 1673); *Morning Ramble; or, Town Humours*, produced at the same theatre in 1673 (4to, 1673), which, though lacking in plot and quick incident, is far from a bad comedy; and *The Siege of Constantinople*, acted by the Duke's company in 1674 (4to, 1675), a tragedy which very sharply lashes Shaftesbury as the Chancellor, especially in Act II, when Lorenzo, upon his patron designing a frolic, says:—

My Lord, you know your old house, Mother Somelie's,
You know she always fits you with fresh girls.

Mother Somelie is, of course, the notorious Mother Mosely.

Henry Payne wrote several loyal pamphlets, and after the Revolution he became, according to Burnet, 'the most active and determined of all King James' agents.' He is said to have been the chief instigator of the Montgomery plot in 1690, and whilst in Scotland was arrested. 10 and 11 December of that year he was severely tortured under a special order of William III, but nothing could be extracted from him. This is the last occasion on which torture was applied in Scotland. After being treated with harshest cruelty by William III, Payne was finally released from prison in December, 1700, or January, 1701, as the Duke of Queensbury, recognizing the serious illegalities of the whole business, urgently advised his liberation. Payne died in 1710. As Macaulay consistently confounds him with a certain Edward Neville, S.J., the statements of this historian with reference to Henry Neville Payne must be entirely disregarded.

p. 72 *The Fair Jilt.* Editio princeps, 'London. Printed by *R. Holt* for *Will. Canning*, at his Shop in the *Temple-Cloysters*' (1688), 'Licensed 17 April, 1688. *Ric. Pocock*', has as title: *The Fair Jilt; or, The History of Prince Tarquin and Miranda*. As half-title it prints: *The Fair Hypocrite; or, The Amours of Prince Tarquin and Miranda*. All subsequent editions, however, give: *The Fair Jilt; or, The Amours of Prince Tarquin and Miranda*. The Dedication only occurs in the first edition.

p. 73 *Scrutore.* Escritoire. cf. Sir T. Herbert, *Trav.* (1677): 'There they sell . . . Scrutores or Cabinets of Mother of Pearl.'

p. 75 *Canonesses, Begines, Quests, Swart-Sisters and Jesuitesses.* Canonesses are very ancient in history. The most important Congregations are the Sepulchrines or Canonesses of the Holy Sepulchre, and the Lateran Canonesses. There was an old community of French Hospitaller

Canonesses of Saint-Esprit. Thomassin tells us that the Béguines were canonesses, and that their name is derived from S. Begghe (*ob.* 689), who founded the Canonesses of Andenne. There are also Chapters of secular canonesses, nearly all Benedictine in origin. Many of these only admitted ladies of the highest rank. The French Revolution swept away a great number of these institutions, and some were suppressed by Joseph II of Austria. Premonstratensian (white) Canonesses were common in Belgium.

Begines. Either founded by S. Begghe, or their name is derived from Lambert de Bègue, a priest of Liège, in 1177. Some place their foundation at the beginning of the eleventh century in the Netherlands or Germany. After three years women who are enrolled are entitled to a little house. No vows are taken, but they assist in choir thrice daily. There are several hundreds at Ghent, and the Béguinage (ten Wijngaarde) of Bruges is famous.

Quests. Quêteuses. Extern Sisters, Poor Clares and Colettines; Lay Sisters, Dominicanesses, who go out and beg for the community. 'To quest' is to go alms-begging. The Sisters of Charity are of later foundation. cf. Translation, D'Emilliane's *Frauds of Romish Monks* (1691): 'The Farmer [of Purgatory Money] sends some of his Emissaries into the Fields to carry on the Quest there for the said Souls'; and *Earthquake . . . Peru,* iii, 303 (1748): 'If the Friars go into the Country a questing for their Monastery.'

Swart-Sisters. Black Nuns. Dominicanesses, a feature of whose dresses is the cappa, a large black cloak and hood, worn from All Saints' Day till the 'Gloria' on Easter Eve, and on all great solemnities.

Jesuitesses. A common misnomer for the original Congregation founded by Mary Ward (*ob.* 1645), and named by her 'The Institute of Mary'. It was not until 1703 that they were fully approved by Clement XI.

p. 78 *Cordeliers.* Observant Franciscans, who follow the strict Rule of Poverty and observe all the fasts and austerities of the Order. This name was first given them in France, where later they were known as Recollects.

p. 130 *I gave 'em to the King's Theatre.* Sir Robert Howard and Dryden's heroic tragedy, *The Indian Queen,* was produced at the Theatre Royal in mid-January, 1663. It is a good play, but the extraordinary success it attained was in no small measure due to the excellence and magnificence of the scenic effects and mounting. 27 January, Pepys noticed that the streets adjacent to the theatre were 'full of coaches at the new play *The Indian Queen,* which for show, they say, exceeds *Henry VIII.*' On 1 February he himself found it 'indeed a most pleasant show'. The grandeur of the *mise en scène* became long proverbial in theatrical history. Zempoalla, the Indian Queen, a fine rôle, was superbly acted by Mrs. Marshall, the leading tragedienne of the day. The feathered ornaments which Mrs. Behn mentions must have formed a quaint but doubtless striking addition to the actress's pseudo-classic attire. Bernbaum pictures 'Nell Gwynn[1] in the true costume of a Carib belle', a quite unfair deduction from Mrs. Behn's words.

---

[1] Nell Gwynne had no part in the play.

p. 168 *Osenbrigs.* More usually 'osnaburg', so named from Osnabrück in North Germany, a kind of coarse linen made in this town. Narborough's Journal, 1669 (*An Account of Several Late Voyages*, 1694), speaks of 'Cloth, Osenbrigs, Tobacco'. cf. *Pennsylvania Col. Records* (1732): 'That to each there be given a couple of Shirts, a Jackett, two pairs of trowsers of Oznabrigs.'

p. 174 *as soon as the Governour arrived.* The Governor was Francis Willoughby, fifth Baron Willoughby of Parham (1613?–1666). He had arrived at Barbadoes, 29 April, 1650, and was received as Governor 7 May, which same day he caused Charles II to be proclaimed. An ardent royalist, he was dispossessed by an Act of Parliament, 4 March, 1652, and summoned back to England. At the Restoration he was reinstated, and arrived the second time with full powers in Barbardoes, 10 August, 1663. About the end of July, 1666, he was lost at sea on board the good ship *Hope.*

p. 177 *my Father . . . never arriv'd to possess the Honour design'd him.* Bernbaum, following the mistaken statement that Mrs. Behn's father, John Amis, was a barber, argues that a man in such a position could hardly have obtained so important a post, and if her 'father was not sent to Surinam, the only reason she gives for being there disappears.' However, since we know her father to have been no barber, but of good family, this line of discussion falls to the ground.

p. 180 *Brother to Harry Martin the great Oliverian.* Henry, or Harry, and George Marten were the two sons of Sir Henry Marten (*ob.* 1641) and his first wife, Elizabeth, who died 19 June, 1618. For the elder brother, Henry Marten, (1602–80), see note Vol. I, p. 457.

p. 193 *The Deputy Governor.* William Byam was 'Lieutenant General of Guiana and Governor of Willoughby Land', 1661–7. Even previously to this he had gained no little influence and power in these colonies. He headed the forces that defended Surinam in 1667 against the Dutch Admiral Crynsens, who, however, proved victorious.

p. 198 *my new Comedy. The Younger Brother; or, The Amorous Jilt,* post-humously produced under the auspices of, and with some alterations by, Charles Gildon at Drury Lane in 1696. George Marteen, acted by Powell, is the young and gallant hero of the comedy.

p. 200 *his Council.* In *The Widow Ranter* Mrs. Behn draws a vivid picture of these deboshed ruffians.

p. 207 *one Banister.* Sergeant Major James Banister being, after Byam's departure in 1667, 'the only remaining eminent person' became Lieutenant-Governor. It was he who in 1668 made the final surrender of the colony. Later, having quarrelled with the Dutch he was imprisoned by them.

THE HISTORY OF THE NUN.

p. 262 *The Dutchess of Mazarine.* Hortense Mancini, niece of the great Cardinal, was born at Rome in 1646. Her beauty and wit were such that Charles II (whilst in exile) and other princes of royal blood sought her hand. She married, however, 28 February, 1661, Armand-Charles de la Meilleraye, said to be 'the richest subject in Europe'. The union was unhappy, and in 1666 she demanded a judicial separation. Fearful, however, lest this should be refused, she fled from Paris 13 June, 1668, and, after several years of wandering, in 1675 came to London at the invitation of Charles II, who assigned her a pension. Her gallantries, her friendship with Saint-Evremond, her lavish patronage of the fine arts and literature are well known. She died at her Chelsea house in the summer of 1699. Her end is said to have been hastened by intemperance. Evelyn dubs her 'the famous beauty and errant lady.'

The Lucky Mistake.

p. 351 This Dedication only appears in the first edition (12mo, 1689), 'for R. Bentley'. George Granville or Grenville,[1] Lord Lansdowne, the celebrated wit, dramatist and poet, was born in 1667. Having zealously offered in 1688 to defend James II, during the subsequent reign he perforce 'lived in literary retirement'. He then wrote *The She Gallants* (1696, and 4to, 1696), an excellent comedy full of jest and spirit. Offending, however, some ladies 'who set up for chastity' it made its exit. Granville afterwards revived it as *Once a Lover and Always a Lover*. *Heroick Love*, a tragedy (1698), had great success. *The Jew of Venice* (1701), is a piteously weak adaption of *The Merchant of Venice*. A short masque, *Peleus and Thetis* accompanies the play. *The British Enchanters*, an opera (1706), is a pleasing piece, and was very well received. At the accession of Queen Anne, Granville entered the political arena and attained considerable offices of state. Suspected of being an active Jacobite he was, under George I, imprisoned from 25 September, 1715, till 8 February, 1717. In 1722 he went abroad, and lived in Paris for ten years. In 1732 he returned and published a finely printed edition of his complete *Works* (2 Vols., 4to, 1732; and again, 3 Vols, 1736, 12mo). He died 30 January, 1735, and is buried in St. Clement Danes.

p. 398 *double Union*. In a collection of Novels with running title : *The Deceived Lovers* (1696), we find No. v *The Curtezan Deceived*, 'An Addition to The Lucky Mistake, Written by Mrs. A. Behn.' This introduction of Mrs. Behn's name was a mere bookseller's trick to catch the unwary reader. *The Curtezan Deceived* is of no value. It has nothing to do with Aphra's work and is as commonplace a little novel as an hundred others of its day.

The Unfortunate Bride.

p. 401 *To Richard Norton*. This Epistle Dedicatory is only to be found in the first edition of *The Unfortunate Bride ; or, The Blind Lady a Beauty*, 'Printed for Samuel Briscoe, in Charles-Street, Covent-Garden, 1698', and also dated, on title page facing the portrait of Mrs. Behn, 1700.

Southwick, Hants, is a parish and village some 1¾ miles from Portchester, 4½ from Fareham. Richard Norton was son and heir of Sir Daniel Norton, who died seised of the manor in 1636. Richard

---

[1] The spelling 'Greenvil' 'Greenviel' is incorrect.

Norton married Anne, daughter of Sir William Earle, by whom he had one child, Sarah. He was, in his county at least, a figure of no little importance. Tuesday, 12 August, 1701, Luttrell records that 'an addresse from the grand jury of Hampshire . . . was delivered by Richard Norton and Anthony Henly, esqs. to the lords justices, to be laid before his majestie.' He aimed at being a patron of the fine arts, and under his superintendence Dryden's *The Spanish Friar* was performed in the frater of Southwick Priory,[1] the buildings of which had not been entirely destroyed at the suppression. Colley Cibber addresses the Dedicatory Epistle (January, 1695) of his first play, *Love's Last Shift* (4to, 1696), to Norton in a highly eulogistic strain. The plate of Southwick Church (S. James), consisting of a communion cup, a standing paten, two flagons, an alms-dish, and a rat-tail spoon, is silver-gilt, and was presented by Richard Norton in 1691. He died 10 December, 1732.

The Dumb Virgin.

p. 429 *Dangerfield.* This name is not to be found in any one of Mrs. Behn's plays, but as it does occur in Sedley's *Bellamira; or, The Mistress* (1687), one can only conclude that Aphra gave it to Sir Charles and altered her own character's nomenclature. Mrs. Behn, it may be remembered, was more than once extraordinarily careless with regard to the names of the Dramatis Personæ in her comedies. A striking example occurs in *Sir Patient Fancy*, where the 'precise clerk' is called both Abel and Bartholomew. In *The Feign'd Curtezans* Silvio and Sabina are persistently confused, and again, in *The Town Fop* (Vol. III, p. 15 and p. 20), the name Dresswell is retained for Friendlove. Sedley's *Bellamira* is derived from Terence's *Eunuchus*, and Dangerfield is Thraso; the Pyrgopolinices, Miles Gloriosus, of Plautus.

The Wandering Beauty.

p. 451 *two Pinners.* A pinner is 'a coif with two long flaps one on each side pinned on and hanging down, and sometimes fastened at the breast . . . sometimes applied to the flaps as an adjunct of the coif'. —*N. E. D.* cf. Pepys, 18 April, 1664: 'To Hyde Park . . . and my Lady Castlemaine in a coach by herself, in yellow satin and a pinner on.'

The Unhappy Mistake.

p. 477 *the Jack.* The small bowl placed as a mark for the players to aim at. cf. *Cymbeline* ii, 1: 'Was there ever man had such luck! when I kissed the jack upon an up-cast to be hit away!'

p. 477 *the Block.* cf. Florio (1598). '*Buttino*, a maister or mistres of boules or coites whereat the plaiers cast or playe; some call it the blocke.'

p. 495 *vor Mainly be our Country Word, zure.* Wright, *English Dialect Dictionary*, gives apposite quotations for 'mainly' from Gloucester,

---

[1] The house was one of Black (Austin) Canons.

Wilts and Devon. He also has two quotations, Somerset and West Somerset for 'main' used adverbially. But 'mainly' is also quite common in that county.

p. 495   *the Gun.*   A well-known house of call.   2 June, 1668, Pepys 'stopped and drank at the Gun'.

p. 496   *a Broad piece.*   This very common name was 'applied after the introduction of the guinea in 1663 to the "Unite" or 20 shilling pieces (Jacobus and Carolus) of the preceeding reigns, which were much broader and thinner than the new milled coinage.'

p. 509   *Appendix. Oronooko : Epistle Dedicatory.*   Richard Maitland, fourth Earl of Lauderdale (1653–95), eldest son of Charles, third Earl of Lauderdale by Elizabeth, daughter and heiress of Richard Lauder of Halton, was born 20 June, 1653. Before his father succeeded to the Lauderdale title he was styled of Over-Gogar; after that event he was known as Lord Maitland. 9 October, 1678, he was sworn a Privy Councillor, and appointed Joint General of the Mint with his father. In 1681 he was made Lord Justice General, but deprived of that office three years later on account of suspected communications with his father-in-law, Argyll, who had fled to Holland in 1681. Maitland, however, was in truth a strong Jacobite, and refusing to accept the Revolution settlement became an exile with his King. He is said to have been present at the battle of the Boyne, 1 July, 1690. He resided for some time at St. Germains, but fell into disfavour, perhaps owing to the well-known protestant sympathies of his wife, Lady Agnes Campbell (1658–1734), second daughter of the fanatical Archibald, Earl of Argyll. From St. Germains Maitland retired to Paris, where he died in 1695. He had succeeded to the Earldom of Lauderdale 9 June, 1691, but was outlawed by the Court of Justiciary, 23 July, 1694. He left no issue. Lauderdale was the author of a verse translation of Virgil (8vo, 1718 and 2 Vols., 12mo, 1737). Dryden, to whom he sent a MS. copy from Paris, states that whilst working on his own version he consulted this whenever a crux appeared in the Latin text. Lauderdale also wrote *A Memorial on the Estate of Scotland* (about 1690), printed in Hooke's *Correspondence* (Roxburghe Club), and there wrongly ascribed to the third Earl, his father.

The Dedication only occurs in the first edition of *Oronooko* (1688), of which I can trace but one copy. This is in the library of Mr. F. F. Norcross of Chicago, whose brother-in-law, Mr. Harold B. Wrenn, most kindly transcribed and transmitted to me the Epistle Dedicatory. It, unfortunately, arrived too late for insertion at p. 129.